SHIRE NATURAL I G000166491

GRASSHOPPERS AND BUSH-CRICKETS
of the British Isles
ANDREW MAHON

CONTENTS

To Sara and Kim for their patience during bush-cricket hunts.

COVER: *Common Field Grasshopper (Chorthippus brunneus).*

Series editors: Jim Flegg and Chris Humphries

Copyright © 1988 by Andrew Mahon. First published 1988.
Number 25 in the Shire Natural History series. ISBN 0 85263 946 5.

Set in 9 point Times roman and printed in Great Britain by C. I. Thomas & Sons (Haverfordwest) Ltd, Press Buildings, Merlins Bridge, Haverfordwest, Dyfed.

Life history

The grasshoppers and bush-crickets belong to the order Orthoptera and are closely related to the crickets, cockroaches, earwigs and stick-insects. The order has some 17,000 members worldwide but only six hundred or so occur in Europe and the British total is just thirty. This includes eleven species of grasshopper from the family Acrididae and ten species of bush-cricket which belong to the family Tettigoniidae.

The grasshoppers and bush-crickets are stout insects characterised by enlarged, muscular hind legs adapted for jumping, biting mouthparts and a saddle-shaped pronotum, a protective shield over the thorax. Most have two pairs of wings. The fore wings are much tougher, thicker and narrower than the more delicate membranous hind wings for which they provide some protection. Metamorphosis is incomplete without a pupal stage: there are several nymphal instars which all have a basic resemblance to the adult. Perhaps the best known characteristic is the ability to stridulate or 'sing' by the rubbing together of certain parts of the body.

The bush-crickets may be distinguished from the grasshoppers by their long antennae which give them their alternative but now little used name of long-horned grasshoppers. Other differences are the shape of the female ovipositors, which are long and sword-shaped in the bush-crickets but inconspicuous in the grasshoppers, the mechanism of stridulation and the position on the body of the hearing organ.

Elsewhere in the world there are many destructive members of the Orthoptera, including several cockroach species and the notorious migratory locust. None of the native British representatives are injurious, however, and several of the bush-crickets may assist the gardener and farmer by consuming destructive aphids and caterpillars.

THE LIFE CYCLE

All British grasshoppers and bush-crickets overwinter as eggs and have only a single generation each year. The eggs, laid singly by the bush-crickets but in pods of up to fifteen by the grasshoppers, begin to hatch in late spring when the weather is favourable for nymphal development.

The young insect emerges from the egg as a vermiform or worm-shaped larva but almost immediately sheds the outer skin to reveal the first instar nymph. Favoured grasshopper oviposition sites such as anthills are often littered with discarded skins in early May. The nymphs soon begin to feed and growth is quite rapid. Ecdysis occurs between one and two weeks later when the first instar sheds the restrictive skin to reveal a larger and more developed second instar. This process generally takes place in a sheltered and hidden spot as the newly emerged nymph is most vulnerable to predators and to unfavourable climatic conditions.

The number and duration of instars depends on the species, food supply and weather. Most of the grasshoppers have four instars but there is a variation amongst the bush-crickets from five or six in the smaller species to as many as nine in the Great Green Bush-cricket (*Tettigonia viridissima*). The rudimentary wing buds appear in the second or third instar and become reversed in the later nymphal stages. The ovipositor of the bush-crickets tends to become proportionately longer in comparison with the body in later instars. Some of these increases can be quite remarkable. In the Great Green Bush-cricket, for example, the average ovipositor length in the penultimate nymphal stage is about 8 mm (5/16 inch) compared with around 22 mm (15/16 inch) for the subsequent pre-adult instar. In some species, notably the Grey Bush-cricket (*Platycleis denticulata*), at least one nymphal instar has a different coloration to the adult. In this species early instar nymphs often have emerald green stripes along the lower edges of the pronotum and this spreads along both sides of the thorax and abdomen in the penultimate instar. This is probably an evolutionary adaptation which reflects a difference in habitat choice between nymph and adult. The nymphs feed in the grassy areas of their typical clifftop habitat but the adults move into the more

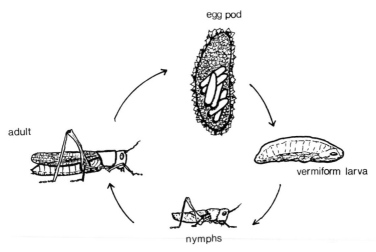

1. *The life cycle of a grasshopper.*

open, warmer parts during breeding. Here their more disruptive mottled grey coloration is of greater value than the green which provided camouflage for the nymphs amongst the grass.

Nymphs have the ability to regenerate lost limbs or antennae during the course of ecdysis, though in later instars the replacement is generally much smaller than normal. A new limb cannot be produced once the insect has become adult but the loss of a leg is not always seriously incapacitating and towards the end of the year a significant proportion of males, in particular, may be missing one of the hind legs.

After a few days of relative inactivity the final moult to the adult grasshopper occurs in late May or June. This stage may not be achieved in the bush-crickets until late July or even August. These are the most vulnerable few hours of the insect's life as the compressed adult form is extracted from the nymphal skin. The greatest change at this time is the production of the fully grown wings from the wing buds. They are slowly inflated to full size as the insect hangs from a grass stem or twig. The bush-crickets often carry out this process whilst clinging to their old skin with the fore and mid legs. It is often some time before full use of the hind legs is achieved. During this period the vul-

nerability is further increased because the exoskeletal plates which normally overlap to provide protection for the soft body tissues are slightly separated and draw together only slowly. The exposure of the neck region between the head and pronotum is particularly obvious. Once ecdysis is complete the adult may eat the shed skin before moving off in search of the more usual diet.

Sexual maturity is not reached for some time. The males use their newly found powers of stridulation within a couple of days but it may be a fortnight before the female is ready to accept the persistent attentions of a male. Meantime she will forcibly reject any overzealous advances by kicking out with the hind legs.

STRIDULATION

The songs of the grasshoppers and bush-crickets are used primarily during courtship but also function as territorial signals between males and perhaps also as a contact between members of a colony. The stridulatory mechanism consists of a file and a scraper which are found on two different parts of the body. The song is produced by the rubbing of the scraper, a thickened ridge, over the file, a line of pegs. In the grasshoppers a file is situated on the inside of each of the

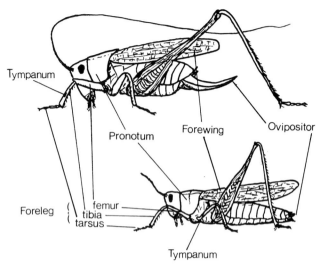

2. *Glossary of terms used in the text for parts of the body: a typical bush-cricket (above) and grasshopper (below).*

hind femora and the scrapers are provided by the thicker veins of the folded fore wings. It is the resonance of the fore wings which is heard as a song. There is one British exception to this mechanism. The Large Marsh Grasshopper (*Stethophyma grossum*) does not possess the usual file and scraper and its characteristic popping song is produced by the flicking of the flexed fore wings by the hind feet alternately.

The bush-cricket mechanism is contained entirely on the wings. The file is a toothed vein on the left fore wing and this is rubbed by the hind edge of the right fore wing. A clear membranous area known as the mirror helps to amplify the song and this is the only section of the wings that remains in the male Dark (*Pholidoptera griseoaptera*) and Speckled Bush-crickets (*Leptophyes punctatissima*). Female bush-crickets do not stridulate and they lack the specially adapted stridulatory areas of the wings. As with the grasshoppers there is one exception to the general mechanism of bush-cricket stridulation. The male Oak Bush-cricket (*Meconema thalassinum*) lacks the wing mechanism and produces his song by drumming one hind foot against the surface of a leaf. This occurs in bursts of about one second during which time the leg is raised and lowered an incredible 65 times.

The distinctive and individual songs of the various species arise from a combination of different densities of pegs and speed and repetition of leg or wing movement. Each note of the song results from one to and fro movement of the scraper across the pegs. In species such as the Meadow Grasshopper (*Chorthippus parallelus*) the notes are repeated relatively slowly at a rate of about six per second and each can be detected by the human ear. Other species move the legs so rapidly that the individual notes are produced at a frequency that is far too fast to be distinguished. Even within a species there is some variation in the density of the pegs and therefore in the song. Furthermore the apparatus takes time to become fully hardened and a deeper quality is gradually achieved with age, especially in the bush-crickets. The colour and density of the mirror alters correspondingly during this period. The song changes once again towards the end of the season as the file and scraper begin to wear. The actual rate of leg and wing movement during stridulation is particularly influenced by the ambient temperature.

The hearing organs which receive the song signals are located differently in the grasshoppers and bush-crickets but func-

4

3. *Long-winged Cone-head nymph showing the inverted wing buds.*

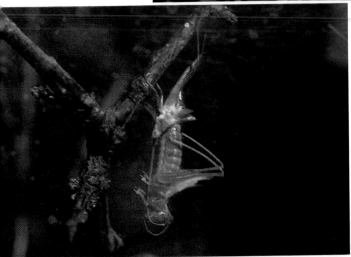

4. *A female Long-winged Conehead during the final ecdysis to adult.*

5. *Twenty minutes after release from the nymphal skin the Long-winged Conehead begins to 'inflate' the wings.*

tion in much the same way. In the grasshoppers the tympanal membranes are set in openings in either side of the first abdominal segment, often partly concealed by the folded wings. The hearing organs of the bush-crickets are in the fore legs. An opening on either side of each tibia leads to a pair of tympanal membranes. Some species, such as the Dark Bush-cricket, have flaps which reduce the opening to a narrow slit but in others it is quite unrestricted.

COURTSHIP

The British grasshoppers and bush-crickets all go through some form of courtship display prior to mating. In grasshoppers it would appear that stridulation is the most important factor though in most species some form of antennae waving or contact also occurs. The Rufous Grasshopper (*Gomphocerippus rufus*) also indulges in a lively courtship dance which makes good use of the white-tipped antennae to accentuate the movements. Most grasshoppers produce a variety of songs depending on the stage of courtship and the Stripe-winged Grasshopper (*Stenobothrus lineatus*), for instance, has a courtship song comprising a rapid series of clicks most unlike its usual wheezing stridulation. Some species have a third version which is only employed during copulation. Female grasshoppers also indulge in stridulatory movements during courtship but most produce at best only a rather weak version of the male's song.

The normal mating position for the grasshoppers is with the male on the back of the female. He bends his abdomen down to probe the underside of the female abdomen until a linkage is secured. The male then produces a spermatophore, a whitish gelatinous mass which contains the sperm. Part dissolves into the female's reproductive organs and the remainder drops off as it dries.

Courtship in the bush-crickets is also marked by a mixture of visual stimuli and song, though the female bush-crickets do not stridulate at all. In some species, including the Grey Bush-cricket, courtship is a rather complex procedure. The female first circles a singing male then approaches from the rear and touches the end of the abdomen with her antennae. This causes the male to heighten his stridulation and to arch his abdomen, lifting the wings to reveal the dorsal surface to the female. She will then use her mouthparts apparently to feed on a secretion from her suitor's back though neither the fluid nor a gland which might produce it have been found. After several minutes the male will reverse beneath the female and attempt to reach up with his claspers. As contact is made with the base of the ovipositor, the female moves over the male dragging him abdomen over head until he flips over. The spermatophore is inserted beneath the female's subgenital plate and the embrace is held for a variable period which may last up to thirty minutes. The experience seems to exhaust the male which takes some hours to recover fully. Stridulation may not occur again until the male is ready to breed several days later. Meanwhile the female bush-cricket eats the remainder of

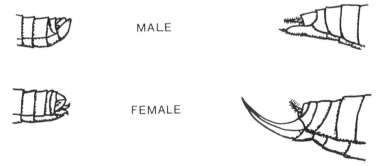

MALE

FEMALE

6. *The differences between a male and female grasshopper (left) and bush-cricket (right).*

6

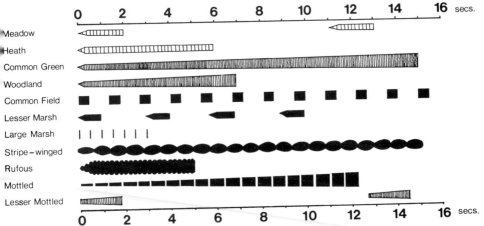

7. Song bars representing the stridulation of each grasshopper species. Each vertical line represents a distinct note. Where the bar is solid the frequency of notes is too great for the human ear to distinguish them. The width of the bar is an indication of the relative loudness of the song.

the spermatophore from beneath her ovipositor. A day or two later the female will lay the fertilised eggs and spend some further time feeding and resting until she also is ready to mate once again.

The actual position at mating varies between species. Another common variation is seen in the Long-winged Cone-head (*Conocephalus discolor*) where the partners mate end to end, often in a vertical position on an upright grass leaf.

OVIPOSITION

Most of the British bush-crickets lay eggs singly and differ in this respect from the grasshoppers. The shape and curvature of the ovipositor reflects the preferred oviposition site of each species as does the shape of the egg. The huge sword-shaped ovipositor of the Great Green Bush-cricket is used to deposit cigar-shaped eggs deep into the soil, a medium also favoured by the Grey Bush-cricket and the Wartbiter (*Decticus verrucivorus*). The other bush-crickets lay into various types of vegetation. The cone-heads have long slender ovipositors which lay very thin, pointed, cylindrical eggs into the hollow stems of rushes and grasses. Crevices in bark or decaying wood are favoured by others, including the Speckled Bush-cricket, which bears a toothed ovipositor which is used rather like a saw to insert the atypical flat, disc-shaped eggs into bark crevices.

The apparently single-unit ovipositor is in fact made up of three pairs of valves held together by tongue and groove joints. These slide over each other quite freely to help move the eggs along the ovipositor. The abdomen is usually bent at an alarming angle of up to ninety degrees to facilitate penetration of the substrate and the two sides of the ovipositor are then pushed alternately into the soil or vegetation to drill the necessary hole before the egg is passed down to the tip to be laid.

The grasshoppers have a much less obvious ovipositor which comprises two main valves at the end of the abdomen. In the majority of British grasshoppers the ovipositor is inserted into the soil in a closed position then opened to force the soil outwards to create a hole. The process is repeated until the required depth is reached. The exceptions are the Stripe-winged Grasshopper, which lays at the soil surface just above grass roots, and the Large Marsh and Lesser Marsh Grasshopper (*Chorthippus albomarginatus*) which, in common with the Common

7

8. *Great Green Bush-cricket.*

Green Grasshopper (*Omocestus viridulus*), lay in vegetation, generally at the base of dense, grassy tussocks. Grasshopper eggs are laid in groups of up to fifteen, depending on species, and a frothy liquid is secreted around them which hardens to form a protective egg pod.

The eggs undergo a primary development before entering a diapause phase as ambient temperatures fall below a critical level. This phase will not end until the following spring when development continues once again. The complex physiological changes that take place during diapause prevent eggs from further development in unseasonal warm spells early in the year and so reduce the risk of exposing the vulnerable young nymphs to inclement weather. Most bush-crickets produce eggs which hatch over a period of years, with the majority not developing until the second spring after laying. Only a very small proportion hatch the following spring, possibly those laid early in the season, and the remainder will not produce nymphs until the third or subsequent years.

Ecology

MOVEMENT AND DISPERSAL

The ability to hop or jump is a particular characteristic of Orthoptera and is achieved by the sudden straightening of the long, powerful hind legs, which are generally held in a sharply angled position. The movement can hurl the insect to a distance and height many times its own length while the small size and tough external skeleton prevent injury on landing.

Ironically, walking is the more usual method of locomotion of all British grasshoppers and bush-crickets and most make use of their muscular hind legs to hop only when disturbed. A few species will take to the wing to escape danger though the clumsy flights seldom cover more than a few metres and are directed more by the wind than the will of the insect. One exception is the Oak Bush-cricket, which is often attracted to well lit houses during its active nocturnal flights. The flying ability of the Meadow Grasshopper and five of the bush-cricket species is further restricted by the reduced or vestigial nature of the wings.

9 (above left). *Grey Bush-cricket.*
10 (above right). *A female Dark Bush-cricket sunbathing.*
11 (below). *A male Dark Bush-cricket showing the much shortened wings.*

In the Dark and Speckled Bush-crickets the hind wings are totally absent and the fore wings reduced to minute flaps used only for stridulation.

The early instar nymphs migrate from the often crowded hatching zone into more favourable feeding areas around, though the bush-crickets that lay eggs singly have less need to travel. Adults seldom move far and males are often faithful to the same song location once the colony has established a stable territory pattern. Following mating in the feeding grounds the females of some species must move back to more suitable areas for oviposition. This is particularly true of those grasshoppers that lay in warm, open sites such as anthills.

FEEDING

Grasshoppers and bush-crickets locate their food by sight, smell and taste and test its suitability with sensory cells on the antennae and mouth parts. These can assess both the physical and chemical characteristics of the food. Grasshoppers are plant feeders, taking mainly narrow-leaved grasses such as *Agrostis* and *Festuca* and occasionally the leaves of forbs (or meadow herbs) like clover. The bush-crickets take a great variety of food ranging from the mainly herbivorous diet of the coneheads to the carnivorous tastes of the adult Oak Bush-cricket. Some animal protein seems to be a dietary requirement of all of the bush-crickets but especially for adult females, which may need the protein for satisfactory egg development, and both nymphs and adults need an energy-rich diet. In the autumn when most flowers are over it is not unusual to find late Great Green Bush-crickets stripping ivy blooms of their nectar and pollen.

ADAPTATION AND VARIATION

The success of the grasshoppers and bush-crickets is largely due to their adaptability. The huge range of colour variations in several grasshopper species ensures good camouflage for at least a proportion of a colony under a diversity of environmental conditions. The basic pattern of coloration reflects the habitat preference of each species so that, for instance, the Mottled Grasshopper (*Myr-*

meleotettix maculatus) blends perfectly with the mottled background provided by dunes and open heathland, while the longitudinal stripes on a basically green conehead provide just enough disruption to disguise the insect stretched out along a grass stem.

Grasshoppers and bush-crickets are least susceptible to inclement weather at the egg stage, when some protection is afforded by the soil or dense vegetation in which they were laid. In such circumstances the eggs will survive conditions of cold and dampness which would prove fatal to a nymph or adult. The staggered hatching of the eggs over the course of a season is a vital factor in ensuring that a period of unfavourable weather will not jeopardise the whole colony. Recently hatched nymphs of most species can be found throughout the summer so some breeding and oviposition can take place even if early developing individuals are wiped out before achieving adulthood. The bush-crickets that take this process a stage further by producing eggs that hatch over several years avoid the possibility of extinction due to one particularly poor year, a real danger to any species at the edge of its geographical range that completes its life-cycle in less than twelve months and therefore relies on successful development and breeding each and every year.

MORTALITY

The variation in diet places grasshoppers and bush-crickets at different levels in the food chain and indeed nymphal or even adult grasshoppers may be taken by the larger bush-crickets. Despite their camouflage and other adaptations a large proportion of grasshopper nymphs and some adults fall victim to a wide variety of predators, including spiders, hunting wasps, birds and reptiles. Bush-crickets also form part of the diet of a range of predators, especially birds. Tits and Goldcrests will feed on Oak Bush-crickets while larger birds of scrubby areas like the Yellowhammer occasionally take Dark and Great Green Bush-crickets. Magpies and Kestrels have also been recorded taking Orthoptera.

Less obvious is the importance of parasitism and disease in regulating the

10

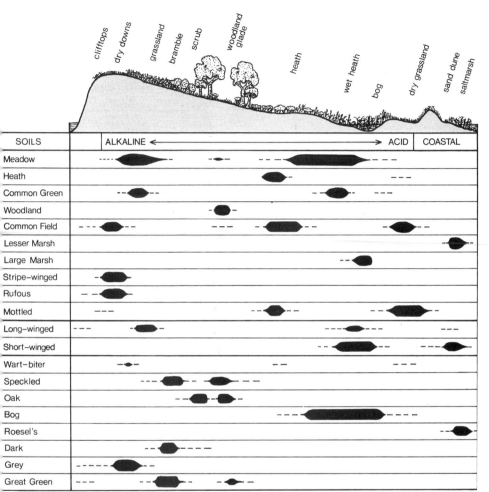

12. *The preferred habitats of each of the species. Solid bars indicate the favoured and dotted lines the less favoured habitat.*

population of grasshoppers and bush-crickets. The eggs are prone to bacterial and fungal diseases as well as a variety of hymenopteran wasps. Parasites of adults include nematode worms and the larvae of certain flies. Climatic factors are another major influence on survival and heavy rain or unseasonal cold weather at or soon after hatching can prove fatal. Several of the species restricted to the southern coasts of Britain are more wide-spread inland in Europe. This suggests that for species such as the Grey Bush-cricket it is not necessarily availability of suitable habitat that is restricting distribution but a climatic factor. The oceanic climate of the British Isles, with cool summers and a high probability of late spring and early autumn frosts, is not a favourable one for most grasshoppers or bush-crickets but is at its least severe along the south coast where the sea exerts a moderating influence on extremes of temperature.

11

13. *Speckled Bush-cricket.*

14. *Wartbiter.*

15. *Oak Bush-cricket.*

16 (above left). *Long-winged Conehead.*
17 (above right). *Short-winged Conehead.*
18 (below left). *The green variety of the Bog Bush-cricket.*
19 (below right). *The brown variety of the Bog Bush-cricket.*

HABITAT PREFERENCE

Most Orthoptera species have specialised requirements and are therefore restricted to a particular habitat. In many cases this is related to the physical or microclimatic nature of the oviposition site or to a dietary factor. The habitat requirements of some species are so precise that they provide a reliable additional identification guide. The Large Marsh Grasshopper, for instance, is never encountered away from the boggy heaths on which it is totally dependent. Others, such as the Meadow Grasshopper, occur in a wider range of habitats and can be associated both with typical wet heathland species like the Bog Bush-cricket (*Metrioptera brachyptera*) and elsewhere with the Stripe-winged Grasshopper of dry downlands. Figure 12 summarises the preferred habitats of the British grasshoppers and bush-crickets.

Identification and distribution

The colour and shape of each of the British bush-crickets is sufficiently distinctive to allow identification from the photographs and following descriptions. The situation is less clear with the grasshoppers, all of which have the same basic shape and most of which occur in a range of colour varieties. The flow diagram (figure 21) can be used to identify adult grasshoppers though the recognition of some of the critical characteristics takes a little practice. It should be used in conjunction with the song bars and the distribution map and checklist as well as the individual species description to verify the identification. With experience it is possible to distinguish each species by song alone but initially at least it may be necessary to capture specimens in glass tubes and use a hand lens to facilitate close examination of the important features. It should be noted that the capture or collection of the Wartbiter is illegal as the species is fully protected under Schedule 5 of the Wildlife and Countryside Act.

Nymphs are not easily identified in the field and it is important to check that specimens are adult by examination of the wings. Older nymphs have short, inverted wing buds whereas the adults of most species are fully winged. Even the short-winged Meadow Grasshopper can be easily distinguished from nymphs by its papery wings with a network of veins. These contrast with the nymphal wing buds which are more fleshy and have at most a few parallel veins.

DISTRIBUTION

Some of the commonest grasshoppers are found throughout the British Isles in a variety of grassland types but most are restricted to the warmer parts of the country and to specific habitats within that range. Few species penetrate built-up areas, though the Common Field (*Chorthippus brunneus*) and Meadow Grasshoppers may often be found on waste areas and less intensively managed parkland. Bush-crickets are also much more numerous in the southern parts of Britain and only the Dark, Bog and Speckled Bush-crickets extend into Scotland.

BOG BUSH-CRICKET, *Metrioptera brachyptera*

The Bog Bush-cricket occurs in two colour varieties. Both have dark brown sides but the top of the head and pronotum and the margins of the fore wings are green in one and brown in the other. The bright green underside and a broad

20. *Nymphal wing buds (left) compared with short adult wings (right).*

14

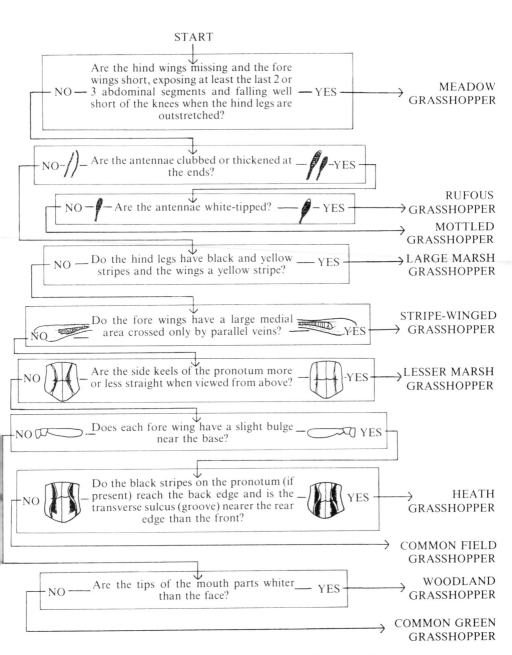

START

Are the hind wings missing and the fore wings short, exposing at least the last 2 or 3 abdominal segments and falling well short of the knees when the hind legs are outstretched? — NO / YES → MEADOW GRASSHOPPER

NO / Are the antennae clubbed or thickened at the ends? — YES

NO / Are the antennae white-tipped? — YES → RUFOUS GRASSHOPPER

→ MOTTLED GRASSHOPPER

NO — Do the hind legs have black and yellow stripes and the wings a yellow stripe? — YES → LARGE MARSH GRASSHOPPER

NO / Do the fore wings have a large medial area crossed only by parallel veins? — YES → STRIPE-WINGED GRASSHOPPER

NO / Are the side keels of the pronotum more or less straight when viewed from above? — YES → LESSER MARSH GRASSHOPPER

NO / Does each fore wing have a slight bulge near the base? — YES

NO / Do the black stripes on the pronotum (if present) reach the back edge and is the transverse sulcus (groove) nearer the rear edge than the front? — YES → HEATH GRASSHOPPER

→ COMMON FIELD GRASSHOPPER

NO — Are the tips of the mouth parts whiter than the face? — YES → WOODLAND GRASSHOPPER

→ COMMON GREEN GRASSHOPPER

21. *Identification flow diagram for the British grasshoppers. The Lesser Mottled Grasshopper is excluded as it is restricted to one site and can be distinguished by its small size. A fully winged variety of the Meadow Grasshopper is also ignored as it is rarely encountered and is always in company with others of the more normal form.*

pale band along the rear edge of the side flaps of the pronotum distinguish this from similar species. The hind wings are almost absent and the fore wings are reduced to short lobes, though a rare fully winged form occurs.

The eggs hatch in May and there are six nymphal instars. The adults appear from late July and are day-loving insects with an incessant stridulation which can be heard throughout suitable damp heathland in warm sunny weather. Adults may be found in apparently dry heathland some distance from bogs but there will generally be an area nearby which becomes marshy in winter. Their mixed diet includes the flowers and leaves of heathers and heathland grasses as well as a range of small invertebrates.

DARK BUSH-CRICKET, *Pholidoptera griseoaptera*

One of Britain's commonest bush-crickets and widespread throughout the south, the Dark Bush-cricket can be recognised by a sharp but not loud chirp given from heavy cover in bramble and shrubs. It can be heard throughout suitable days from August to mid October with a peak of stridulation around dusk. On warm nights it may continue until the early hours of the morning. The female appears almost totally wingless with only tiny remnants of the wings, while the male bears small overlapping flaps which include the stridulatory mechanism. The underside of the abdomen is a characteristic bright yellow or occasionally greenish-yellow colour. Males are generally dark brown and the female rather paler. Both sexes occasionally show a richer chestnut colour on the upper parts of the body.

Although frequently heard, the Dark Bush-cricket is a secretive insect. When disturbed or threatened its first reaction is to drop to the floor into even deeper cover and a stealthy approach is needed to observe specimens that venture out into the open. This is often the first bush-cricket to emerge each year, with nymphs making an appearance during April. The extended period of hatching and irregular growth rates mean that some adults survive through October and

even well into November in mild winters. Both nymphs and adults are omnivorous, with small insects and leaf material being supplemented by pollen, nectar and the flowers of a wide range of plants.

GREAT GREEN BUSH-CRICKET, *Tettigonia viridissima*

At over 40 mm (1¾ inches) long and with a wingspan of some 70 mm (2¾ inches) the Great Green is Britain's biggest bush-cricket. The green colour is broken by a dark brown stripe along the back and two narrow yellow bands beneath, providing excellent camouflage. It is most common in the south, especially along the coast, and occurs in shrubby areas, including hedgerows and mature gardens. The males stridulate on warm evenings, often starting in mid-afternoon and going on well after dark. In keeping with the insect's size, the high-pitched song is very loud, carrying for several hundred metres and often continuing for many minutes or even hours with only occasional, short pauses.

The eggs hatch in May and the nymphs grow quickly to produce adults from around the last week of July. Both nymphs and adults take a wide variety of plant and animal food, including leaves, flowers, seeds, grasshoppers, small butterflies, caterpillars and other insects. The adult females are particularly voracious predators. Mating normally occurs after dark and the eggs are laid in crevices in the soil. The Great Green Bush-cricket is prone to various parasites and fatal wasting diseases though males will continue to stridulate even when most of the abdomen has been lost. Individuals persist into late October or even mid November in favourable years. Adults are able to fly for several metres and occasionally enter houses. They should be handled carefully as the mouthparts are capable of inflicting a painful nip. They must be held by both hind knees as one leg can be cast to effect escape.

GREY BUSH-CRICKET, *Platycleis denticulata*

This species is restricted to the warmer parts of Britain and is concentrated mainly along the southern coast of England. It is rarely encountered more than a few

16

22 (left). *Roesel's Bush-cricket.*

23 (right). *Large Marsh Grasshopper showing the much shorter antennae which distinguish the grasshoppers from the bush-crickets.*

hundred metres from the sea. The ideal habitat is a mixture of rough grassland with some warmer open patches of rock or soil. The adults are a mottled brown to grey colour, sometimes with a chocolate-brown streak along the top of the head and pronotum. The later instar nymphs have bright emerald green sides; newly emerged adults retain this characteristic and in addition show a greenish coloration to the hind legs and wings. A darkening to the more usual grey-brown occurs over the course of a few days, during which time the insects are extremely secretive and remain well hidden in the densest part of the grassland.

By the time sexual maturity is reached all but the sides of the abdomen have attained the grey coloration. About a week or so later typical adult behaviour begins and the insects venture into more open parts of the habitat to breed and lay eggs. The black ovipositor of the female is used to probe cracks in the soil and amongst debris though, if necessary, it will be forced into more compacted soil to lay the eggs. Oviposition always occurs

in the warmest possible places, generally in open areas of soil and usually on south-facing slopes. The mobile substrate of undercliffs and unstable hillsides provide ideal conditions for Grey Bush-crickets and suitable areas may hold dense populations of several thousand insects.

Being fully winged it is unlikely that this species will be confused with any other British bush-cricket. It has an early season with nymphs first appearing in April and adults in mid July. Given suitable weather the adults will survive until November though the warm conditions required for stridulation seldom occur after early October in Britain. The song is a quiet and rapidly repeated chirp. Grass flowers and seeds form the bulk of the diet and a variety of small invertebrates is also taken.

OAK BUSH-CRICKET, *Meconema thalassinum*

The Oak Bush-cricket is encountered perhaps more often than any other bush-cricket in England and Wales due to its

17

habit of entering houses after dark, attracted by the light. It is a delicate-looking creature, pale green in colour and with a narrow light brown and yellow stripe running from the head across the pronotum and on to the top surface of the wings. The antennae are pale with black flecks spaced regularly along their length. The female ovipositor is gently upcurved and the male bears a very obvious pair of long, curved claspers at the end of the abdomen.

It is a most atypical member of the Tettigoniidae in several respects. There is no stridulatory mechanism on the wing and males produce their quiet drumming song by rapidly beating a leaf with the hind feet. The diet is largely carnivorous and consists mainly of caterpillars. Cannibalism also occurs. This is the only British species that lives in the tree canopy though it is not restricted to oak and may be found in almost any sort of deciduous woodland. Its activities are almost entirely nocturnal and the females can be found by torch-light probing the fissured bark of oaks and other trees for suitable oviposition sites. Eggs may also be laid in moss, lichen and even in vacated oak galls. As these preferred sites are more often associated with older trees, Oak Bush-crickets are seldom found far away from areas of mature woodland.

This species has one of the latest seasons of all British Orthoptera and adults are rarely encountered before mid August. Early September is the time of peak activity and records of survival until late November are not unusual.

ROESEL'S BUSH-CRICKET, *Metrioptera roeselii*

A combination of a yellow underside and short fore wings extending only half-way along the abdomen identify Roesel's Bush-cricket. Other distinctive features are the pale, usually yellowish band around the front, bottom and rear sides of the side flaps of the pronotum and pale yellowish patches on the thorax. The usual dark brown general coloration is occasionally tinged with green. The female's ovipositor is short in comparison with her total size and is markedly upcurved. A very rare, fully winged form has both pairs of wings extending beyond the knees of the outstretched hind legs.

Nymphs hatch in late May or early June and adults are commonest in their estuarine saltmarsh habitat in August and September. Stridulation occurs day and night and is a high-pitched and continuous song which may last for a minute or more. It is inaudible to some people, especially the more elderly. The bulk of the diet consists of grass leaves, flowers and seeds. The distribution is mainly around the south-eastern coasts of England, extending along the eastern coast as far north as the Humber estuary. An outlying colony in north Wales is probably the result of an accidental or deliberate introduction.

SPECKLED BUSH-CRICKET, *Leptophyes punctatissima*

This is one of the least variable members of the British Orthoptera. The colour is a bright bramble green with a yellowish-green underside. Close inspection reveals numerous minute brown dots which give the insect its name. Its long, spindly legs, slow crawling habits and lack of wings give it a rather spidery appearance. The female is almost totally wingless while the male bears only small brown overlapping remnants of the fore wings. The poorly developed stridulatory mechanism produces a weak, high-pitched chirp every few seconds. The song carries only a short distance and is inaudible to the human ear more than a metre or so away. The main period of activity is around dusk. The Speckled Bush-cricket occurs over much of Britain though it does not extend far across the Scottish border. Almost any shrubby habitat will support the species, including mature gardens. It is most often associated with areas of dense bramble where its coloration provides excellent camouflage. It occasionally enters houses.

Adults mature from early August and survive until October or a little later in good years. The eggs are laid in plant stems, tree bark and other suitable crevices. The unusual broad, flattened ovipositor of the female is an indication of a rather strange egg shape. Eggs are flat and elliptical, rather like a distorted record, and quite large at some 3.5 mm (0.15 inch) by 2.0 mm (0.1 inch). The

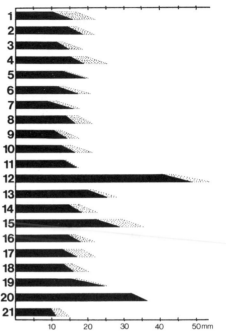

24. The distribution and comparative sizes of the British Orthoptera. Numbers refer to the checklist below. (I) indicates occurrence in Ireland. (Left) the British range of each species. Number 21, the Lesser Mottled Grasshopper, is known only from the Isle of Man. (Above) lengths measured from the front of the head to the tip of the abdomen, wings or ovipositor, whichever is longest. Solid bars are males and the shaded extensions females. The range of size is represented by the different top and bottom lengths of the bar.

1 Meadow Grasshopper; 2 Common Green Grasshopper (I); 3 Mottled Grasshopper (I); 4 Common Field Grasshopper (I); 5 Dark Bush-cricket; 6 Bog Bush-cricket; 7 Speckled Bush-cricket (I); 8 Lesser Marsh Grasshopper (I); 9 Short-winged Conehead; 10 Roesel's Bush-cricket (I); 11 Oak Bush-cricket (I); 12 Great Green Bush-cricket; 13 Grey Bush-cricket; 14 Stripe-winged Grasshopper; 15 Large Marsh Grasshopper (I); 16 Rufous Grasshopper; 17 Woodland Grasshopper; 18 Heath Grasshopper; 19 Long-winged Conehead; 20 Wartbiter; 21 Lesser Mottled Grasshopper.

19

ovipositor bears miniature saw teeth towards its tip which are used to enlarge crevices in bark to facilitate egg laying.

WARTBITER, *Decticus verrucivorus*

The rarest of the British bush-crickets, the Wartbiter is now confined to a handful of sites in the south of England. Its large size distinguishes it from all but the Great Green Bush-cricket and it may be told from this species by the black or brown blotches on the fore wings and a marked ridge on the pronotum. The hind tibiae are generally tinged reddish-brown. Little is known about the Wartbiter in Britain due mainly to its rarity and also because it becomes active only on very warm, sunny days. The song, a series of loud clicks given with increasing rapidly as stridulation progresses, is seldom heard at temperatures below 20 C (68 F). It may be likened to the sound of a fisherman's reel as he hauls in a catch. The adults reach maturity in early August and continue to sing on suitable days through September. The typical habitat is a mosaic of short, open grassland and denser refugia.

The Wartbiter's future in Britain now seems more secure as its main colonies have been designated nature reserves and the species has been scheduled with full protection under the Wildlife and Countryside Act.

LONG-WINGED CONEHEAD, *Conocephalus discolor*

This rare bush-cricket is restricted to the south coast of England and most often associated with long grass and reeds near to cliffs. Around 1983, however, a population explosion occurred and new colonies were established some miles inland around Bournemouth and the New Forest. By 1986 it had spread to many areas and it may now turn up anywhere,in southern Britain where species of grass with hollow flower stems are left uncut. New habitats include areas of derelict downland dominated by Tor Grass (*Brachypodium pinnatum*), pond margins and overgrown allotments and gardens.

Its habits and green coloration are similar to the grasshopper's. The underside and ovipositor are brown and the light brown hind wings project beyond the fore wings. There is a rare brown colour variety. It is an agile and graceful creature which often adopts a cryptic pose, stretched out along a grass stem. Stridulation occurs on sunny days and warm evenings. It is a faint high-pitched rattle typically given in bursts of up to thirty seconds or for several minutes in the presence of a female. Adults appear from late July though nymphs can still be found in late October. Eggs are laid singly in hollow grass, reed and rush stems, the female biting a hole for the ovipositor. The bulk of the diet is grass flowers and seeds though some small invertebrates may be taken.

The 'new' colonies are similar to the European form with extra long wings. This could reflect deliberate or accidental introduction or unprecedented climatic conditions which favoured migration but given the extensive area colonised and the low flight capability of the insect this is unlikely. Laboratory studies have shown that long-winged forms tend to arise in dense populations and this may have occurred in resident colonies.

SHORT-WINGED CONEHEAD, *Conocephalus dorsalis*

Rather smaller than its long-winged relative, this species can be immediately distinguished by the short fore wings and lack of hind wings. Other differences are the lack of spines on the underside of the hind femora and the markedly upcurved ovipositor of the female. These latter characteristics are important for the identification of the very rare fully winged form of the Short-winged Conehead. There are five nymphal instars and the adults emerge from July. They are seldom found beyond mid October. The diet and habits are similar to those of the Long-winged Conehead.

The song consists of a high-pitched hissing interspersed with a rapid clicking: the transition from one version to the other is sudden and occurs every few seconds in a song which may continue for several minutes. This is the more widespread of the coneheads, with a distinctly eastern distribution in England. Though occasionally found in and around freshwater marshes near the coast, saltmarsh appears to be the preferred habitat. Like the Long-winged Conehead it is a day-loving insect which is seldom active long after dusk except on the warmest nights. A rare brown variety is occasionally found.

COMMON FIELD GRASSHOPPER, *Chorthippus brunneus*

This is a fairly large grasshopper with a tremendous range of colour varieties. The side keels of the pronotum are strongly incurved and the fore wings are long, extending beyond the knees when the hind legs are straightened. The dark stripes on the top of the pronotum (if present at all) do not extend to the rear edge. The underside of the thorax is usually densely hairy and there is a marked bulge on the lower edge of the fore wings near their base. The colour varies from purplish to green but the most common varieties are brownish with a degree of black, grey or brown mottling. The more highly coloured varieties tend to dull with age, though an orange flush develops at the end of the abdomen of most individuals, especially males. This is probably the most commonly seen grasshopper and it is often quite numerous in dry parkland areas and waste ground and roadsides. It is an accomplished flyer and a very active insect in warm weather.

The large egg pod is laid below the surface of dry soil. It contains up to fifteen eggs which hatch in May. Adults appear from late June and can survive colder weather than most other grasshoppers. It is not unknown for adults to stridulate on sunny days in December. The song is a series of chirps, each about half a second long. Groups of males often hold 'conversations', chirping in turn, and there is a distinctive ticking version of the song given during the final stages of courtship.

COMMON GREEN GRASSHOPPER, *Omocestus viridulus*

The Common Green Grasshopper is the most widespread member of the family in the British Isles and occurs in all but the driest grassland habitats. It is generally the only grasshopper found on dry moorland and its characteristic song can be heard from July through to late September or early October. It is a rapid ticking noise which starts quietly and builds to full volume after about ten seconds. Each burst lasts about twenty seconds and has been likened to the motor of a car which refuses to start on a cold morning. There is a different courtship song given in the presence of a female which consists of a variable series of loud clicks.

There is nearly always some green on the body though the male occurs in an all-brown variety. Females occasionally show a dark purplish colour on the sides. Both sexes frequently have dark grey or even blackish fore wings, the colour darkening towards the tips. The Common Green Grasshopper can be distinguished from the closely related Woodland Grasshopper (*Omocestus rufipes*) by the lack of orange abdominal coloration and pale but never whitish mouthparts.

HEATH GRASSHOPPER, *Chorthippus vagans*

This is one of the rarest British grasshoppers. It is restricted to dry heaths in south-east Dorset and south Hampshire. The Heath Grasshopper is generally smaller than the similar Common Field Grasshopper but their size ranges overlap and close inspection is necessary to make certain identification in the absense of stridulation. In this species the sulcus, a groove running across the pronotum, is normally towards the rear of the pronotum and the black stripes extend fully to the back edge. The wings just reach the knees of the extended hind legs in the female but fall short in the male. The general coloration is grey-brown with mottling on the wings and an orange colour develops on the abdomen of older adults.

The egg pods are laid just below the surface of warm, well-drained, often sandy soil and contain up to eight eggs. These hatch during May and adults appear from mid June. They are very much warmth dependent and seldom survive beyond September. The song is similar in quality and speed to that of the much commoner Meadow Grasshopper but it is given for longer periods of five to eight seconds.

LARGE MARSH GRASSHOPPER, Stethophyma grossum

By far the most impressive and spectacular British grasshopper, this species can be easily recognised by its black and yellow hind tibiae and a red marking on each of the hind femora. The general body colour is green or yellowish-green though females occur rarely in a reddish-purple variety. It is unfortunately a rare insect, restricted to the wettest heathy bogs where it is associated with Bog Myrtle (*Myrica gale*), Cotton Grass (*Eriophorum* spp.) and Bog Asphodel (*Narthecium ossifragum*). It is only active on hot sunny days when it may undertake flights of several dozen metres if disturbed. Despite its large size and colourful appearance it is difficult to locate once it takes to cover.

The Large Marsh Grasshopper has a late season with adults maturing in late July and August. The egg pods are laid above ground at the base of dense grass tufts. The male lacks a stridulatory mechanism but instead produces a series of about eight popping sounds, a little reminiscent of gorse pods exploding, by kicking the tips of the fore wings with the hind tibiae.

LESSER MARSH GRASSHOPPER, Chorthippus albomarginatus

This is a similar species to the closely related Meadow Grasshopper, with which it is occasionally encountered in its preferred coastal grassland habitat. The wings are fully developed but are quite short and barely reach the knees when the hind legs are outstretched. The side keels of the pronotum are straight or only slightly incurved. The song is a series of four to six chirps over a period of about ten seconds. The rate of leg movement is very rapid, producing a sound not unlike a rather extended version of the Common Field Grasshopper's stridulation. There are several colour varieties but the most common is a pale brown throughout. The others have green on the head and pronotum with almost any combination of green, brown and reddish-pink on the sides. The nymphs appear during May and June and adults mature in July. They are seldom found after early September. The egg pods are laid at the base of

grass tufts. There is a complex array of courtship and mating behaviour. Several males gathering in the presence of a female produce a subdued ticking song most unlike the usual stridulation.

LESSER MOTTLED GRASSHOPPER, Stenobothrus stigmaticus

This is the smallest of the British grasshoppers and was discovered as recently as 1962. There is still only one known site (a heathy peninsula with slate outcrops near the southern tip of the Isle of Man) and the species' absence from the rest of the British Isles is something of a mystery. The simplest explanation would be a deliberate introduction to the area from Europe. While this remains a possibility it must be noted that the Manx specimens are significantly smaller than their European counterparts.

There are several colour varieties but green and brown predominate. The song is a scratchy sound similar to that produced by the Meadow Grasshopper but the notes are issued twice as rapidly. Each burst lasts only a few seconds and it is repeated at irregular intervals.

MEADOW GRASSHOPPER, Chorthippus parallelus

One of the most widespread and commonly encountered species in Britain, the Meadow Grasshopper can be identified by the lack of hind wings and much shortened fore wings. The female's fore wings reach about half-way along the abdomen while those of the male are comparatively longer, though they fall well short of the tip of the abdomen and the knees of the outstretched hind legs. There are various green and brown colour varieties and the former is by far the commonest. Females quite often occur as an attractive purplish variety. Both sexes are occasionally encountered with fully developed wings and as intermediate stages with less stunted wings than the usual form. Only the fully winged variety has the ability to fly.

The Meadow Grasshopper is one of the most cold-tolerant species and nymphs often begin to hatch in mid April in the south of Britain. Adults can be found right through into November or even into December in a mild winter. Their stri-

22

dulation is the characteristic rattle of just a few seconds which is familiar to all visitors to summer meadows. It is repeated frequently but at irregular intervals and is one of the few grasshopper songs which can be heard during hours of darkness on mild evenings. The egg pods are laid below the soil surface and the females search out more open patches within their preferred lush grassy habitat to lay. They can often be found alongside the female Common Field Grasshopper, a species more characteristic of dry, open areas, inserting their egg pods into the surface of large anthills.

MOTTLED GRASSHOPPER, *Myrmeleotettix maculatus*

This is the smallest of the commonly encountered grasshopper species. It can be recognised by the thickened tips of the antennae, most obvious in the male, and the very strongly inflexed side keels of the pronotum. There is an endless variety of colours and these occur, as the name suggests, in a mottled or patchy pattern. Grey, black and various shades of brown are the most usual predominant colours.

Adults mature in late May and can be found through to early November on dry grassy heaths and moorland throughout Britain. Populations can also reach very high densities on fixed dunes and some abandoned quarries. The song is a series of about twenty short chirps which become gradually louder and longer towards the end. A special courtship song is often accompanied by body swaying and antennae waving. The egg pods are laid in warm open soil or sand and contain up to six eggs.

RUFOUS GRASSHOPPER, *Gomphoceripus rufus*

The white-tipped clubbed antennae distinguish this species from all other British grasshoppers. Other features are the short fore wings, which do not extend beyond the hind knees, and a whitish face. There is not much variation in colour and the majority of individuals are brown. A rare purple variety is known amongst females. The name is a reference to the orange coloration which soon develops on the hind tibiae and the tip of the abdomen of both sexes after the final

ecdysis to the adult. The Rufous Grasshopper is more or less restricted to south-facing slopes of chalk and limestone grassland but it is strangely absent from apparently suitable habitat over parts of central southern England. The main areas of distribution are the South Downs of Kent and Surrey.

The Rufous Grasshopper has a relatively late season and adults seldom mature before late July. There is a complex and well-documented courtship display which involves antennae waving, waggling of the mouth parts, head shaking and a quieter version of the normal stridulation. The song is a faint and constantly fluctuating chirp which lasts about five seconds. The fluctuations are produced by changing the angle of the stridulating legs. The clubs on the antennae do not become apparent until later instars and the unique white tips are used to good effect during courtship to accentuate the head and antennae movements. The egg pods are laid in anthills and other patches of soil in the warmest parts of the habitat.

STRIPE-WINGED GRASSHOPPER, *Stenobothrus lineatus*

The Stripe-winged Grasshopper is restricted to dry calcareous grasslands and is typically found on the southern slopes of chalk and limestone downland. The key feature to identification is the much enlarged medial area of the fore wing. This forms a wide band from the base half-way along each fore wing, which is crossed only by parallel veins and not by the network normally found in this zone in other species. The female also has a characteristic tooth on each valve of the ovipositor. The name derives from the white stripe along the base of the fore wing of the female. Both sexes have a very clear white stigma, a comma-shaped mark, two-thirds of the way along each fore wing. The coloration is nearly always green, with some brown or orange on the abdomen and wings. There is rarely a pinkish tinge on the pronotum stripes and on the rear legs.

The adults are active from mid July until September but males will only stridulate in warm sunny weather. The song is a characteristic wheezing most

23

unlike any other British grasshopper. The regular and continuous alternation between subdued and full volume occurs approximately once a second. The stridulatory pegs are very numerous and closely packed and the song is produced by continuous but relatively slow leg movement. Each burst lasts about twenty seconds. The sudden start of the song can be startling and bears a resemblance to a hissing snake. A very different ticking song is used in the immediate presence of a female. The egg pods are not buried but laid just at the interface between the soil and the base of grass clumps.

WOODLAND GRASSHOPPER, *Omocestus rufipes*

The only British grasshopper with a preference for shaded habitat, the Woodland Grasshopper can be identified by its whitish mouthparts and a large area of reddish-orange on the underside of the abdomen. It is seldom found in very dark areas, rather in glades and woodland margins, and it occasionally strays into more open grassland around. The colour is nearly always greyish-brown to black though there is a variety with green along the top surface of the head, pronotum and wings. The Woodland Grasshopper has an early season. The eggs hatch in May and adults mature from late June. They can seldom be found after September.

The egg pods contain up to six eggs and are laid in the soil, often in mossy areas. The song resembles that of its close relative, the Common Green Grasshopper, but lasts only five to ten seconds. During courtship the male produces short chirps. This is one of the rarest species and even well-established colonies frequently have poor years when the population dips to very low numbers. There is therefore always a possibility of local extinction at isolated sites.

Watching Orthoptera

Despite their bright coloration grasshoppers and bush-crickets are notoriously difficult to pinpoint amonst vegetation, especially those which seem to have a curious ability to 'throw' their far-carrying songs. Nevertheless, with practice it is usually possible to track down stridulating males and then females will seldom be far away. Closer inspection is possible if they are captured in glass tubes (75 by 25 mm, 3 by 1 inches), or a larger container for the Great Green Bush-cricket, but specimens are easily damaged and nymphs do not live long in the heat of a glass tube. Several bush-crickets can inflict a painful nip (a further discouragement to collectors). Patient field observation of free individuals is far more rewarding and of greater scientific value.

Most grasshoppers and the coneheads adopt a cryptic posture on vegetation, stretching out and moving to the opposite side of the stem or leaf at any threat such as an inquisitive face or a collecting jar. Bush-crickets found low down often drop to the ground at the first indication of danger and then become difficult to find.

WHERE TO GO

Rivalled only by the New Forest, the Isle of Purbeck in Dorset is one of the richest areas for the study of Orthoptera. Nine of the ten native bush-crickets and all but two of the grasshoppers can be found here. Studland Heath NNR provides ideal habitat for the heathland and bog species, including the rare Heath Grasshopper. To the south, the limestone of Durlston Country Park boasts large populations of Stripe-winged Grasshoppers and the scarce Grey Bush-cricket, amongst a rich insect fauna.

FURTHER READING
Marshall, Judith; and Haes, Chris. *Grasshoppers and Allied Insects of Great Britain and Ireland.* Harley Books, 1988.

ACKNOWLEDGEMENTS
Figures 14 and 22 were photographed by M. Chinery (Natural Science Photos). All other illustrations are by the author.

Grasshoppers and Bush-crickets of the British Isles

The large and often brightly coloured grasshoppers and bush-crickets are amongst the best known of all British insects. The lively movements and jaunty 'songs' of the grasshoppers are familiar to everybody who has walked through a flowery meadow on a sunny day and few late summer holidaymakers visiting the south of Britain can fail to be aware of the exotic evening serenade of the bush-crickets. This book introduces the fascinating life history and ecology of these two closely related families and describes the reasons for, and the mechanisms behind, their songs, which are such an important part of the often complex courtship rituals. The adaptations, habitat preference and distribution of the eleven species of grasshopper and ten species of bush-cricket are described and hints on visual identification are given. Further clues to identity are provided by song tables, a unique bonus in the study of British insects. A final chapter suggests places to visit, concentrating on one of the richest areas, the Isle of Purbeck in Dorset.

Andrew Mahon was born on the Wirral and has always been fascinated by natural history. He read Ecological Science at Edinburgh University, where he developed a special interest in conservation management. An early passion for wild flowers soon widened to include other aspects of downland ecology when he moved to Dorset to work on the coast of the Isle of Purbeck. It is here that he has dedicated much time to the study and conservation of Orthoptera, both in the wild and through captive breeding. Far from being isolated in this work, however, he takes great delight in showing off the rich diversity of wildlife to the tens of thousands of holidaymakers and schoolchildren who visit him each year at Durlston Country Park near Swanage.

Shire Natural History

This series aims to fill the gap between brief guides of general interest and full-length books for the specialist. Each book deals concisely with a single subject, written by experts for the interested layman or student. Titles include:

£

SHIRE £2.50

ISBN 0 85263 946 5   9

At Black Diamond we are obsessed with great gear, we're constantly evolving the way we think about biners. In 1994 we introduced the Hotwire. The wiregate gives more strength, less weight, a wider gate opening and more security as **"wiplash"** gate opening is virtually eliminated. This every bit as light, every bit as strong. The lightest full service biner made.

NEUTRINO

Black Diamond Europe
CH-4153 Reinach BL
Phone ++41 (0) 61 71 31 61 0
E-mail bdeurope@bdel.com

First Ascent
Matlock - Derbyshire, DE4 3EJ
Phone   01629 580 484
E-mail sales@firstascent.co.uk

www.BlackDiamondEquipment.com

This book is dedicated to

Terry Tullis

and with fond memories of

Ed Stone, Pascal Deces, and Julie Tullis

Acknowledgements:

A volume as large as this requires help from so many different areas, and it is to everyone that has helped in the production of this guide that I thank. Firstly to Carrie, for some excellent photographs and endless patience with my countless hours of sketching and computerizing; and secondly to Andy and Jayne Meyers who always were ready with a brew on the, horrible, grim, rainy sketching days. A big thank you to all those who helped out with the photography, doing a climb when they would have preferred to have been off to the pub, and whose names are on the photographs, and the others that did not make the cut.

With a lot of thought in checking the grades, problems and general heavy drinking sessions; Malcom McPherson, Robin Mazinke, Barry Knight, Frank Shannon, Mick Fowler, Chris Murray, Ian Butler, Mike Eden, Luc Percival, Guy McLelland and Ian Stronghill

With tremendous help in translations for foreign climbers; Virginet Bernier (France), Rudiger Jooss (Germany), Matteo Gandini (Italian), Juan Carlos y Eva (Spain), Maki Itekuchi (Japan)

My other Sandstone climbing partners over the years, with which I have had many great days and great fun; Chris Arnold, Justin Beeley, Fliss Butler, Pete Church, Gordon DeLacy, Theseus Gerard, John Godding, Chris Griffiths, Paul Hayes, Joe Healey, John and Pat Horscroft, Graeme Hughes, Paul Innes, Jon Kenton, Julien Morgan, Bruce Nottage, Henry Nottage, Geoff Odds, Sandy Ogilvie, Jamie Ogilvie, Geoff Pearson, Gerry Peel, Martin Randall, Matt Saunders, Jasper Sharp, Dave Shoesmith, Gordon Stainforth, Alan Staley, Jon Thedham, Tip Tipton, Dave Turner, Gary Wickham, Paul Widdowson, Dave Williams, Blob Wyvill.

All previous guidebook writers and contributors; Edward Pyatt, Dave Fagan, John Smoker, Les Holliwell, Tim Daniells, Trevor Panther, Dave Turner, and Mike Vetterlein.

All photographs are by David Atchison-Jones, and Cazzoo of course.

David Atchison-Jones
Chief Editor

Sandstone – South East England
Jingo Wobbly – Euro Guides
First Published in Great Britain in December 2000.
By Vision Poster Company
Holmwood House, 52 Roxborough Park,
Harrow-on-the-Hill, London. HA1 3AY

Copyright © David Atchison-Jones

Image Scanning – Professional Film Company, London
Printing – Fratelli Spada SPA, Rome

A CIP catalogue record is available from the British Library

ISBN   1-873 66511 3

Every effort has been made to ensure that the information included in the guidebook is as up to date as possible at the time of going to press. Historical details may vary when new sources become available, and a new routes book is usually kept at either the Crown pub, Groombridge; or the Huntsman pub at Eridge. Any information included within the advertisements are the sole responsibility of the advertiser. The publisher cannot accept responsibility for any consequences arising from the use of this book.

Up to date latest information can be found at the www.jingowobbly.com website
To buy this guide on line see page 252, or any climbing shop website. Local stockists see page 266.

Photos:
Cover top; Robin Mazinke on October 4c, Bowles Rocks
Cover Left: Angela White on Wooly Bear 6b+. Harrison's Rocks
Cover Right: Carrie Atchison-Jones on Hate 6a, Bowles Rocks
Cover Bottom: Guy McLelland on Digitalis 6a, Bowles Rocks
Frontispiece: Angela White on Wooly Bear 6b+, Harrison's Rocks
Title page: Barry Knight on Cardboard Box 6b, Bowles Rocks

SANDSTONE
South East England

JINGO WOBBLY EURO GUIDES

Contents

What is climbing! Is it a sport, a pastime, a fun hobby, an endurance caper, a self inflicted terror weekend, or one of the easiest and quickest ways to have an accident and die? The latter is certainly the most accurate - if not the most warming, and should always be paramount in anybody's mind, who wants to climb.

Accidents, which result in injury or death, are not unknown, so the real question of today is – who is therefore to blame? Well, until the square suits of Whitehall, frog march us out of the city suburbs to the foot of the crags, and gives the order 'climb, or be shot!' It's our decision. It is ourselves that are to blame for this most ridiculous of pastimes; our decision to visit the rocky cliffs, gormenghasts that have always been associated with perilous danger. We take that deliberate choice to leave the comfort of our safe homes, for the hard and uncompromising vertical world. What is important though, is how we should prepare ourselves to enter this unruly arena. Are there rules? Can climbing be actually made safe? Do we even want it to be safe?

In climbing, there are no rules and no umpires. You only need rules when you compete with other people. In climbing, you only compete with yourself, and for that you need no rules; which makes it so special. So if there are no rules, then how do we play the game? When do we get on, and when do we get off? The game is generally about self-fulfillment. You do it because you want to, and how you want to. If you decide against using ropes or safety equipment - then you do. It is that fine edge danger point and physical freedom, which will give you your own self fulfillment. On the other hand, if you are wary of injury, then get all the professional instruction under the sun, even get a professional climbing guide to hold your hand – there is nothing wrong or sissy about staying alive. The point, is that you too will get your own personal fulfillment.

So there are no rules, but there is one abiding law; the Law of Gravity – it, never fails; only you can! In climbing across Europe, there are many documents about cliff stability, and the metal rings that are used for safety points. In summary, general opinion is that they are all completely unsafe!! This of course sounds completely ridiculous, because everyone uses them. But it does solve the two subjective safety dilemmas. Firstly – liability; anyone who places a ring, has put it in for their own use only, and is not putting it in for others safety! A climber cannot return every day to check every bolt ring in Europe – there are millions. You cannot have a safety system without daily checks. Secondly, and more importantly – Judgement; By using the ring and knowing that it is not guaranteed, you personally assess the situation visually – how lucky do you feel today eh!!! You choose whether or not to accept responsibility of use, with the full knowledge that it may fail. It is risky, climbing is! If you don't like the risk and the consequences – don't use the rings, don't even climb.

There are two styles of climbing book: an instruction manual (this book is not an instruction manual), which will teach you many points of climbing and safety: And a Climbing Guide, which teaches you nothing, but illustrates where climbs have been done. This point is very important, there is certainly no guarantee that the climb will still be in the same condition or difficulty as on the first ascent, or when the guidebook was compiled. If a climb or footpath is illustrated in this guide, it does not give you any trespass right whatsoever. With regard to access, a right to roam freely, should be applicable to everyone and everywhere in the UK – it is our country lets face it. But 'a roaming right,' should be just that – not a rambling massive thoroughfare, or a constant vertical rambling ravine. The countryside for its part, needs to be looked after, and this is only possible, with part-national and part-private ownership. Climbers and walkers should therefore respect the rights and requests of landgoverners, conservationists and environmentalists, who actually really care for the countryside. Some cliffs in this guide have restricted climbing; please accept restricted climbing - as part of not having to give up our basic roaming rights. (refer to current notices at the cliffs themselves).

6

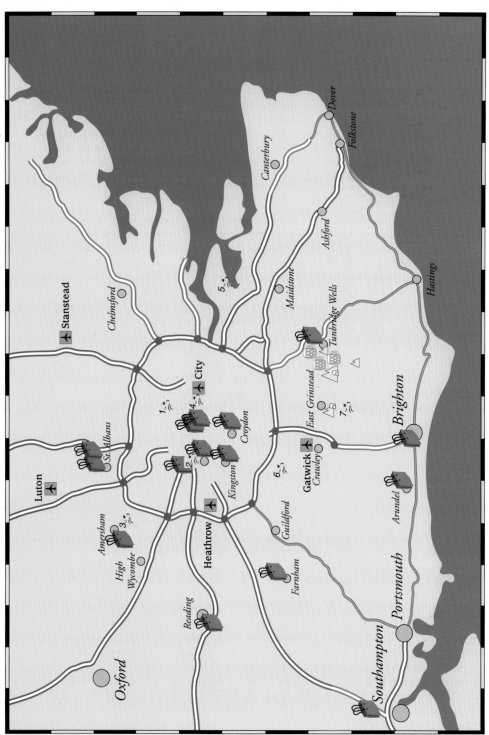

Advertisers Index

Indoor Climbing Walls

1. **The Castle**, Green Lanes, Stoke Newington, London N4 2HA 020 8211 7000 [inside back cover]
2. **Westway Sports Centre**, 1 Crowthorne Road, London W10 6RP 020 8969 0992 [p-148]
3. **The Climb**, Benshiem Way, Chiltern Ave, Amersham HP6 5AH 01494 586 809 [p-312]
4. **Mile End Wall**, Haverfield Road, Mile End, London E3 5BE 020 8980 0289 [p-113]
5. **Arethusa Venture Centre**, Lower Upnor, Rochester, Kent ME2 4XB 01634 719 933 [p-299]
6. **High Sport Wall**, Unit 6, Orchard Business Centre, Bonehurst Road, Salfords, Nr. Redhill, Surrey RH1 5EL 01293 822 884 [p-292]
7. **Blackland Farm**, Grinstead Lane, East Grinstead RH19 4HP 01342 810 493 [p-325]

Equipment

Mammut - www.mammut.ch
Black Diamond - www.blackdiamondequipment.com
Boreal - www.boreal-club.com
Beal - www.bealropes.com
Petzl - www.petzl.com
Berghaus - www.berghaus.com
HB - www.hb.wales.com
Mountain Hard Wear - www.mountainhardwear.com
S7 - www.s7.co.uk
Lost Arrow - www.lost-arrow.de
Jingo Wobbly Euro Guides - www.jingowobbly.com

Inner M25 London Shops

Cotswold, 72-76 Clarence St, Kingston-on-T, London KT1 1NW 020 8549 9500 [p-262]
Cotswold, 42-46 Uxbridge Rd, Shepherd's Bush, London W12 8ND 020 8743 2976 [p-262]
Rock On, Mile End Wall, Haverfield Rd, Mile End London E3 5BE 020 8981 5066 [p-24]
Rock On, YHA Adventure, Southampton Row, Covent Garden, London WC2E 7HY 020 7212 9979 [p-24]
Urban Rock, Castle Climbing Centre, Green Lanes, Stoke Newington N4 2HA 020 8211 0475 [p-48]
Field and Trek, 105 Baker Street, London W1M 1FE 020 7224 0049 [p-68]
Lang and Hunter, 12 Thames Street, Kingston, London KT1 1PE 020 8546 5427 [p-54]

Pubs and Inns

The Huntsman, 80 metres from A26, Eridge Station, Eridge, near Tunbridge Wells Kent TN3 9LE [p-30]
The Crown Inn, the Green on B2110, Groombridge, near Tunbridge Wells, Kent TN3 9QH [p-86]
Toad Rock Retreat, 300m from A264, Denny Bottom, Rusthall, nr T. Wells Kent TN4 8NX 01892 520 818 [p-125]

Physiotherapy

Wimpole Street Physiotherapy Clinic
59 Wimpole Street, London W1G 8AF
Tel: 020 7935 7344 [p-112]

South East Shops

Cotswold, 13 Lower Northam Road, Hedge End, Southampton SO30 4FN 01489 799 555 [p-262]
Peglers, 69 Tarrant Street, Arundel. West Sussex BN18 9DN 01903 883 375 Peglers [p-117, 278, 330]
Open Spaces, 69 Trafalgar Street, Brighton, Sussex BN1 4EB 01273 600 897 [p-84]
Country Trails, 39 Mount Pleasant, Tunbridge Wells, Kent. TN1 1PN 01892 539 002 [p-98]
Breaking Free, The Borough, Farnham, Surrey GU9 7NA 01252 724 347 [p-210]
Fox's, 1 London Road, Amersham, Bucks HP7 0HE 01494 431 431 [p-214]
Urban Rock, The Climb, Benshiem Way, Chiltern Ave, Amersham HP6 5AH 01494 431 641 [p-187]
Breaking Away, 36 London Road, St. Albans, Herts AL1 1NG 01727 833 586 [p-250]

Climbing Instructors

Chris Tullis, Dower House Mews, Leyswood, Groombridge, TN3 9PH
Tel: 01892 863 659 [p-59]
Email: chris@softrockclimbing.co.uk
www.softrockclimbing.co.uk

Keith Fleming, 3 the Twitten, Burgess Hill, West Sussex RH15 8BX [p-316]
Tel: 01444 235258 or 07710 345322
Email: keith@mtn-activities.co.uk
www.mtn-activities.co.uk

GOOD FORM on Sandstone, is to enjoy the climbing - and the day out, whilst leaving as little scars of erosion as possible. The rock is soft, and therefore very susceptible to quick wear from ropes, heavy footwear, and general over thuggyness. Without doubt, safety precautions get the highest priority, but in most situations, this can be achieved without causing large damage to the rock.

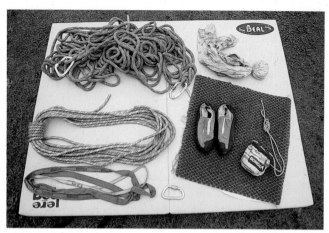

A local kit of Dynamic rope, non stretch belay slings and extensions, locking karabiners, soft slippers, carpet and crash mat, chalk and resin.

The climbing equipment used, should be in first class condition and thoroughly checked, every time before use! Climbing safety - use a dynamic rope, which absorbs the impact of a fall; choose your own belaying system, but use one that does not transfer any shock load to anchors.

Arrange a belay at the top of the cliff which is safe, with correctly tied knots. Here use a Static-non stretch system, and keep the running karabiner, clear of the edge. This will result in no rope running over the rock under tension – which is the worst and quickest erosion problem. In a fall, shock impact should be absorbed by the dynamic rope and belayer.

Bad Form: Do not run the rope simply around the trunk of a tree, or the ring of an in-situ bolt. This will soon saw the tree in half with concentrated weekend use.

Most beginners do not have the finger strength to pull off holds, but they do have bashing plodders to kick the hell out of the rock. Please use soft-soled footwear such as specialist climbing shoes, there are many modern

SANDY BITS AND PIECES

Choose your own belay system, and if you use devices, check then thoroughly

lightweight slippers which are very kind to the rock, and succeed on the climbs of the very top standard.

Bad Form: Climbing on the rock when it is wet. The rock soaks up the moisture and becomes incredibly soft and brittle, a strong or heavy climber will simply pull off any fragile holds.

When you climb, feel free and do what you want, but stick to climbing the rock, and not get winched up the climb. Climb at all times free from aid, and leave

winch grinding to the America's Cup. Importantly, the moment that you give someone a tight rope, the rope will most probably come into contact with the rock, and under tension will act like a band saw, cutting through the hard crust and into the soft under rock. Chalk and resin are used, some agree, some disagree! Feel free to have an opinion, neither seems to erode the rock differently – in fact resin can polish the rock, which must mean that it is not being worn away – you can't have it both ways.

When you reach the top, make sure that you are safe and talk to your belayer. Then untie and use a proper walk way down, one which is organised and designed for lots of use. This will in turn, protect the rock from needless erosion in lowering off. Ground slip and settlement is an ongoing problem, so trees and plants have been used to bind the soil together. A huge amount of effort has been put into the careful planning of paths, descents and drainage routes. The management of the rocks is working, but can only succeed with the help of all visiting climbers.

Bad Form: Abseiling: DO NOT ABSEIL ON SANDSTONE. Abseiling on soft rock such as Sandstone, wears away the crust very quickly and within a few years, the whole area turns to soft sand! Artificial climbing walls offer excellent abseil facilities, and proper safety regulations should be in force.

Most importantly, the climbing area in the South East is popular and well frequented by a lot of people. There is no one to clear up after you, so leave all areas as you find them – use only the proper toilet facilities, and leave no litter.

SANDY BITS AND PIECES

This topo climbing guidebook, uses pictorial drawings to illustrate the cliff faces, and then a series of coloured lines to show the various routes at each difficulty. Inside the two ends of the book, there are maps to the East and West areas of climbing. These show the rough location of the cliffs, and give the page number to the crag chapters. At each crag there is a small location map, which should be ample to locate the cliff and the various sections within it. From here one can quickly locate the individual buttress and topo diagram. The diagrams themselves should be easy to follow, but sometimes there have been sneaky cheats - like unwrapping a curved boulder onto a flat sheet (like a world map). The climbs are illustrated with colour to reflect difficulty, and at the point of the crux, there is often a symbol which illustrates the type of crux. There is a general index to these on the inside back flap. Below are the route names and historical details. On each line, there are symbols to illustrate the style of climb, and the index to these is on the inside front flap.

Wobbly - bow ties
UK - Mantleshelf
F- Small sharp holds
I - Pocket pulling
ES- Overhanging thuggy
CH- Slopy smooth holds
A - Techno grooves
D - Pebble pulling
Scotland - Cracks

There are 8 different Wobbly symbols to show technical and difficult crux moves, the bow tie will illustrate the actual style of move.

The Jingo on the route is to show a really devilish move, often very powerful and not easy to read, but is only relative to the actual grade of the climb.

A parachute symbol is used to show the direction of the way up and down. If there is a numbered circle on it, then you actually have to use that route as the way.

Never forget to take notice of the reach ruler, if it's there, then you will be at full stretch to get the holds, levels vary from 5ft to 6ft 3ins.

Each route is marked with a corresponding number, and is listed with its name, and sometimes a nickname or a different first ascent name that has been.

The grade and date of the first ascent is given, and the names of any known first ascentionists.

There are two symbols which best represent the style of climbing to be found on the route, with the left symbol often reffering to the lower part. and right-upper part.

At Jingo Wobbly we like stars - we like climbing. All are relative to the crag, and not Yosemite. We also think some climbs are disgusting so we show them. the dustbin.

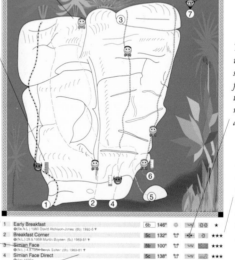

1	Early Breakfast		6b	146°				★
	☺(6a,N.L.) 1980 David Atchison-Jones (6b) 1992-5 ▼							
2	Breakfast Corner		5c	132°				★★★
	☺(N.L.) 28.6.1959 Martin Boysen (5c) 1969-81 ▼							
3	Simian Face		5b	100°				★★★
	☺(N.L.) 4.9.1958 Derek Suter (5b) 1969-81 ▼							
4	Simian Face Direct		5c	138°				★★★
	☺(5c) 1970's							

There is the solo trophy award, for the first known solo; falling off the last move does not count! The name and date are listed where possible.

The current grade is given in the main box, which is colour coded to match the route. The colours used are intended to be as close to Fontainebleau circuits as possible.

This is the sunshine box for sun in the morning, all day, evening, and not at all. If there is green encroaching, then in heavy summer the trees will shade the rock.

The angle of the hard part of the climb is given, which has been taken using the highly comical Atchison-Angleometer.

When you have had it up to your eyeballs with the hustle and bustle of London, or when the stress of work takes you to screaming point, fear not! There is the tranquil and elegant rural countryside of East Sussex and Kent to escape to. Apart from the bluebell woodlands and lush meadows, there are the hop wires and vineyards, which service the wonderful country pubs.

In a few places of the Wealden basin, the sandstone bed, breaks through to give around 10 different outcrops. This rock is soft and fine-grained, not hard like Fontainebleau, and has no pebbles like the Pfalz in Germany. The years of weathering, have given the rounded breaks a crusty surface, and in many place a fine honeycomb texture. It has, and continues to wear, so every effort must be made to reduce erosion to a minimum (see environmental photos). Beginners will have great fun here, but will find it difficult since that rock gives very few good juggy holds. The middle grade climber (4a-5a) will have plenty to struggle with, and with all climbing being done on a top rope (because the rock is so weak), you can take it to the limit.

The real finesse with sandstone lies in the high grades (5b-6a), you need not be strong, but technique and footwork will be of the essence. Many of the local climbers have practiced the routes for years, so be prepared to be shown up; however, this guide now at least gives you 'the numbers' for the crux's. For nearly every route in this guide, there is more than one way to climb it, which makes it one of the most enjoyable and entertaining areas in the UK.

The equipment that is used will vary from climber to climber, but the rocks are only 30ft high at the most, and leading using traditional protection is both bad for the rock – and incredibly dangerous. A non stretch sling for a tree or bolt belay is the norm, and in places where this is a long way back, you should extend using a non stretch rope, and protect the edge of the cliff from erosion with a mat or beer towel. Screwgate karabiners only, and please always walk down after a climb – it helps reduce wear enormously. A tiny mat with a waterproof underside is essential; you can then start the climb with clean shoes.

There is not a huge amount of bouldering here, but what there is – is hard and good. Please never boulder on wet sandstone, it is incredibly weak and breaks

Firefly 6b, High Rocks; Dave Woodburn

instantly. There have been some excellent problems developed in this guide, and with the label system for the holds you should be able to develop you own as well – see the jingowobbly.com website for local, up to date, desperates.

Our friend and guardian for the rocks is Sheriff TT. So if you see a sticker or sign for him, then you most probably should not be climbing there. If he is on a topo in this guide, you should really question as to why you are climbing there! We have included the all the topo's - 'open and restricted,' because it gives a good overall description of climbing in the past 50 years.

Overuse is by far the biggest problem to any rural activity within striking distance from London. With so many people coming to the area, firstly please make every effort to use the toilet facilities at Harrison's, Bowles and High Rocks (the 3 major outcrops). Large instructional groups, can contact Chris Tullis, at Harrison's Rocks Tel: 018092 863 659 for general co-ordination advice. If you visit for more than the day, there is the Julie Tullis memorial campsite at Harrison's. There is only a small fee; for a lovely woody camping area, drinking water, hot water and washing facilities.

La campagne anglaise est très agréable car très verdoyante du fait des nombreuses pluies que l'Angleterre subit. La région du sud-est de Londres reste cependant assez sèche et est certainement la région la plus ensoleillée du continent britannique. Ainsi d'avril à octobre, le climat y est parfait pour l'escalade. Sandstone est un endroit très calme, et même si quelques dimanches vous trouvez un peu plus de monde, surtout à Harrison Rocks, vous aurez en général plus de mal à vous frayer un chemin entre les paniers de piquenique qu'entre les grimpeurs. L'escalade est située sur des petits blocs de grès, qui sont formés tels de longues dalles avec quelques cimes isolées. Ils sont pour la plus part d'une hauteur de 7 à 10 mètres et sont situés sur de basses collines ondulées et boisées. La roche est naturellement tendre et parfois fragile, notamment lorsqu'il a plu et qu'elle est encore humide. Le grès est similaire dans sa forme à Fontainebleau notamment à celui des blocs de la Dame Jouanne et de l'Eléphant, mais il n'est pas à grain fin et n'a pas de dépôt de quartz. Il est également très similaire à certains endroits de Pfalz, en particulier Berdorf. A

Look Sharp 6b+, High Rocks; Ian Butler

cause de sa fragilité, il est à certains endroits très usé et de nombreuses prises arrondies se sont créées, ce qui rend l'escalade plus difficile pour les grimpeurs débutants. Sur les voies plus difficiles, les prises les plus petites ont pratiquement toutes disparues et par conséquent, du fait du surplomb de certaines voies, l'adresse et la force d'un orang-outang sont nécessaires pour grimper. Pour les grimpeurs locaux, Sandstone est simplement appelé "The Rocks", et la plus part des sites sont appelés par leurs premiers noms.

Les blocs

Harrison's Rocks, avec plus de 350 voies, est le secteur d'escalade le plus important, en particulier pour les grimpeurs débutants et de niveau moyen. Il est orienté ouest et reçoit beaucoup d'ensoleillement dans l'après-midi. Les voies sont d'environ 8 mètres de haut et offrent différents types de technique de grimpe. Le site est situé dans un très joli décor, à la bordure d'un bois et à environ 15 minutes de marche du principal parking. Bowles Rocks, qui est le second plus important sîte de blocs, est parfait pour les grimpeurs moyens et est également utilisé comme centre aéré. L'escalade est excellente, mais on ne retrouve pas cette sensation de nature qu'il y a à Harrison. High Rocks - sans nul doute - offre les meilleures voies pour les grimpeurs confirmés. Les voies sont en moyenne de 10 mètres de haut mais avec un angle de 110 degrés celles-ci ne paraissent pas toujours très longues. Malheureusement "High" est très ombragé et reste donc très humide, et même si cela n'empêche pas toujours de grimper, ça rend les 6b beaucoup plus difficiles. Les autres secteurs d'escalade plus petits sont moins fréquentés. Ils offrent des voies de qualité et l'opportunité de profiter des joies de la grimpe dans le calme et la sérénité.

Technique

Tout comme une première visite à Fontainebleau, vous serez très surpris de voir comme les grimpeurs du coin sont très bons et ceci est simplement dù à une bonne utilisation de leur technique sur les blocs de Sandstone. En effet, pour la plus part des voies (excepté les voies les plus difficiles), vous n'avez pas besoin d'être fort ou d'avoir beaucoup d'endurance, mais simplement d'une bonne technique. La roche est très sableuse et l'adhérence est difficile à obtenir. Il est donc indispensable de nettoyer la semelle de vos chaussures avant de grimper, et vous remarquerez très rapidement que les grimpeurs se promènent toujours avec un petit tapis pour s'essuyer les pieds avant de commencer une voie. Le sable a tendance à tomber du haut des voies sur les réglettes qui se trouvent un peu plus bas. Une petite serviette est donc également très pratique afin de nettoyer les prises et de permettre une bonne adhérence. Parfois lorsque la roche est humide, la serviette est posée entre la roche et le chausson afin de conserver l'adhérence. Sur ce type de roche les prises ayant tendance à être glissantes, les pieds et les chevilles doivent être bien détendues afin de permettre un contact total entre la semelle et le rocher. La plus part des voies faciles peuvent se faire en parfaite équilibre et une bonne utilisation du croche talon a sa récompense. De nombreuses voies ont leur crux en haut et nécessitent une bonne technique de rétablissement. Du fait de ces fins difficiles, très peu de grimpeurs tentent des solos. Vous trouverez dans ce livre différentes sections sur l'escalade à bloc. Il vaut la peine de visiter un des secteurs les plus faciles afin d'avoir une bonne introduction de l'escalade sur les blocs de Sandstone.

Equipement

Les chaussons d'escalade légers sont parfaits et un crash pad est toujours utile. L'escalade est une activité dangereuse et il est de la responsabilité de chaque grimpeur de bien s'assurer de sa sécurité. Il y a des ancrages et des arbres au sommet des blocs, cependant ne présumez pas de leur parfaite sécurité. Choisissez toujours plusieurs points d'ancrage au cas ou l'un d'entre eux lâche. Assurez-vous de placer le mousqueton de sécurité juste en dessous du bord du sommet du bloc et d'utiliser une sangle non élastique. Ceci permet d'éviter tout frottement sur la roche (des sangles de 5 mètres pour Harrison et Bowles, 15 mètres pour la plus part des autres sites d'escalade ou les arbres sont plus éloignés). L'escalade se fait en moulinette, vous aurez donc besoin d'une bonne corde d'excellente qualité, relativement courte - 30 mètres de long. Enfin, un bon harnais pour chaque grimpeur et de préférence un système d'assurage de type grigri.

Comment utiliser ce topo

Ce guide a été réalisé autour de symboles qui sont montrés au dos de la couverture avant. Chaque bloc a été schématisé et les voies sont indiquées avec des couleurs spéciales - qui sont identiques aux couleurs utilisées pour les cotations de Fontainebleau. Il y a

Matterhorn Arête, High Rocks; Ian Butler

des visages souriants pour montrer les mouvements difficiles et des démons rouges pour montrer les mouvements experts; parfois ils sont associés avec une règle pour illustrer les voies qui sont particulièrement difficiles ou impossibles pour les grimpeurs de petite taille. Un index en dessous du topo donne le nom de la voie avec sa cotation, la date de la première ascension et la date de la première ascension solo. La cotation générale de la voie est indiquée à côté de la partie la plus difficile de la voie. Une catégorie avec des soleils est utilisée pour indiquer l'ensoleillement des blocs, ceci car certaines voies orientées sud sont malgré tout très ombragées par les arbres. Enfin, les étoiles sont données pour la qualité de la voie. Vous trouverez à l'intérieur des couvertures, des cartes qui vous guideront aux différents sites d'escalade, et pour chaque site, vous trouverez un plan des blocs.

Restrictions

La roche étant très fragile, il y a un grand problème d'érosion. Chaque grimpeur se doit donc d'être vigilant et doit éviter d'aggraver ou d'accélérer ce processus d'érosion. Si possible essayez de grimper de manière contrôlée afin d'éviter de casser les prises. Une fois la voie terminée dénouez la corde de votre harnais et redescendez en marchant. En effet, la descente en rappel est une technique qui détruira la roche très rapidement. Si vous vous lancez dans une voie sur un bloc dont la descente est difficile, assurez-vous que vous pourrez effectuer cette descente par vos propres moyens. Un parachute est utilisé sur les schémas pour montrer ou se situe la descente. Lorsqu'un numéro est rattaché à ce parachute, cela signifie qu'il vous faut utiliser cette voie pour redescendre. Ce guide contient deux pages de photos qui illustrent la plus part des bonnes et mauvaises choses à faire et à ne pas faire aux sites d'escalade de Sandstones, étudiez-les attentivement. En général les oiseaux ne font pas leurs nids autour du standstone, il n'y a donc pas de restrictions à ce niveau. A Eridge Green, il y a quelques plantes et des espèces de mousses et de lichen qui sont très rares. Les grimpeurs opèrent donc une politique de non-escalade pour certains endroits de Eridge et le guide indique ces endroits. Le secteur général de restrictions change très souvent et le National Climbing Organisation met à jour régulièrement une liste des restrictions qui est affichée à l'entrée de chaque site.

Cotations

Les cotations anglaises sont souvent données par rapport au mouvement le plus difficile de la voie. Dans le secteur standstone, la cotation représente la difficulté générale de la voie, et les symboles du démon et du sourire, représentés sur les schémas, sont utilisés pour les crux moves. Chaque site a une liste de voies par ordre de difficulté et les cotations de chaque secteur sont similaires tout au long de ce guide. Certaines voies particulières, nécessitent de grimper en utilisant certaines prises bien spécifiques. Pour l'escalade de bloc, nous avons utilisé les cotations de Fontainebleau.

Logement et accès

A Harrison's Rocks, vous trouverez le terrain de camping à la mémoire de Julie Tullis. C'est un terrain de camping assez petit mais très sympathique, à l'intérieur d'un petit bois. Il y a des toilettes et des bacs avec de l'eau chaude pour nettoyer la vaisselle. Une modique somme d'argent est demandée par personne et par nuit. Ces installations ainsi que le parking de Harrison's rocks sont mis à la disposition du public sur la condition que les visiteurs fassent une donation à chacune de leur visite. S'il vous plait respectez cette règle, puisque cet argent permet de conserver les installations propres et en en bon état et de garder le site d'escalade dans de bonnes conditions. Vous trouverez localement de très bons pubs et des fermes faisant chambres d'hôte. Il est très utile d'avoir une voiture afin de se déplacer d'un site à un autre, cependant des trains circulent régulièrement entre Londres et Tunbridge Wells ou il y a en général des taxis qui peuvent vous conduire jusqu'à Harrison. Enfin il y a les bus qui depuis Tunbridge Wells circulent tout autour des principaux sites d'escalade.

Tobacco Road bouldering, Bowles; Ian Stronghill

Die schöne grüne Landschaft Englands lässt es ahnen: hier regnet es nicht zu wenig. Doch es ist der grosse Vorteil der Region südöstlich von London, dass es der trockenste und mit Sicherheit der sonnigste Landesteil von Gross-Britannien ist. Von April bis Oktober ist das Klima perfekt zum Klettern und es kommt nur an wenigen Sonntagen einmamal vor, dass es am Harrison Rock eng zugeht. Und selbst dann wird man eher über Picknickkörbe als über engagierte Kletterer stolpern. Geklettert wird an kleinen Sandsteinfelsen, die lange Felsenbänke mit einigen freistehenden Nadeln bilden. Die meist 7 bis 10 Meter hohen Felsen fügen sich harmonisch in die waldreichen Hügelländer ein. Der von Natur aus ohnehin weiche Sandstein wird nach Regenfällen besonders nachgiebig, da dann das Bindemittel teilweise gelöst wird. Die Felsformen erinnern an Fontainebleau, etwa an die Gebilde der 'Dame Jouanne' oder des 'Elephant', aber in Harrison's ist der Sandstein nicht so feinkörnig und enthält keinen härtenden Quarz. Das Gestein erinnert stark an die Pfalz und ganz besonders an Berdorf. Aufgrund der Weichheit werden die Griffe im Laufe der Zeit immer runder, was vor allem den Unterarmen von Anfängern stark zu schaffen macht. In den schweren, meist stark überhängenden Touren sind die kleineren Griffe mit der Zeit verschwunden, weswegen der Kletterstil eines bärig starken Orang Utans den meisten Erfolg versprechen wird. Die Locals nennen das Gebiet einfach „The Rocks" und die meisten Felsen werden nur mit ihrem ersten Namen bezeichnet.

Die Felsen

Harrison's Rock ist mit seinen 350 Touren der bedeutendste Fels des Klettergebiets für den Durchschnittskletterer. Er ist vorwiegend nach Westen ausgerichtet und erhält dadurch angenehme Nachmittagssonne. Die Kletterungen sind etwa 8 Meter hoch und sehr abwechslungsreich. Der Fels liegt wunderschön am Waldrand 15 Minuten vom Haupt-Parkplatz entfernt. Bowles Rock, das andere grosse Gebiet, ist optimal für den Durchschnittskletterer geeignet und wird auch als Outdoor-Center genützt. Die Kletterei ist genial, doch fehlt das natürliche Ambiente von Harrison's. High Rocks bietet zweifellos die besten Touren für den ambitionierten Kletterer. Die Felsen sind zwar meist nur 10 Meter hoch, doch bei einem Überhang von 110 Grad ergeben sich recht lange Kletterungen. Leider ist High sehr schattig und kann lange feucht sein, was das Klettern natürlich nicht unmöglich macht, sondern nur die 6b's ein gutes Stück schwerer! An den restlichen, kleineren Felsen geht es wunderbar ruhig zu; sie bieten Kletterei in Spitzenqualität und eine gute Gelegenheit für genüßliches Klettern in Ruhe und Frieden.

Technik

Wie beim ersten Besuch in Fontainebleau ist man überrascht, wie gut die Locals hier klettern. Das liegt an einer sehr speziellen Technik. In den Überhängen sieht das natürlich anders aus, aber für die meisten Touren muss man weder stark sein noch eine gute Ausdauer haben. Das Gestein ist sandig und bietet daher wenig Reibung. Gründliches Reinigen der Sohle ist obligatorisch vor jeder Tour und die Locals haben immer ein kleines Stück Teppich dabei von dem aus sie einsteigen. Da Sandkörner in einer Tour abwärts fallen und auf Leisten liegen bleiben, erweist sich ein Handtuch als sehr nützlich, um Griffe und Tritte zu säubern. Wenn ein Tritt schmierig ist, wird das Handtuch manchmal sogar darauf gelegt, damit die Sohle sauber bleibt und die nötige Reibung erzielt wird. Die Tritte sind in der Regel abschüssig, sodass die Fußgelenke gut locker sein müssen, damit die volle Sohlenfläche den Fels berühren kann. Die meisten leichteren Touren kann man hochbalancieren; Heelhooks erweisen sich als Schlüssel mancher schweren Stelle. Die Crux vieler Touren befindet sich am Ausstieg und verlangen eine saubere Mantle-Technik. Aufgrund dieser schwierigen Ausstiege wird nur wenig solo geklettert. In diesem Führer wird auch das Bouldern ausführlich beschrieben; leichteres Bouldern ist eine sehr gute Einführung in die Eigenheiten der Kletterei hier.

Ausrüstung

Normale Reibungskletterschuhe sind am besten geeignet. Ein Crashpad bei Bouldersessions dabei zu haben, ist nie ein Fehler. Klettern ist nicht ungefährlich und es liegt an jedem / jeder selber für seine / ihre Sicherheit zu sorgen. Zwar gibt es Bohrhaken und Bäume an den Ausstiegen, doch sind diese Fixpunkte nicht unbedingt sicher! Es sollten immer mehrere Haken gleichzeitig zum Sichern verwendet werden, für den Fall, dass einer ausbricht. Ganz wichtig ist es, den Schraubkarabiner, in dem das Toprope-Seil läuft, so am Ausstieg zu platzieren, dass das Toprope-Seil nicht über die Felskante reibt. Dazu wird der Schrauber in einem extra Seil eingehängt, dass an den teilweise recht weit von der Felskante entfernten Bäumen fixiert wird. Dieses Seil wird zum Schutz vor Abrieb mit nicht dehnbarem Tape umwickelt wird (5 Meter für Harrison's und Bowles, 15 Meter für viele der anderen Felsen). Es wird nur Toprope geklettert, ein relativ kurzes handelsübliches Kletterseil (30 Meter) reicht aus. Desweiteren braucht jeder Kletterer einen Klettergurt und eines der gängigen Sicherungsgeräte.

Zum Gebrauch dieses Führers

Als roter Faden dieses Führers dienen die Symbole, die im vorderen Innencover erklärt werden. Jeder Fels ist künstlerisch wertvoll skizziert und die Touren in verschiedenen Farben, die den Schwierigkeitsgraden in Fontainebleau entsprechen, dargestellt. Glückliche Gesichter weisen auf harte Züge hin und rote Teufel auf absolut knallharte Moves. Ein Reichweiten-Meterstab deutet auf Größenprobleme hin, die besonders schwer oder gar unmöglich für kleine Kletterer sind. Jeweils unterhalb der Topos folgt eine Übersicht, die Tourenname, Schwierigkeitsgrad, Erstbegeher samt Datum sowie die erste bekannte Solobegehung enthält. Die Gesamtbewertung der Tour ist neben der Wandneigung des schwierigsten Teils angegeben. Eine Besonnungsskala informiert über die tatsächliche Sonneneinstrahlung auf den Fels, da Südwände durch Bäume oder andere Felsen auch stark beschattet sein können. Zwei Symbole geben Auskunft über die Art der Kletterei in der Reihenfolge des Kletterns. Eine Kante wird immer mit der Seite gezeigt, auf der sie geklettert wird; ein Überhang der bereits aus dem Symbol der Wandneigung ersichtlich ist, wird nicht nochmals ausgewiesen, usw. Die Qualität der Kletterei wird, immer bezogen auf das jeweilige Klettergebiet, mit Sternen bewertet. Übersichtskarten weisen den Weg zu den Felsen. Für jeden Fels zeigen Detailkarten den Weg zu den einzelnen Sektoren.

Kletterbeschränkungen

Da das Gestein sehr weich ist, stellt die Erosion ein großes Problem dar. Jeder Kletterer sollte sich dessen bewusst sein und nach Möglichkeit alles vermeiden, was diesen Prozess fördern oder sogar beschleunigen könnte. Wenn möglich klettert bitte kontrolliert ohne die Griffe aus der Wand zu reißen. Am Ausstieg solltet Ihre Euch ausbinden und hinunter zu den Einstiegen laufen. Es leuchtet jedem ein, dass Ablassen, Abseilen oder das Ausbouldern einer Tour das Gestein sehr schnell in Mitleidenschaft ziehen und unnötig ist. Wenn Ihr eine Tour auf eine Nadel oder einen größeren Felsblock angeht, die einen schwierigen Abstieg haben, vergewissert Euch vorher, dass Ihr auch alleine wieder hinunterkommt. Ein Fallschirmsymbol zeigt den Weg des Abstiegs und wenn eine Nummer dabei steht bedeutet dies, die entsprechende Tour abzuklettern. Bitte beachtet auch die zwei Foto-Seiten, die praktische Hinweise für dieses Klettergebiet geben. Vögel nisten nicht regelmäßig hier im Sandstein, sodass es glücklicherweise keine jahreszeitlichen Felssperrungen gibt. Bei Eridge Green gibt es einige seltene Pflanzen, schmierige grüne Moose und Flechten. Die Kletterer waren hier mit einem freiwilligen Kletterverzicht sehr erfolgreich, die Regelung ist im Führer dargestellt. Das Gebiet mit den meisten Einschränkungen wechselt häufig. In der Regel informieren Infotafeln der National Climbing Organisation an den Zustiegen über die aktuelle Situation.

Wooly Bear 6b+, Harrison's Rocks; Angela White

Unterkunft und Anreise

Julie Tullis Memorial Campsite ist ein kleiner und sehr schöner Campingplatz bei Harrison's Rock mit kleinen Zeltplätzen inmitten eines jungen Wäldchens. Da Parkplätze, Toiletten und Waschmöglichkeiten mit Warmwasser zur Verfügung gestellt werden, sind die Besucher aufgefordert freiwillig eine gewisse Summe zu hinterlassen. Daran sollte sich auch jeder halten! Die letzten Jahre haben gezeigt, dass die Bemühungen um Sauberkeit unschätzbaren Wert haben. Die Felsen und ihre Umgebung sind - im Gegensatz zu manch anderem beliebten Klettergebiet - absolut sauber, die Kletterei wird akzeptiert. Es gibt auch sehr nette Pubs und Bauernhöfe in der Umgegend, die 'Bed and Breakfast' anbieten. Ein Auto ist hilfreich um an die Felsen zu gelangen, doch gibt es auch eine gute Bahnverbindung von London nach Tunbridge Wells, wo in der Regel Taxis für die 6 Meilen lange Fahrt nach Harrison's zur Verfügung stehen. Zudem gibt es noch Busverbindungen, deren Routenverlauf sich jedoch immer mal wieder ändert! Von hier nach da und dort und wieder zurück oder auch mal nicht.

Bewertung

Die in England übliche Schwierigkeitsbewertung bezieht sich häufig auf einen harten Zug in der Tour. In diesem Sandsteingebiet ist der Schwierigkeitsgrad als Gesamtbewertung einer Route zu verstehen, der Smiley und der Teufel veranschaulichen die Art der Schlüsselstelle. Für jeden Felsen gibt es eine Liste der Routen, sortiert nach ihrer Schwierigkeit. Wir haben uns bemüht, die Bewertung in diesem Führer für alle Gebiete einheitlich ausfallen zu lassen. Einige der Routen sind definiert, sodass der Grad nur dann zutrifft, wenn gewisse Griffe oder Tritte weggelassen werden (die Symbole verdeutlichen dies). Für die Bewertung der Boulder wurde die Fontainebleau-Skala verwendet, die tendenziell etwas härter ist und eine exaktere Bewertung in den mittleren und höheren Graden zulässt.

L'Inghilterra presenta una piacevole campagna con alberi molto verdi, il che significa che piove molto; la zona a sud- est di Londra però ha il grande vantaggio di essere la più asciutta e certamente la più soleggiata dell'intero Regno Unito. Da Aprile ad Ottobre il clima è perfetto per arrampicare, ed accade solo occasionalmente alla Domenica che Harrison's Rock risulti troppo affollato per arrampicare; anzi è addirittura più probabile inciampare in cestini da picnic che in veri e propri climbers!

Le vie si trovano su piccoli affioramenti di roccia arenaria calcarea formati da lunghe lamine con alcune isolate cime. La loro altezza si aggira attorno ai 7-10 metri, e si trovano in ondulate colline coperte d'alberi della bassa pianura. La roccia si presenta per sua natura tenera, ed eccezionalmente poco resistente, soprattutto quando risulta bagnata dalle pesanti piogge. L'arenaria calcarea è simile nella forma a Fontainebleau a Dame Joanne e all' Elephant, ma non è così granulata e non presenta depositi di quarzo duro. E' molto simile alle zone dello Pfalz, e specialmente del Berdorf. A causa della sua morbidezza presenta dei pezzi molto consumati, con prese molto tonde, che risultano alquanto faticose per i principianti. Sulle vie dure gli appigli più piccoli sono quasi interamente scomparsi, e vista anche la natura strapiombante della roccia, queste vie richiedono capacità e prestazioni di un potente orangotango. Per la gente del posto questa zona è semplicemente chiamata "The Rocks", e la

maggior parte dei sassoni vengono chiamati solamente con il loro primo nome.

I massi

Harrison' s Rocks (le rocce di Harrison) è la più importante zona destinata all'arrampicata per climber di medio livello, e presenta più di 350 ascensioni. E' rivolta principalmente a ovest e riceve così gran parte del piacevole sole pomeridiano. Le vie hanno pressappoco un' altezza di 8 metri, ed offrono parecchi modi diversi di arrampicata. Harrison' s Rocks si trova in un bellissimo scenario, confinante con un bosco, ed è facilmente raggiungibile in 15 minuti a piedi dal parcheggio. Bowles Rocks, che è l'altra principale roccia, risulta perfetta per arrampicatori di medio livello, ed è anche usata come centro d'arrampicata all'aperto. Arrampicare qui è eccellente, ma manca la sensazione che si prova arrampicando ad Harrison' s. Le High Rocks senza dubbio offrono le migliori vie per climber di alto livello. Queste massi presentano perlopiù un'altezza di 10 metri, che con un angolo di 110 gradi, conferiscono uno sviluppo maggiore alla via. Sfortunatamente le High rimangono molto tempo all'ombra, risultando piuttosto umide; questo non impedisce sicuramente di arrampicare, rende solamente una via di 6b molto più impegnativa! Gli altri sassi più piccoli risultano meno frequentati ed ottimi per arrampicare, offrendo infatti un'arrampicata di primo livello e l'opportunità di piacevoli arrampicate in pace e serenità.

'Guy McLelland'
The 1980's
Legendary
boulderer

Tecnica

Proprio come ad una prima visita a Fontainebleau, rimarrete molto sorpresi nel vedere l'ottimo livello degli arrampicatori del posto, ed è soprattutto pura tecnica locale. Le vie molto erte sono certamente differenti tra loro, ma per molti climbers non è necessario essere forti fisicamente od avere molta resistenza. La roccia è arenosa ed è difficile rimanere in aderenza, la pulizia della suola delle scarpe prima di ogni ascesa è essenziale, potete infatti riconoscere la gente del posto per fatto di avere un pezzo di tappeto su cui stare prima di toccare la parete. Dal momento che pezzi di arenaria tendono a cadere sulle sporgenze più basse delle vie, un piccolo asciugamano risulta utile per pulire gli appigli e assicurare l'aderenza. Alle volte quando la roccia si presenta unta, l'asciugamano viene messo sull'appiglio sia per mantenere la suola delle scarpe pulita sia per ottenere l'aderenza necessaria. I numerosi svasi presenti obbligano a tenere le caviglie rilassate per permettere il pieno contatto della suola con la roccia. La maggior parte delle vie possono essere fatte in perfetto equilibrio, e un buon uso del tallonaggio risulta essere molto gratificante. Molte delle vie hanno il loro passaggio più difficile verso la fine, il che richiede un eccellente tecnica di ristabilimento. A causa di questi difficili ultimi passaggi, pochi scalatori riescono in solitaria su queste vie. Ci sono molte sezioni riguardanti il bouldering in questa guida, è comunque sufficiente visitare uno dei settori più facili per farsi un'idea del tipo di arrampicata presente in queste zone.

Equipaggiamento

Un paio di normali e leggere scarpe da arrampicata sono perfette qui, ed un tappetino da bouldering risulta sempre utile. L'arrampicata è un'attività pericolosa, ed è la responsabilità di ogni singolo alpinista che la rende più o meno sicura. Ci sono parecchie catene e alberi in cima ai sassi, ma non possono tutti essere considerati sicuri! Scegliete sempre più di un ancoraggio nel caso uno si rompesse. E' importante chiudere l'ultimo moschettone proprio sulla cima della via ed usare fettucce statiche. Questo per evitare lo sfregamento della corda sulla roccia (5 mt di fettuccia per Harrison's e Bowles, 15 mt per molti degli altri sassoni dove l'ancoraggio avviene agli alberi).E' consigliabile utilizzare una corda di ottima qualità da 10 mm di diametro e 30 metri di lunghezza; un buon imbrago per ogni alpinista, e preferibilmente un sistema di autobloccaggio.

Come usare questa guida

L'intera guida è stata progettata in base ai simboli, che vengono mostrati nel taschino interno della copertina. Ogni sasso è stato disegnato in modo artistico, e le vie sono state segnate con colori speciali, che sono identici ai gradi presenti a Fontainebleau. Ci sono "facce sorridenti" per i movimenti duri, e "diavoli rossi" per descrivere movimenti veramente disperati; alle volte sono combinati con il simbolo del righello per indicare passaggi molto difficili o addirittura impossibili per alpinisti di bassa statura. Un indice delle vie al di sotto dei luoghi descritti da il nome alla via stessa, insieme al grado, la data e i records della prima ascensione; poi anche la registrazione della prima ripetizione solitaria conosciuta. E' anche indicato l'attuale grado complessivo della via assieme all'inclinazione della parte più dura. Una categoria di esposizione viene usata per indicare la presenza del sole sulla roccia, questo perché alcune delle vie sulla parete sud sono ampiamente ombreggiate dagli alberi. Ci sono poi due simboli rappresentanti lo stile d'arrampicata, in ordine di salita: un "dulfer" indicherà la posizione, a destra o a sinistra, da assumere, ricordate però che il simbolo dello "strapiombo" non verrà segnalato se sarà già stata indicata l'inclinazione della via. Le stelle vengono date per la qualità, in considerazione della zona locale. Ci sono mappe poste all'interno della copertina, che vi guideranno ai singoli sassi. Per ogni sasso c'è un piano individuale per individuare ogni singolo settore.

Limitazioni

A causa della friabilità della roccia, è presente un grosso problema di erosione, che ogni climber deve conoscere e cercare di non fare niente che possa aumentare o accelerere l'erosione. Se possibile cercate per favore di arrampicare in maniera controllata, con uno stile che non stacchi gli appigli, e quindi raggiunta la cima, slegati, tornate indietro camminando. E' piuttosto evidente che calarsi o lavorare una via tenda a distruggere alquanto velocemente la roccia, ed è di certo inutile. Se state provando una via su un campanile o su di un boulder con una difficile discesa, siate sicuri di poter raggiungere la discesa senza aiuto, prima di scendere. Viene usato un paracadute per illustrare dove si trova la discesa che viene segnalata da un numero, quindi usate per favore le discese segnalate. Esaminate per favore le due pagine di fotografie, queste infatti illustrano la maggior parte di buone e

cattive idee pratiche da conoscere in questa zona.
Generalmente in questa zona non nidificano uccelli di
nessun tipo non presentando così nessuna restrizione
stagionale causata da eventuali volatili. A Eridge Green
sono presenti alcune piante rare, perlopiù vischiosi
muschi e licheni verdi; gli alpinisti hanno promosso
una politica di non-arrampicata in alcune zona di
queste aree, chiaramente illustrate nella guida. Le zone
di restrizione spesso cambiano, ed è di solito
l'organizzazione Nazionale di Arrampicata che pone
appositi segnali all'entrata di ogni sasso che servono
quali utile guida.

dimostrato ottimo. Di conseguenza le rocce ed in
genere l'intera area sono igienicamente molto pulite,
a dispetto di altre zone per l'arrampicata, viene così
pienamente frequentata ed apprezzata da tutti. Pubs e
fattorie offrono inoltre il servizio bed and breakfast. E'
utile avere una macchina per raggiungere le zone di
arrampicata, le principali linee ferroviarie comunque
vanno da Londra a Tunbridge Wells, dove potete tro-
vare di solito taxi che aspettano i clienti per quelle
6 miglia che vi separano da Harrison's. Alternativa-
mente, corriere coprono l'intero tragitto ininterrot-
tamente.

Gradi

I gradi inglesi sono spesso usati per
indicare il movimento più duro. In
questa area invece il grado rappre-
senta la difficoltà media dell'intera
via, con il simbolo del sorriso e del
diavolo usati per illustrare movimenti
chiave. Ogni affioramento ha una
lista in ordine di difficoltà, e i gradi
usati in ogni singola area dovrebbero
essere simili nell'intera guida. Alcune
vie vengono "eliminate" poichè richiedono "un'arrampicata usando solo
certi appigli", pur mantenendo il
grado corretto (i simboli aiuteranno
a rendere tutto più chiaro). Abbiamo
utilizzato i gradi di Fontainebleau per
il bouldering, risultando così un po'
più arduo dando però più spazio nei
gradi medi ed in quelli più alti.

Old Kent Road, F6b+ High Rocks; Carrie Atchison-Jones

Alloggi e spostamenti

Ad Harrison's Rocks c'è il Julie Tullis
Memorial Campsite. E' un posticino
molto piacevole con piccoli spiazzi
proprio nel bel mezzo di un bosco.
C'è un piccola quota da pagare per
la notte, però questo posto presenta
bagni e zone per lavarsi munite
di acqua calda. Queste possibilità
assieme al parcheggio della macchina
sono disponibili lasciando però una
piccola donazione per ogni visita.
Siete pregati di lasciare questa donazione visto che negli anni l'alto
standard dei servizi si è sempre

Inglaterra tiene agradables campos y árboles verdes, con lo que esto significa que llueve un montón; sin embargo, la gran ventaja del sureste de Londres es que es la zona más seca y, realmente, la más soleada de Gran Bretaña. Desde abril a octubre, el clima es perfecto para escalar y solamente algún que otro domingo encontrarás Harrison´s Rocks lleno de gente; eso sí, tropezarás con más cestas de picnic que con escaladores reales. Las zonas de escalada están situadas en pequeñas formaciones de arenisca, en forma de largos filos y con alguna aguja aislada. Tienen entre 7 y 10 metros de alto aproximadamente y están situadas en redondeadas y arboladas colinas. La roca es bastante blanda y excepcionalmente débil cuando está húmeda después de una fuerte lluvia. La arenisca, a simple vista, es parecida a la de Fontainebleau en Dame Jouanne y Elephant, pero el granulado no es tan fino ni tiene depósitos de cuarzo duro. Es muy similar a algunas partes de Pfalz y especialmente a Berford. Debido a su blandura, está muy gastada en algunos sitios, creándose agujeros redondeados que son muy costosos para los principiantes. En las vías duras, casi todos los agujeros pequeños han desaparecido y teniendo también en cuenta el desplome que tienen por naturaleza, estas vías requerirán la ayuda y la habilidad de un orangután bastante fuerte. Para los escaladores locales, la zona es simplemente "The Rocks" y la mayoría de los sectores son conocidos únicamente por su primer nombre.

Sectores

Harrison´s Rocks es el sector más importante para el escalador medio ya que tiene unas 350 vías. La mayoría están orientadas al oeste y esto les proporciona agradables horas de sol por las tardes. Las vías tienen unos 8 metros de altura y ofrecen gran cantidad de tipos de escalada. Está situado en un bello emplazamiento, en el límite de un bosque, después de andar 15 minutos desde el aparcamiento principal. Bowles Rocks, el otro sector principal, es perfecto para el escalador medio y además se utiliza como un centro de recreo. La escalada aquí excelente, pero eso le hace carecer de la sensación propia de Harrison's. High Rocks –sin duda- ofrece las mejores vías para el escalador de élite. Las vías tienen, en su mayoría, 10 metros de altura que con un ángulo de 110 grados hace que parezcan vías realmente largas. Desafortunadamente, "High" se encuentra a la sombra y hay sensación de humedad, pero eso no impide escalar, ¡sólo hace los 6b bastante más duros! Los otros sectores

más pequeños son muy tranquilos e idílicos; ofrecen escaladas de alta calidad y una gran oportunidad de disfrutar en paz y serenidad.

Técnica

Al igual que en la primera visita a Fontainebleau, te sorprenderás de lo buenos que son los escaladores de la zona, y es gracias a una pura técnica local. Por supuesto que en las escaladas más duras es diferente, pero en la mayoría de las vías no necesitas estar fuerte ni tampoco tener resistencia. La roca es arenosa y la adherencia es difícil de conseguir; limpiar la suela de tus pies de gato antes de cada vía es esencial, y puedes copiar a los locales, que tienen una pequeña alfombra para estar de pie antes de tocar la roca. Como la arena tiende a caer en las regletas de la parte inferior, una pequeña toalla es muy útil para limpiar los agujeros y asegurar la adherencia. Algunas veces, cuando la roca está resbaladiza, la toalla se coloca en uno de los agujeros para los pies y consigues dos cosas, mantener el pie de gato limpio y una adherencia suficiente para progresar. Estos agujeros suelen estar inclinados, por ello, los tobillos deben estar relajados, lo que permitirá un mayor contacto de la suela contra la roca. La mayoría de las vías más fáciles se pueden escalar sólo en equilibrio, y es muy aconsejable un buen uso de los talonajes. Un montón de vías tienen su paso clave al final, y requieren una excelente técnica de paso de mostrador. Debido a estos finales difíciles, muy pocos escaladores realizan vías en 'solo integral'. Hay muchas secciones de boulder en esta guía, y visitar uno de los sectores más fáciles puede ser una buena introducción al tipo de escalada que se da en esta zona.

Equipamiento

Unos pies de gato ligeros son perfectos para esta zona, y una colchoneta para los boulders es siempre útil. Escalar es una actividad peligrosa, y es responsabilidad de cada escalador preocuparse por la seguridad de uno mismo. Hay anclajes de parabolt y árboles en la parte superior de cada pared – ¡pero no puede darse por sentado que son seguros! Elige siempre varios anclajes por si uno de ellos fallara. Muy importante –instala una triangulación (con mosquetón de seguro) en la parte superior de la pared, utilizando cinta plana. Esto hará que no se produzcan roces contra la roca (5 metros de cinta para Harrison's y Bowles y 15 metros para muchos otros sectores donde los árboles están bastante más atrás). La escalada se realiza en top rope, así que necesitarás una buena cuerda de escalada y relativamente corta –30 metros de largo. Un buen arnés para cada escalador y preferiblemente un cabo de anclaje para la reunión.

Cómo utilizar la guía

La guía completa se ha diseñado para funcionar por medio de símbolos, los cuales se explican en la solapa interior de la portada. Cada formación se ha dibujado de manera artística y las vías se han marcado con colores especificativos –que son idénticos a la graduación de Fontainebleau. Hay caras sonrientes para mostrar los pasos duros y diablillos rojos para mostrar los pasos realmente al límite; y algunas veces, combinado con una regla para indicar las vías que son particularmente difíciles o imposibles para los escaladores más bajos. Un índice de vías debajo de los croquis indica el nombre de la vía, así como el grado, la fecha y los datos de la primera ascensión; después, los datos del primer 'solo integral' conocido. Se muestra el grado total de la vía junto con el ángulo de la parte más dura de la ascensión. Las indicaciones sobre las horas de sol muestran las horas reales, dado que algunas de las vías orientadas al sur son muy sombrías debido a los árboles. Hay dos símbolos que representan el tipo de vía, en orden de escalada; en las aristas se indicará el lado por el que escalar, un desplome no se indicará si el ángulo de la vía ya lo muestra, etc. Las estrellas se otorgan por la calidad –con referencia al resto de vías locales. Hay mapas situados en las tapas que te guiarán hasta los distintos sectores. De cada uno de ellos hay un plano individual para encontrar cada zona en particular.

Restricciones

Debido a que la roca es blanda, hay un mayor problema de erosión, por lo que el escalador debe tener cuidado con eso, e intentar no hacer nada que incremente o, posiblemente, acelere la erosión. Si es posible, escala de forma controlada, de manera que no se vayan rompiendo los agarres, una vez llegues arriba, desencuérdate y baja andando hasta el suelo. Es bastante obvio que descolgar, rapelar o ensayar una vía va a destrozar la roca más rápidamente y, por supuesto, es innecesario. Si vas a intentar escalar una vía, una aguja o un boulder con un descenso difícil, asegúrate de que puedes efectuarlo sin ayuda, antes de subir. Hemos puesto un paracaídas para ilustrar la dirección de descenso y si hemos añadido un número, usa esa

vía para descender. Por favor, examina las dos páginas de fotografías que muestran prácticamente la mayoría de buenas y malas ideas relevantes en cada sector.
Los pájaros no anidan generalmente en arenisca y no se tienen que aplicar restricciones por nidificación.
En Eridge Green hay algunas plantas poco frecuentes, musgos verdes y líquenes; los escaladores han tenido mucho éxito en ejecutar un plan voluntario de no escalada, la guía muestra estas zonas en particular. El área general de restricción cambia a menudo, y la Organización Nacional de Escalada coloca postes de señalización en la entrada de cada sector que sirven como un buen tablón de noticias.

Los grados ingleses se utilizan a menudo para marcar un paso individual. En esta área, el grado representará la dificultad total de la vía, con una Cara Sonriente o un Diablillo que marcarán los pasos clave. Cada sector tiene una lista de vías ordenadas por dificultad, y la graduación de cada zona intenta ser similar en toda la guía. Algunas de las vías son 'de eliminación', es decir, requieren utilizar 'sólo algunos de los agarres' para que resulte el grado correcto (los símbolos te ayudarán a aclararte). Hemos usado la graduación de Fontainebleau para el boulder, que tiende a ser un poco más duro y deja más margen en los grados medios y superiores.

Alojamiento y viaje

En Harrison's Rock encontraremos la Zona de Acampada en Memoria de Julie Tullis . Es un sitio pequeño y agradable, con algunos largos dentro de un pequeño bosquecillo. Hay una pequeña cuota por día, y tiene baños y duchas con agua caliente. Estos servicios, así como el aparcamiento de Harrison's se ofrecen, entendiendo que la gente deja un donativo cada vez que los visita. Por favor, hazlo; a lo largo de los años, este ejemplar cuidado se ha probado como incalculable. Gracias a ello, las paredes y toda la zona en general están maravillosamente limpias, al contrario que otras populares zonas de escalada, se trabaja para mantenerlo y es apreciado por todos. Hay buenos bares locales y las granjas ofrecen alojamiento en régimen de 'bed and breakfast' (alojamiento y desayuno). El coche es útil para llegar hasta los sectores, pero hay líneas de tren desde Londres a Tunbridge Wells, desde donde tienes taxis esperando a los clientes para realizar el trayecto de 6 millas hasta Harrison's. Otra alternativa son los autobuses que realizan diversas rutas, de un lado a otro, de forma intermitente.

JINGO WOBBLY ▲ EURO-GUIDES

SPORT ▲ VERTICAL

DECEMBER 2001

The 1st edition of our
Grand European Guide:
Crags, Maps, shops, campsites; a
climbing guide to all the best climbing
areas in Europe. All the major
and lesser known crags, with access
and details. Over 400 pages and 300
colour photos, 300 location maps.
On sale at all good climbing stores

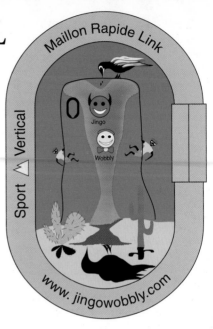

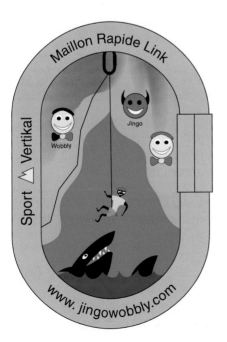

A truly international guide with
a whole range of whacky Jingo
Wobbly symbols. A must for any
sport climber, or Alpinist who wants
somewhere to go when the 4000m
peaks are covered in cloud. We have
split Europe into 100 areas with
14 cliffs in each area. Every area is
designed for enough climbing on
a 2 week vacation. If you have any
information on an area that you feel
should be in the guide, email us on
info@jingowobbly.com

www.jingowobbly.com

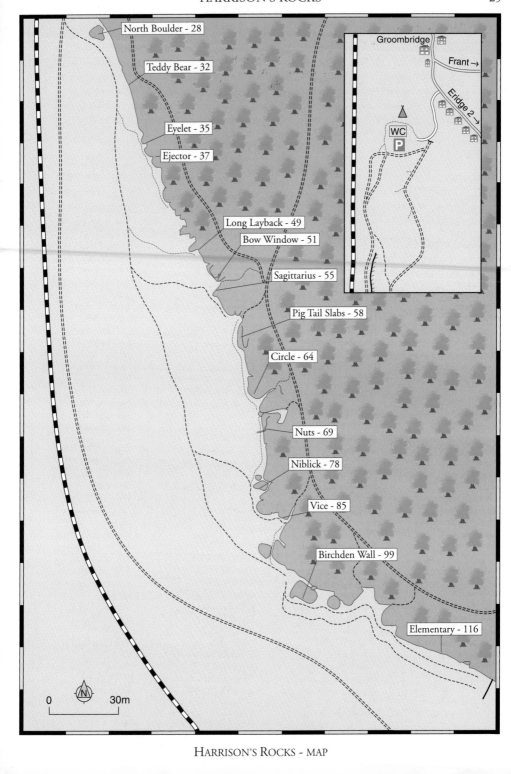

North Boulder - 28
Teddy Bear - 32
Eyelet - 35
Ejector - 37
Long Layback - 49
Bow Window - 51
Sagittarius - 55
Pig Tail Slabs - 58
Circle - 64
Nuts - 69
Niblick - 78
Vice - 85
Birchden Wall - 99
Elementary - 116

Groombridge
Frant →
Eridge 2 →
WC
P

0   30m
N

HARRISON'S ROCKS - MAP

Harrison's Rocks is the largest and most popular outcrop in the whole area, and deservedly so, for it offers excellent climbing in all grades. The crag is made up of a twisting, woodland edge, which clears the tops of the trees in winter to dry quickly, yet in summer will still have cool shady mornings. It is best approached from the lower footpath on the first visit, where you can easily see the rock and decide where to climb. It can get very busy on Sunday's, but rarely do you have that many people actually climbing. Please make a donation to the car park when leaving, this helps in the upkeep of the rocks, and the toilet facilities.

GRADED LIST

6c
Lager Frenzy
A Killing Joke
Tempestivity
What Crisis
Soft Rock

6b+
Oliver James
Dr. Pepper
Blue Murder RH
The Limpet
Pincnib
Lager Shandy
Woolly Bear
Primate Shot
Powder Monkey
Wellington's Boot

6b
Magic Wall
Stubble
Jumping Jack Flash
Hector's House
Bonanza Direct
Finger Popper
Kicks
Force of Destiny
Alexander Beetle
Corridor-Uncertainty
Supernatural
Shytte
Twiglet
Teddy Bear's Picnic
Icarus 5-7a
Desperation
Krypton Factor
That Man's an Animal
River Dance
Chip Shop Excursion
Glendale Crack
Crossbow
Karen's Kondom
Tiptoe through Lichen
Reach for the Sky
Eric

The Republic
Crusing D.J.
Skin Job
The Bolts
Psycho
Purple Nasty

6a+
Powder Finger
Monkey's Bow
The Nuts
Pascale
Hangover III
Jingo Wobbly
Diversion Direct
Neighbours
Le Cuvier Rêmparts
Phillipa
Sossblitz

6a
Flakes Direct
Rowan Tree Wall
Wisdom
Fang
Incisor
Brookslight
Bioplastic
Crucifix
Groove Wall
The Actress - Bishop
Psychedelic Tortoise
Max
Neutral
Tight C-Slab Direct
Stardust
Hangover I
Hangover II
In Limbo
Healey Peeleys
Cannibals
Meat Cleaver
Missing Link
Bostic
The Sod
Sharp Dressed Man

Noisome Wall Direct
Plagiarism
Gall Stone
The Knam
The Mank
Bloody Fingers
Inimitability
Mr. Spaceman
Deep Thought
Awkward Crack
Guy's Problem
Rotton Thump
New Hat
Photina
Jurrasic Park
Grant's Wall
Coronation Crack
Gardeners Q Time
Right Unclimbed
Fat and Middle-Aged
Down - Funny Farm
Blue Madness
Panther's Wall
The Wallow
Battle of the Bulge
Root Route II
South West Corner

5c+
The Flakes
Second Chance
Forester's Wall Direct
Blackeye Wall Direct
The Sting
Desperate Dan
Celestial's Reach Var
Celestial's Reach
On the Edge
Muscle Crack
Grist
Wizzards Shuffle
Sand Piper
Edward's Effort
Indian Summer
Forget-me-Knot
Sandbag

Slim Finger Crack

5c
Orangutang
Boysen's Arête
Finger Stain
Archer's Wall Direct
Last Chance
Rift
Witches Broomstick
Toad
Sticky Wicket
Counterfeit
My Dear Watson
Baskerville
Archer's Wall
Patient Parmar
Rotton Stump Wall
Slanting Crack
Blackeye Wall
Mantlepiece
Smiliodan D-Start
Green Fingers
Smiliodan
Simon's Wall
Wizzard's Progress
Sewer Wall
Halibut Giblets
Little Sagittarius
Directors
Toxophilite
Vulture Crack
Piecemeal Wall
Sullivan's Stake
Central Groove
Dynamo
Wailing Wall
Toevice
Handvice
Bad Finger
Plumb Line
Bloody Sunday
Good Friday
Left Circle
Knight's Move
Bovver Boot

L.H.T.
Crowborough Corner
The Scoop
Biceps Buttress
Soft Rock'er
Reverse Traverse
North West Corner
Luncheon Shelf
Serendipity
Victoria
Bow Window L-H
Bow Window Dir
Soft Cock
Lady Jane
Woodside Blossom
Bootless Buzzard
Pete's Reach
El Loco
Blue Peter
Ten Foot Pole
Smear Campaign
Bonanza
Araldite Wall
Birch Tree Var

5b+
Diversion
Solstice
Corner
Elastic
Bulging Wall
Spout Buttress
Ear-ring
Carrera
Pullover
Shodan
Spider Wall
Birchden Corner
West Wall
Finger Stain
Wildcat Wall Direct
Edward's Wall
Quiver
Elementary

5b
Quarterdome
Snout
Sliding Corner
Dinosaurus
Root Route III
Stranger than Friction
Singlet
Spout Crossing
Set Square Arête
Usurper
Noisome Wall
Tubesnake Boogie

Squank
Flower Far Left
Power Jules
Small Wall
Long Stretch
Belts and Braces
Stag
Knight's Gambit
Yosemite Big Climb
Saint's Wall
Stupid Effort
Birch Nose
Big Cave Wall
Tiptoe thru the Tulips
Cabbage Patch Blues
Cunning Stunts
Rum and Coke
The Niblick
Thingamywobs
Whatsaname
Boulder Route
Slab Crack
Half Crown Corner
Tired Fingers
Jagger
Cave Wall Traverse
Rough Boy
Baldrick's Boulderdash
Sewer Rowan Conn
Pipe Cleaner
The Sandpipe
Signalbox Arête
Forester's Wall
Caroline
Unclimbed Wall
Birchden Wall

5a+
Sagittarius
Casement Wall
Ringlet

5a
Zig Zag
Transparent A-Banana
Sun Ray
The Clamp
Weeping Slab
Garden Slab Left
Wander at Leisure
Garden Slab Right
Senarra
Dark Chimney Buttress
Giant's Ear
Pelmet
Fallen Block Elim
Fallen Block Wall
Two Toed Sloth
Little Cousin

Grant's Crack
Penknife
Root Route I.V
Pince Nez
Matt's Fingertip
Long Reach
Sinners Progress

4c
Long Layback
Coffin Corner
Birch Tree Wall
Deadwood Crack
Kukri Wall Direct
The Sewer
Slab Direct

4b
Saint Gotthard
Sabre Crack
Long Crack
Tight Chimney Slab
Gilbert's Gamble
Ejector
Grand Pic Route
Downfall
Eyelet
The Vice
Breadknife Buttress
Hell Wall
Quasimodo
Moonlight Arête
Starlight
Thingy
Rum and Ribena

4a
Wildcat Wall
The Fonz
Fallen Block Mantleshelf
Toeing the Line
Sashcord Crack
Sunshine Crack
Right Circle
Greasy Crack
Trees are Green
Bow Window
Root Route 1
Simplon Route
Elbow Traverse
Steph
Right Hand Crack
Corridor Route

3
Cottonsocks Traverse
Grand Morin
Bow Window

Jetsam
Snout Crack
Wellington's Nose
Kukri Wall
Big Toe Wall
Happy Days
Birch Tree Crack
Slab
Big Crack
Dave
Beech Corner
A Small bit of Black
Horizontal Birch
Noisome Cleft No.II
Tight Chimney
Sinner's Wall
Back Passage
Tight Chimney
Butterfly Traverse
Easy Cleft Right
Charon's Chimney
Don

2a-c
Utopia
Open Chimney
Small Chimney
Flotsam
Noisome Cleft No.I
Boulder Bridge Route
Big Cave Route I
The Chimney & Traverse
Corner (Left Edge)
Tame Variant
Back Crack
Passage Chimney
Longbow Chimney
Little Cave
Big Cave Route II
Smith's Traverse
Giant's Staircase
Arrow Crack
Dark Chimney
Windowside Spout
Original Route
Scout Chimney Left
Easy Cleft Left

1a-c
Fingernail Crack
Scout Chimney Right
Junend Arête
Snake's Crawl
Isometric Chimney

THE HUNTSMAN

CLIMBER FRIENDLY PUB
WITH LARGE GARDEN*

*Situated midway between Harrison's Rocks
and Bowles Rocks*

5 Well kept cask conditioned beers available
Award winning scrumpy cider & real German Weissbier
Tea, Coffee & Hot Chocolate available
Good selection of snacks & hot food - lunchtime & evenings
Open all day Sunday from May to September
* Sorry - no climbing wall available!

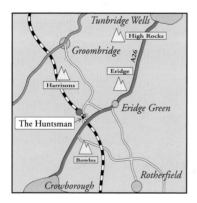

THE HUNTSMAN

ERIDGE ROAD, ERIDGE,
NR TUNBRIDGE WELLS, KENT TN3 9LE
Tel: 01892 864 258

*From Harrison's - Turn right out of car park,
go up the lane, past the phone on the right, for 1 mile
and the pub is on the right before the main road.
From Bowles - Turn left out of car park, right at
the main road and go down hill for 500m, take left
turn to Eridge station, and pub is 50m further on.*

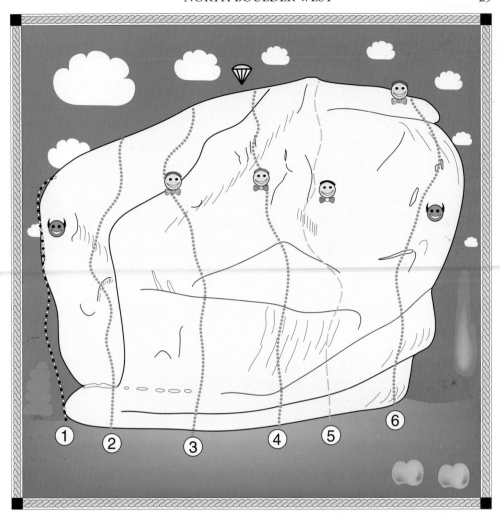

1	Alligator Snatch	6b			4	Sunset Wall	5b		
2	Groovy Graeme	5b+			5	Layaway Cure	5c		
3	Letterbox	5b+			6	Torque Wrench	6a+		

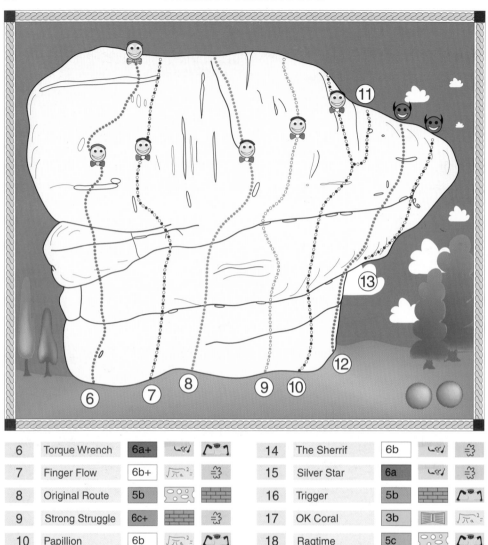

6	Torque Wrench	6a+			14	The Sherrif	6b		
7	Finger Flow	6b+			15	Silver Star	6a		
8	Original Route	5b			16	Trigger	5b		
9	Strong Struggle	6c+			17	OK Coral	3b		
10	Papillion	6b			18	Ragtime	5c		
11	Reve	6b+			19	Ziggy	6a		
12	Back Breaker	6a			20	Red River	6a		
13	Full On Fling	6a			21	Piano	6b+		
					1	Alligator Snatch	6b		

Torque Wrench 6a, Andy Valentine

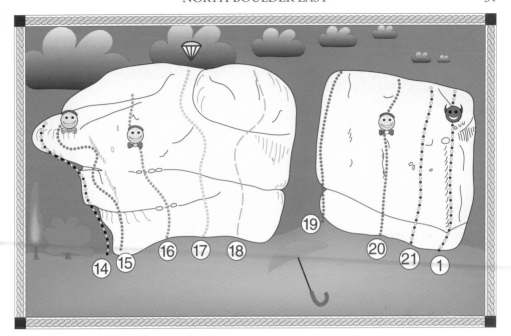

HARRISON'S ROCKS - TOPO 3

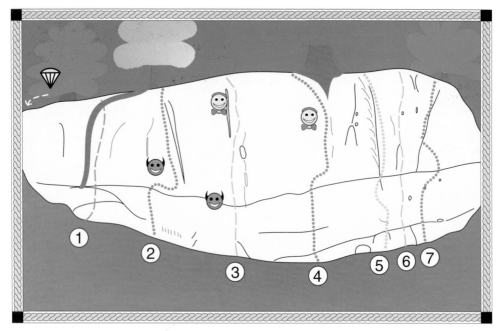

1	**Trees are Green**									
	❶(4a) 30.5.1993 ⚑ Teresa Hill, Brian Kavanagh, Robin Mazinke	4a	72°					
2	**Photina**									
	❶(6a.N.S.) 30.5.1993 Robin Mazinke: (6a) 4.6.1993 ⚑ Tim Allen	6a	82°					
3	**Teddy Bear's Picnic**									
	❶(5c) 1969-81: (6b) 29.6.1996 ⚑ John Patterson	6b	86°				★	
4	**New Hat** ⚑									
	❶(6a.N.S.) 5.6.1993 Robin Mazinke	6a	86°				★	
5	**Central Groove**									
	❶(3b) 1969-81 ⚑	5c	80°				★	
6	**Dynamo**									
	❶(5b) 1969-81	5c	83°				★★	
7	**Usurper**									
	❶(5b) 1969-81 Tim Daniells	5b	80°				★★	

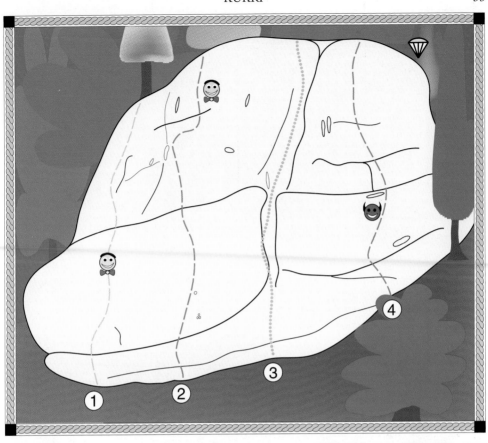

1	**Penknife**	5a	79°			
	❶(5a) 17.4.1995 Robin Mazinke					
2	**Breadknife Buttress**	4b	80°			★
	❶(5a) Pre-1956					
3	**Kukri Wall**	3b	70°			
	❶(4a) Pre-1956					
4	**Kukri Wall Direct**	4c	78°			
	❶(3a) Pre-1956					

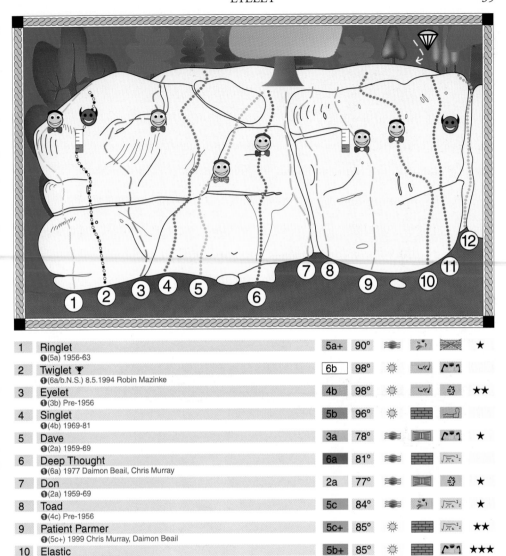

1	Ringlet ❶(5a) 1956-63	5a+	90°	≋	🏊	▨	★
2	Twiglet ⚘ ❶(6a/b.N.S.) 8.5.1994 Robin Mazinke	6b	98°	☀	◡	⌒	
3	Eyelet ❶(3b) Pre-1956	4b	98°	☀	◡	≋3	★★
4	Singlet ❶(4b) 1969-81	5b	96°	☀	▦	⌐	
5	Dave ❶(2a) 1959-69	3a	78°	≋	▤	⌒	★
6	Deep Thought ❶(6a) 1977 Daimon Beail, Chris Murray	6a	81°	≋	▦	√x²	
7	Don ❶(2a) 1959-69	2a	77°	≋	▤	≋3	★
8	Toad ❶(4c) Pre-1956	5c	84°	≋	🏊	√x²	★
9	Patient Parmer ❶(5c+) 1999 Chris Murray, Daimon Beail	5c+	85°	☀	▦	√x²	★★
10	Elastic ❶(5b) 19.9.1958 John Smoker	5b+	85°	☀	▦	⌒	★★★
11	Bioplastic ❶(6a) 1981 David Atchison-Jones	6a	85°	≋	▦	√x²	★
12	Tight Chimney ❶(4a) Pre-1956	3a	85°	≋	⊷☺⊷	≋3	★

Eyelet 4b, Carrie Atchison-Jones

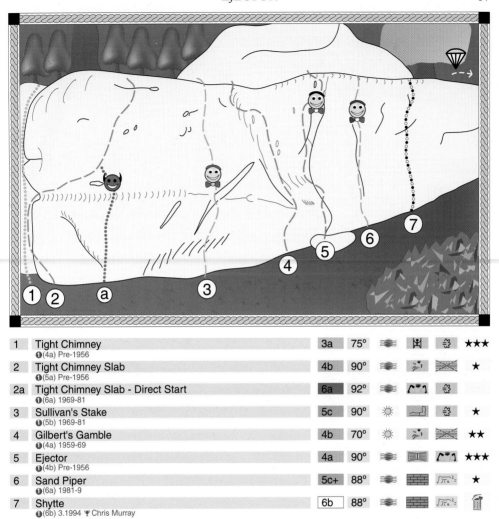

1	**Tight Chimney** ❶(4a) Pre-1956	3a	75°				★★★
2	**Tight Chimney Slab** ❶(5a) Pre-1956	4b	90°				★
2a	**Tight Chimney Slab - Direct Start** ❶(6a) 1969-81	6a	92°				
3	**Sullivan's Stake** ❶(5b) 1969-81	5c	90°	☀			★
4	**Gilbert's Gamble** ❶(4a) 1959-69	4b	70°	☀			★★
5	**Ejector** ❶(4b) Pre-1956	4a	90°				★★★
6	**Sand Piper** ❶(6a) 1981-9	5c+	88°				★
7	**Shytte** ❶(6b) 3.1994 ♉ Chris Murray	6b	88°				

Ejector 4b, Carrie Atchison-Jones

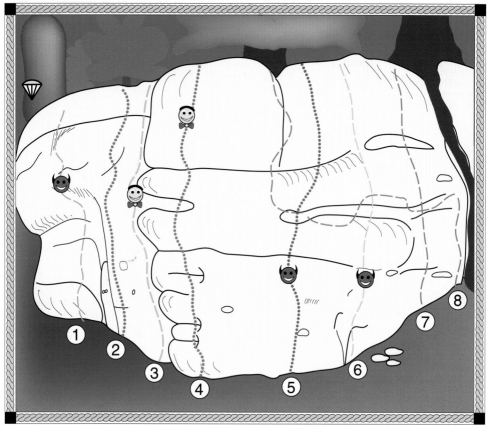

1	Trip of the Psychedelic Tortoise	6a	100°			
	❶(5c) 1981-9 Paul Stone					
2	Carrera	5b+	80°			★
	❶(5b) 1969-81 Tim Daniells					
3	Open Chimney	2b	78°			★★
	❶(2b) Pre-1956					
4	Root Route 3	5b+	87°			★★
	❶(5b.N.L.) 1969-81: (5b) 1982 ❦ David Atchison-Jones					
5	Root Route 2	6a	88°			★
	❶(3b) Pre-1956: (6a) 1992-5					
6	Root Route 1.5	5a	78°			★
	❶(5a) 1981-9					
7	Root Route 1	4a	80°			
	❶(5a) 1981-9					
8	Cottonsocks Traverse	4a	80°			★★★
	❶(2b) Pre-1956					

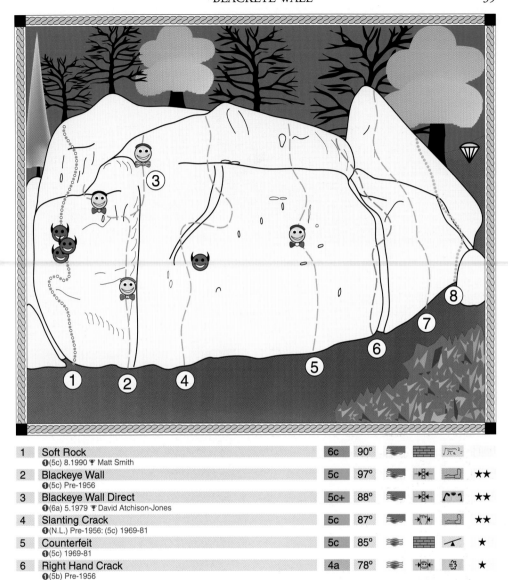

1	Soft Rock	6c	90°				
	❶(5c) 8.1990 ♛ Matt Smith						
2	Blackeye Wall	5c	97°				★★
	❶(5c) Pre-1956						
3	Blackeye Wall Direct	5c+	88°				★★
	❶(6a) 5.1979 ♛ David Atchison-Jones						
4	Slanting Crack	5c	87°				★★
	❶(N.L.) Pre-1956: (5c) 1969-81						
5	Counterfeit	5c	85°				★
	❶(5c) 1969-81						
6	Right Hand Crack	4a	78°				★
	❶(5b) Pre-1956						
7	Serendipity	5c	83°				★
	❶(5c) 11.1989 ♛ Matt Smith, R. Tipton						
8	A Small bit of Black	3a	66°				
	❶(3a) Pre-1956						

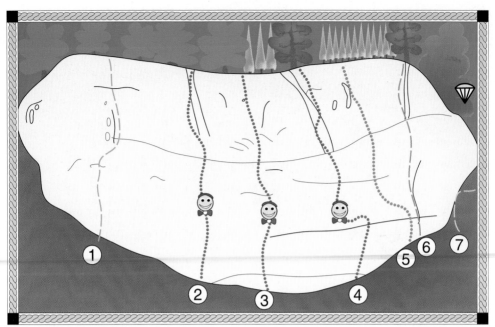

1	Smear Campaign ♥		5c	87°			
	❶(5c.N.S.) 1.8.1990 Chris Tullis						
2	Wisdom		6a	87°			
	❶(5b) 1969-81						
3	Fang		6a	87°			
	❶(5b) 1969-81						
4	Incsior		6a	87°			
	❶(4b) 1969-81						
5	Stranger than Friction		5b	82°			
	❶(5b) 26.7.1990 ♥Chris Tullis, Matt Smith						
6	Steph		4a	80°			
	❶(4a) 1990 ♥Chris Tullis						
7	Weeping Slab		5a	70°			
	❶(N.L.) Pre-1956: (5a) ♥ The Merry Monk						

Counterfeit 5c, David Atchison-Jones

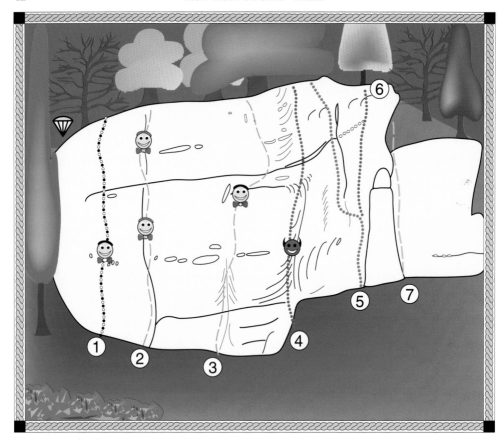

1	**Corridor of Uncertainty**	6b	90°			
	❶(6b.N.S.) 14.8.1990 M.Vetterlein, P.Widdowson: (6b) 5.1992 ❦John Patterson					
2	**Sticky Wicket**	5c	90°			★★
	❶(5c.N.L.) 1969-81: (5c) 1981 ❦ David Atchison-Jones					
3	**Rotten Stump Wall**	5c	88°			★★
	❶(N.L.) Pre-1956: (5c) ❦ 1969-81					
4	**Rotten Thump Arête**	6a	95°			★
	❶(6a) Pre-1995					
5	**Sliding Corner**	5b	92°			
	❶(5b) Pre-1956					
6	**Awkward Crack**	6a	92°			
	❶(6a) 1989-95					
7	**Fingernail Crack**	1b	67°			
	❶(2a) Pre-1956					

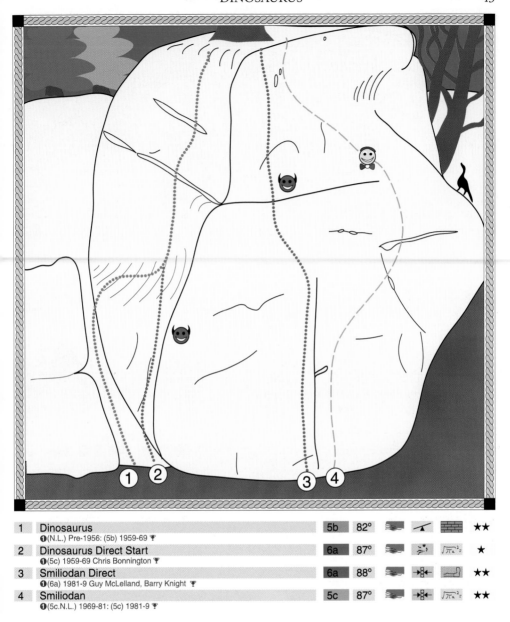

1	**Dinosaurus**		5b	82°				★★
	❶(N.L.) Pre-1956: (5b) 1959-69 ⚲							
2	**Dinosaurus Direct Start**		6a	87°				★
	❶(5c) 1959-69 Chris Bonnington ⚲							
3	**Smiliodan Direct**		6a	88°				★★
	❶(6a) 1981-9 Guy McLelland, Barry Knight ⚲							
4	**Smiliodan**		5c	87°				★★
	❶(5c.N.L.) 1969-81: (5c) 1981-9 ⚲							

1	Simon's Wall - Tomcat	5c	87°	★
	❶(5b.N.L.) 3.1975 Simon Matthews, Nigel Bradburn, T.Panther: (5c) 1981 ☘ D-AJ			
2	Panther's Wall	6a	88°	★★★
	❶(5c) 1954-8 Trevor Panther: (5c) 1959-69 ☘			
3	Snout	5a+	82°	★★
	❶(4b) Pre-1956			

HARRISON'S ROCKS - TOPO 13

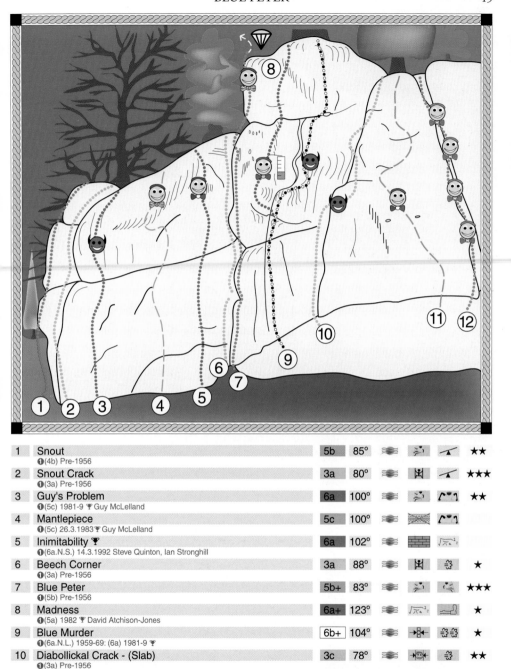

1	Snout		5b	85°				★★
	❶(4b) Pre-1956							
2	Snout Crack		3a	80°				★★★
	❶(3a) Pre-1956							
3	Guy's Problem		6a	100°				★★
	❶(5c) 1981-9 ☘ Guy McLelland							
4	Mantlepiece		5c	100°				
	❶(5c) 26.3.1983 ☘ Guy McLelland							
5	Inimitability ☘		6a	102°				
	❶(6a.N.S.) 14.3.1992 Steve Quinton, Ian Stronghill							
6	Beech Corner		3a	88°				★
	❶(3a) Pre-1956							
7	Blue Peter		5b+	83°				★★★
	❶(5b) Pre-1956							
8	Madness		6a+	123°				★
	❶(5a) 1982 ☘ David Atchison-Jones							
9	Blue Murder		6b+	104°				★
	❶(6a.N.L.) 1959-69: (6a) 1981-9 ☘							
10	Diabollickal Crack - (Slab)		3c	78°				★★
	❶(3a) Pre-1956							
11	Slab Direct		4a	78°				★★
	❶(5a) Pre-1956							
12	Slab Crack		5b	75°				
	❶(5b) Pre-1956							

Limpet 6b+, Angela White

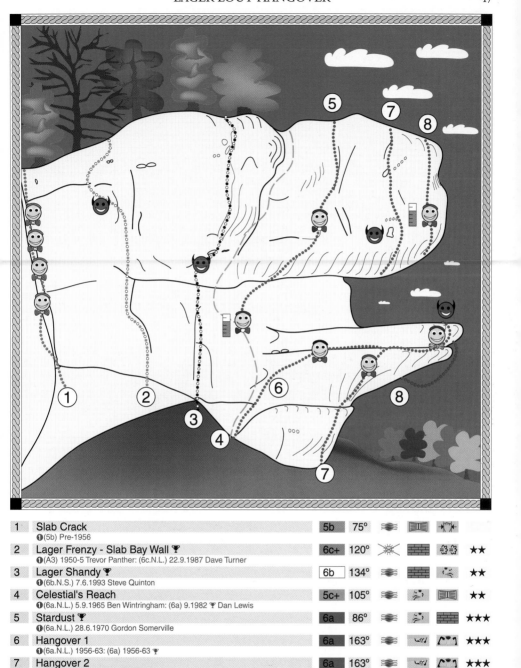

1	Slab Crack	5b	75°			
	❶(5b) Pre-1956					
2	Lager Frenzy - Slab Bay Wall ♈	6c+	120°			★★
	❶(A3) 1950-5 Trevor Panther: (6c.N.L.) 22.9.1987 Dave Turner					
3	Lager Shandy ♈	6b	134°			★★
	❶(6b.N.S.) 7.6.1993 Steve Quinton					
4	Celestial's Reach	5c+	105°			★★
	❶(6a.N.L.) 5.9.1965 Ben Wintringham: (6a) 9.1982 ♈ Dan Lewis					
5	Stardust ♈	6a	86°			★★★
	❶(6a.N.L.) 28.6.1970 Gordon Somerville					
6	Hangover 1	6a	163°			★★★
	❶(6a.N.L.) 1956-63: (6a) 1956-63 ♈					
7	Hangover 2	6a	163°			★★★
	❶(6a.N.L.) Pre-1956: (5c) 1956-63 ♈					
8	Hangover 3	6a+	163°			★★★
	❶(6a.N.L.) 1959-69: (6a) 1979 ♈ Andy Meyers					

Coronation Crack 6a, Jusu Turbe

urbanRock ⊙ .com
a climbing shop with attitude

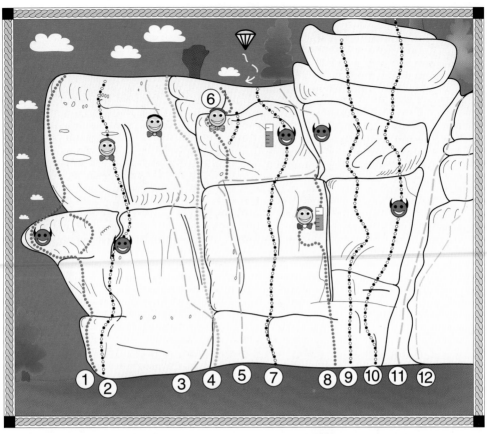

1	Hangover III	6a+	145°				★★★
	❶(6a) 1959-69: (6a) 1979 ♣ Andy Meyers						
2	Crusing D.J. ♣	6b	110°				★★
	❶(6b.N.L.) 7.1982 David Atchison-Jones: 1983 Dan Lewis						
3	Luncheon Shelf	5c	88°				★★
	❶(N.L.) Pre-1956: (5c) 1969-89						
4	Long Layback (Spider Crack - Originally)	4c	87°				★★★
	❶(5b) 1926-9 Jean Morin, Eric Shipton and Party: (5b) Pre-1956						
5	The Flakes	5c+	90°				★★★
	❶(6a.N.L.) 5.1965 Ben Wintringham: (5c) 1969-81 ♣ Andy Meyers 1979						
6	Flakes Direct	6a	110°				★★★
	❶(6a.N.L.) 1976 Martin Randall: (6a) 1983 ♣ David Atchison-Jones						
7	Force of Destiny ♣	6b	110°				★★★
	❶(6b.N.L.) 1989 David Atchison-Jones						
8	Coronation Crack	6a	100°				★★★
	❶(6a.N.L.) 1959-69 Martin Boysen: (6a) 1975-81 ♣ Stevie Haston						
9	Supernatural ♣	6b	105°				★★
	❶(6b.N.S.) 3.1999 Daimon Beail, Chris Murray						
10	The Limpet	6b+	110°				★★
	❶(6a.N.L.) 4.1965 Ben Wintringham: (6b) 1992 ♣ Chris Murray						
11	Dark Chimney	2a	65°				★★★
	❶(2a) Pre-1956						
12	Dark Chimney Buttress	5a	80°				★
	❶(5b) Pre-1956						

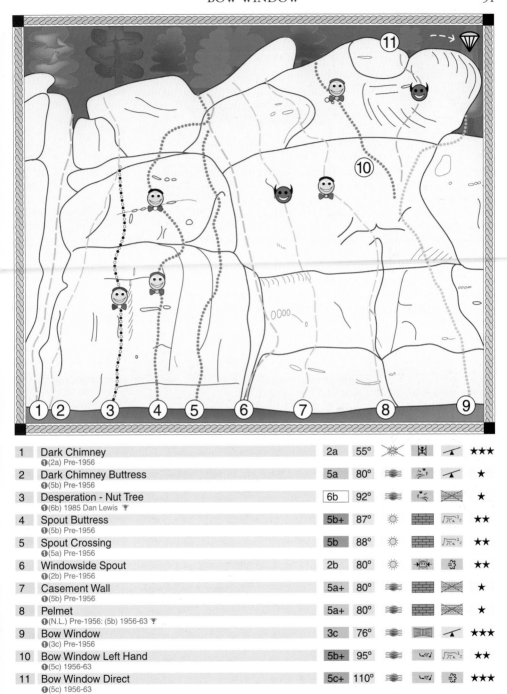

1	**Dark Chimney** ❶(2a) Pre-1956	2a	55°	☀	⛹	◤	★★★
2	**Dark Chimney Buttress** ❶(5b) Pre-1956	5a	80°	≋		◤	★
3	**Desperation - Nut Tree** ❶(6b) 1985 Dan Lewis ♟	6b	92°	≋		▨	★
4	**Spout Buttress** ❶(5b) Pre-1956	5b+	87°	☼	🧱	√π̅²=	★★
5	**Spout Crossing** ❶(5a) Pre-1956	5b	88°	☼	🧱	√π̅²=	★★
6	**Windowside Spout** ❶(2b) Pre-1956	2b	80°	☼		₃⁄₃	★★
7	**Casement Wall** ❶(5b) Pre-1956	5a+	80°	≋	🧱	▨	★
8	**Pelmet** ❶(N.L.) Pre-1956: (5b) 1956-63 ♟	5a+	80°	≋	🧱	▨	★
9	**Bow Window** ❶(3c) Pre-1956	3c	76°	≋	📖	◤	★★★
10	**Bow Window Left Hand** ❶(5c) 1956-63	5b+	95°	≋		√π̅²=	★★
11	**Bow Window Direct** ❶(5c) 1956-63	5c+	110°	≋		₃⁄₃	★★★

Bow Window 3c, Kate Semple

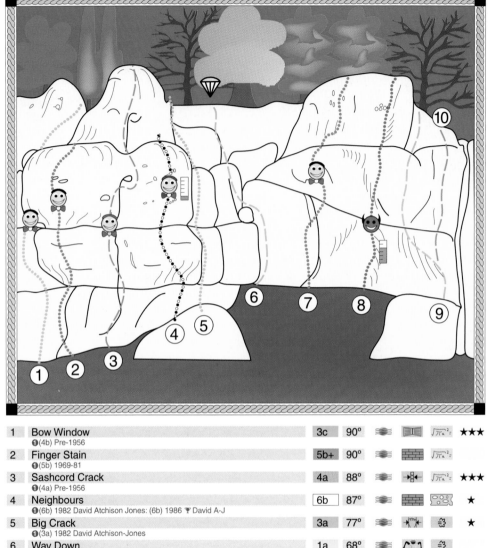

1	Bow Window		3c	90°				★★★
	❶(4b) Pre-1956							
2	Finger Stain		5b+	90°				
	❶(5b) 1969-81							
3	Sashcord Crack		4a	88°				★★★
	❶(4a) Pre-1956							
4	Neighbours		6b	87°				★
	❶(6b) 1982 David Atchison Jones: (6b) 1986 ♛ David A-J							
5	Big Crack		3a	77°				★
	❶(3a) 1982 David Atchison-Jones							
6	Way Down		1a	68°				
	❶(1a) Pre-1956							
7	Quarterdome		5b	88°				★★★
	❶(5b.N.S.) 2.1998 Chris Tullis: (5.1998) ♛ Robin Mazinke							
8	Yosemite Big Wall Climb		6a	94°				★
	❶(6a.N.S.) 15.4.1995 Robin Mazinke ♛							
9	Giant's Staircase		2b	75°				★
	❶(2b) Pre-1956							
10	Lost Arrow Wall		4b	81°				★
	❶(4b) Pre-1956							

Long Layback 4c, Sarah Spence

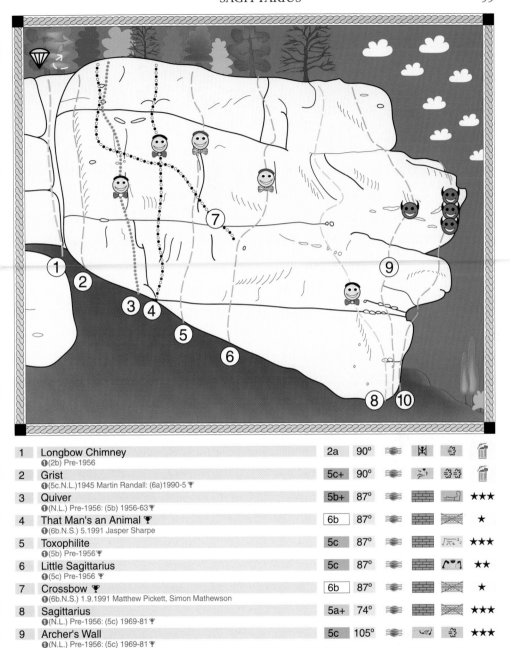

1	Longbow Chimney	2a	90°				
	❶(2b) Pre-1956						
2	Grist	5c+	90°				
	❶(5c.N.L.)1945 Martin Randall: (6a)1990-5 ♈						
3	Quiver	5b+	87°				★★★
	❶(N.L.) Pre-1956: (5b) 1956-63♈						
4	That Man's an Animal ♈	6b	87°				★
	❶(6b.N.S.) 5.1991 Jasper Sharpe						
5	Toxophilite	5c	87°				★★★
	❶(5b) Pre-1956♈						
6	Little Sagittarius	5c	87°				★★
	❶(5c) Pre-1956 ♈						
7	Crossbow ♈	6b	87°				★
	❶(6b.N.S.) 1.9.1991 Matthew Pickett, Simon Mathewson						
8	Sagittarius	5a+	74°				★★★
	❶(N.L.) Pre-1956: (5c) 1969-81♈						
9	Archer's Wall	5c	105°				★★★
	❶(N.L.) Pre-1956: (5c) 1969-81 ♈						
10	Archer's Wall Direct	5c+	125°				★★★
	❶(N.L.) 1956-63: (5c) 1969-81♈						

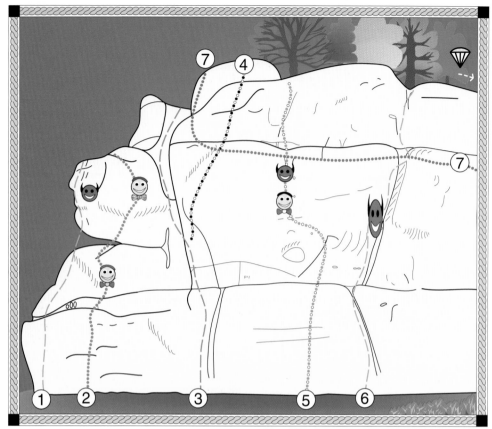

1	Archer's Wall Direct	5c+	120°				★★★
	❶(5c.N.L.) 1956-63: (5c) 1969-81 ♈						
2	Stupid Effort	5b	110°				★★★
	❶(5b) Pre-1956 ♈ Johnnie Lees						
3	Long Crack (Boulder Crack - Originally)	4b	88°				★★
	❶(5a) 1926-9 Jean Morin, Eric Shipton and party						
4	River Dance ♈	6b	82°				★
	❶(6b.N.S.) 27.5.1996 Barry Franklin						
5	What Crisis	6c	105°				★★★
	❶(6b/c.N.L.) 1985 Guy McLelland: (6c) ♈ 1993 Chris Murray						
6	Slimfinger Crack	5c	80°				★★★
	❶(5c) Pre-1956 Clifford Fenner: (5c) ♈ 1947-50 Tony Moulam						
7	Missing Link ♈	6a	90°				★★
	❶(6a.N.L.) 1974-6 Trevor Panther						
8	Vulture Crack	5c	62°				★★★
	❶(N.L.) Pre-1956: (5c) 1969-81♈ Laurie Holliwell						
9	The Sting	6a	100°				★
	❶(6a.N.L.) 1975-9 Martin Randall: (6a) 1982 ♈Dan Wajzner						
10	Marcus's Arête	6a	100°				★
	❶(6a) 13.7.1996 Pete Church, Pete Atkinson: (5c) ♈ Pete Atkinson						
11	Horizontal Birch	3a	80°				
	❶(3b) Pre - 1956						
12	Jumping Jack Flash ♈	6b	96°				★★
	❶(6b.N.S.) 14.8.1990 Paul Widdowson						
13	Downfall	4b	82°				★
	❶(3a) Pre-1956						

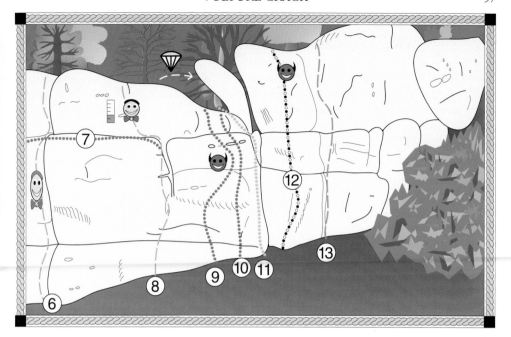

Toxophilite Wall 5c, Tim Daniells   *Sagittarius 5a+, Phil Kelly*

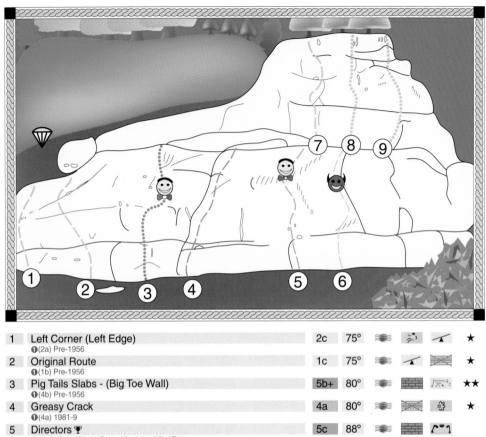

1	Left Corner (Left Edge) ❶(2a) Pre-1956	2c	75°				★
2	Original Route ❶(1b) Pre-1956	1c	75°				★
3	Pig Tails Slabs - (Big Toe Wall) ❶(4b) Pre-1956	5b+	80°				★★
4	Greasy Crack ❶(4a) 1981-9	4a	80°				★
5	Directors ♥ ❶(5c.N.S.) 1989-91 Robin Mazinke, Mike Eden	5c	88°				
6	Giant's Ear ❶(5a) Pre-1956	5a	78°				★
7	The Fonz ❶(4a) Pre-1956	2b	76°				★★
8	Happy Days ❶(3b) Pre-1956	3b	76°				★★
9	Junend Arête ❶(2b) Pre-1956	3c	76°				★★
10	Fallen Block Mantleshelf ❶(4b) Pre-1956	4a	86°				★★★
11	Fallen Block Eliminate ❶(5b) 1969-81	5b	86°				
12	Fallen Block Wall ❶(5a) Pre-1956	5a	86°				★★
13	Snake's Crawl ❶(2a) Pre-1956	1a	77°				★

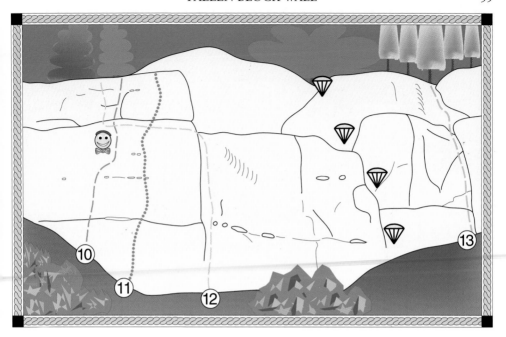

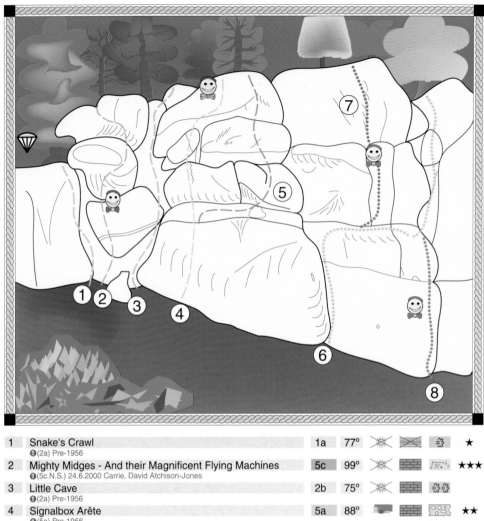

1	Snake's Crawl	1a	77°				★
	❶(2a) Pre-1956						
2	Mighty Midges - And their Magnificent Flying Machines	5c	99°				★★★
	❶(5c.N.S.) 24.6.2000 Carrie, David Atchison-Jones						
3	Little Cave	2b	75°				
	❶(2a) Pre-1956						
4	Signalbox Arête	5a	88°				★★
	❶(5a) Pre-1956						
5	Mountain Railway	4b	83°				★★
	❶(4b) Pre-1956						
6	Sinner's Wall	3a	76°				
	❶(3a) Pre-1956						
7	The Actress and the Bishop	6a	100°				
	❶(6a.N.S.) 17.7.1994 Robin Mazinke						
8	Very Sinfull	5b	86°				
	❶(5b) Pre-1956						

Saint's Wall 5b+, Rex Brangwyn

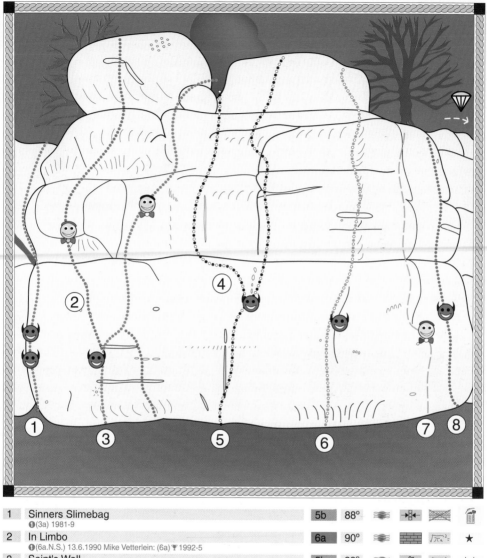

1	Sinners Slimebag	5b	88°					
	❶(3a) 1981-9							
2	In Limbo	6a	90°				★	
	❶(6a.N.S.) 13.6.1990 Mike Vetterlein: (6a) ⚑ 1992-5							
3	Saint's Wall	5b+	88°				★★	
	❶(5b) 1926-9 Jean Morin and Party: (5a) Pre-1956							
4	Chip Shop Excursion (Gretta)	6b	100°				★★★	
	❶(6b.N.L.) 28.4.1984 Jerry Peel, D. Atchison-J, J. Healey: (6b)1984 ⚑ D-AJ							
5	Glendale Crack	6b	100°				★★★	
	❶(6b/c.N.L.) 12.10.1969 Trevor Panther, H. Griffiths: (6c) 1975 ⚑ Stevie Haston							
6	A Killing Joke	6c+	106°				★	
	❶(6a) 4.1983 ⚑ Dan Wajzner							
7	Left Circle	5c+	98°				★★★	
	❶(5a) Pre-1956							
8	Healey Peeleys (Take that Chainsaw)	6a	102°				★★	
	❶(6a) 3.1982 ⚑ Joe Healey, Jerry Peel, Gaz Healey, Will							

Saint's Wall 5b+, Rex (Dynamo) Brangwyn

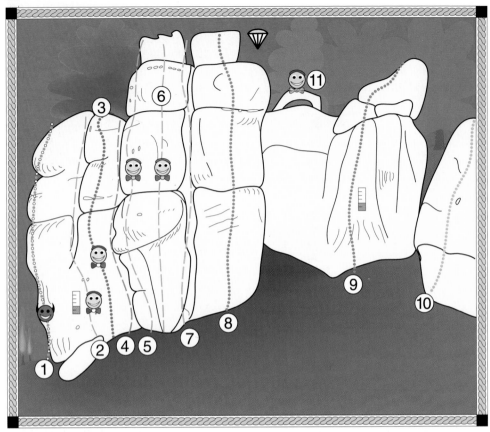

1	A Killing Joke	6c	106°				★
	❶(6a) 4.1983 ☕Dan Wajzner						
2	Left Circle	5c+	98°				★★★
	❶(5a) Pre-1956						
3	Healey Peeleys (Take that Chainsaw)	6a	102°				★★
	❶(6a) 3.1982 ☕Joe Healey, Jerry Peel, Gaz Healey, Will						
4	Right Circle	4a	99°				★★★
	❶(3a) Pre-1956						
5	Bloody Sunday	5c	90°				★★
	❶(5b) 1969-81						
6	Good Friday	5c	106°				★★
	❶(N.L.) Pre-1956: (5c) ☕ 1956-63						
7	Small Chimney	2b	79°				★★
	❶(2a) Pre-1956						
8	Small Wall	5b	86°				★★
	❶(4b) Pre-1956						
9	Long Stretch	5b	96°				★
	❶(5b) Pre-1956						
10	Coffin Corner	4c	77°				★
	❶(5a) Pre-1956						
11	Goats Do Roam - A Class Red Wine	6a	14%				★★★
	❶(6a) A full bodied problem						

Left Circle 5c+, Gerry Gilmartin

Goats do Roam 6a+, Theseus Gerard

Glendale Crack 6b, Rob Houston

Glendale Crack 6b, Rob Houston

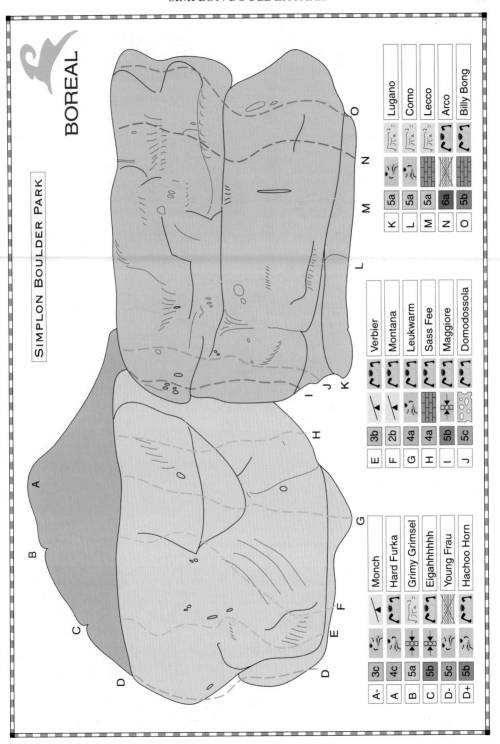

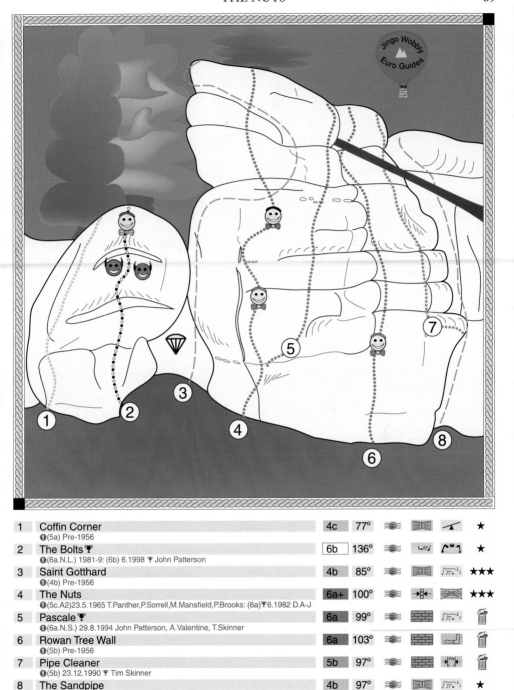

Jingo Wobbly
Euro Guides

1	**Coffin Corner** ❶(5a) Pre-1956	4c	77°	〰	▤	⬆	★
2	**The Bolts** ❣ ❶(6a.N.L.) 1981-9: (6b) 6.1998 ❣ John Patterson	6b	136°	〰	⌣	⌐❶	★
3	**Saint Gotthard** ❶(4b) Pre-1956	4b	85°	〰	▤	√π²	★★★
4	**The Nuts** ❶(5c.A2)23.5.1965 T.Panther,P.Sorrell,M.Mansfield,P.Brooks: (6a)❣6.1982 D.A-J	6a+	100°	〰	⧓	▨	★★★
5	**Pascale** ❣ ❶(6a.N.S.) 29.8.1994 John Patterson, A.Valentine, T.Skinner	6a	99°	〰	▦	√π²	🗑
6	**Rowan Tree Wall** ❶(5b) Pre-1956	6a	103°	〰	▦	⬐	🗑
7	**Pipe Cleaner** ❶(5b) 23.12.1990 ❣ Tim Skinner	5b	97°	〰	▦	⧓	🗑
8	**The Sandpipe** ❶(3b) Pre-1956	4b	97°	〰	▤	√π²	★

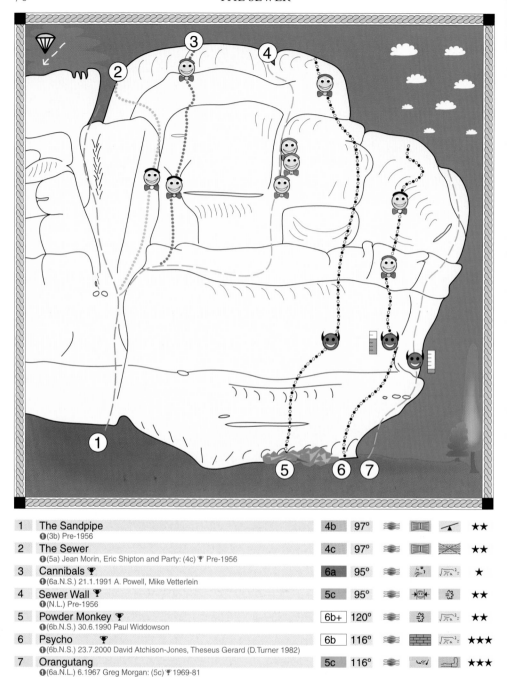

1	The Sandpipe		4b	97°				★★
	❶(3b) Pre-1956							
2	The Sewer		4c	97°				★★
	❶(5a) Jean Morin, Eric Shipton and Party: (4c) ♟ Pre-1956							
3	Cannibals ♟		6a	95°			$\sqrt{\pi a^2}$	★
	❶(6a.N.S.) 21.1.1991 A. Powell, Mike Vetterlein							
4	Sewer Wall ♟		5c	95°				★★
	❶(N.L.) Pre-1956							
5	Powder Monkey ♟		6b+	120°			$\sqrt{\pi a^2}$	★★
	❶(6b.N.S.) 30.6.1990 Paul Widdowson							
6	Psycho ♟		6b	116°			$\sqrt{\pi a^2}$	★★★
	❶(6b.N.S.) 23.7.2000 David Atchison-Jones, Theseus Gerard (D.Turner 1982)							
7	Orangutang		5c	116°				★★★
	❶(6a.N.L.) 6.1967 Greg Morgan: (5c) ♟ 1969-81							

Orangutang 5c, Frank Shannon (no hands rest)

1	**Psycho** ♆ ❶(6b.N.S.) 23.7.2000 David Atchison-Jones, Theseus Gerard	6b	116°			★★★
2	**Orangutang** ❶(6a.N.L.) 6.1967 Greg Morgan: (5c) 1969-81♆	5c	116°			★★★
3	**Primate Shot** ♆ ❶(6b/c.N.L.) 5.1987 Paul Stone	6b	120°			★★
4	**Oliver James** ♆ ❶(6b.N.S.) 24.9.1989 Theseus Hereward Lucas Gerard	6b+	107°			★★★
5	**Monkey's Bow** ❶(N.L.) Pre-1956: (6b) 1995-6 ♆ Mike Ball, Carl Martin	6a+	107°			★★★
6	**Brookslight** ♆ ❶(6a.N.L.) 16.5.1965 R. Brookes	6a	106°			★
7	**Moonlight Arête** ❶(5b) Pre-1956	4b	81°			★★★
8	**Starlight** ❶(4b) Pre-1956	4b	81°			★★

Moonlight Arête 4b, Shyama Ruffell

Small Chimney 2b

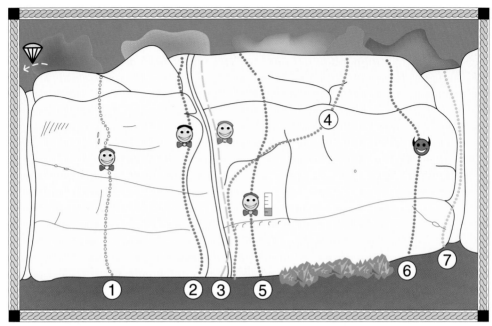

1	Tempestivity 👕	6c	80°				★★
	❶(6c.N.S.) 28.7.1995 John Patterson						
2	Bostic 👕	6a	92°				
	❶(6b.N.L.) 19.9.1965 P. Sorrell, Mike Mansfield						
3	Noisome Cleft No.1	2b	80°				
	❶(3a) Pre-1956						
4	Noisome Wall	5b	85°				
	❶(5b) Pre-1956						
5	Noisome Wall Direct 👕	6a	88°				
	❶(6a.N.S.) 3.5.1995 Robin Mazinke						
6	Plagarism 👕	6a	92°				
	❶(6a.N.S.) 4.5.1992 Robin Mazinke						
7	Noisome Cleft No.2	3a	85°				
	❶(3a) Pre-1956						

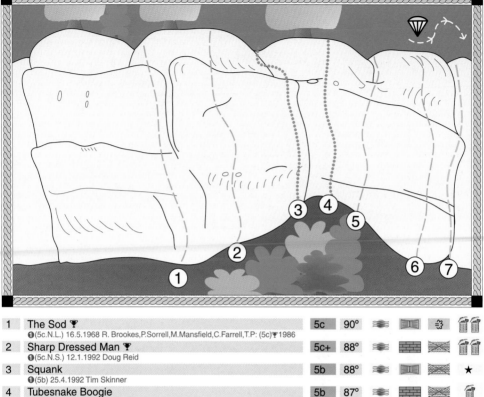

1	The Sod ♀		5c	90°					
	❶(5c.N.L.) 16.5.1968 R. Brookes,P.Sorrell,M.Mansfield,C.Farrell,T.P: (5c)♀1986								
2	Sharp Dressed Man ♀		5c+	88°					
	❶(5c.N.S.) 12.1.1992 Doug Reid								
3	Squank		5b	88°					★
	❶(5b) 25.4.1992 Tim Skinner								
4	Tubesnake Boogie		5b	87°					
	❶(5b) 25.4.1992 ♀Chris Murray								
5	El Loco ♀		5c	88°					
	❶(5c.N.S.) 11.11.1990 Tim Skinner								
6	Ten Foot Pole		5c	88°					
	❶(5c) 25.4.1992 ♀ Tim Skinner								
7	Passage Chimney		2a	90°					
	❶(2a) Pre-1956								

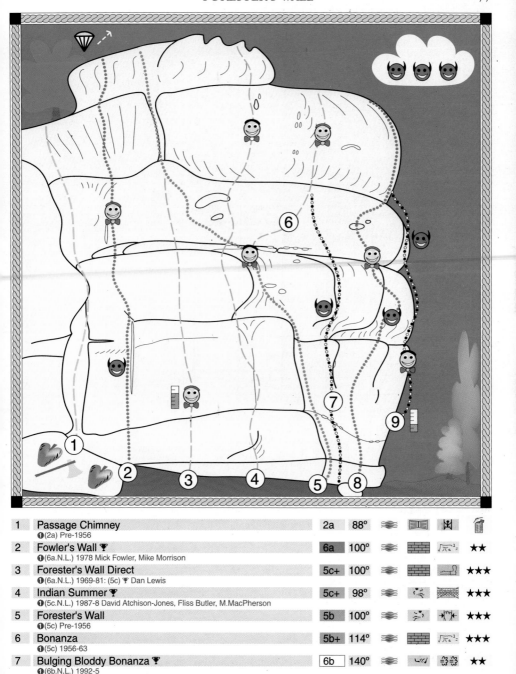

1	Passage Chimney		2a	88°				
	❶(2a) Pre-1956							
2	Fowler's Wall ♈		6a	100°				★★
	❶(6a.N.L.) 1978 Mick Fowler, Mike Morrison							
3	Forester's Wall Direct		5c+	100°				★★★
	❶(6a.N.L.) 1969-81: (5c) ♈ Dan Lewis							
4	Indian Summer ♈		5c+	98°				★★★
	❶(5c.N.L.) 1987-8 David Atchison-Jones, Fliss Butler, M.MacPherson							
5	Forester's Wall		5b	100°				★★★
	❶(5c) Pre-1956							
6	Bonanza		5b+	114°				★★★
	❶(5c) 1956-63							
7	Bulging Bloddy Bonanza ♈		6b	140°				★★
	❶(6b.N.L.) 1992-5							
8	Sossblitz		6a+	128°				★★★
	❶(6a.N.L.) 4.4.1965 Trevor Panther, P. Sorrell: (6a) 1979 ♈ Andy Meyers							
9	Republic		6b	88°				★★★
	❶(6b.N.L.) 9.6.1983 Dan Lewis: (6b) 6.8.1992 ♈ Steve Quinton							

Sossblitz 6a+, Frank Shannon

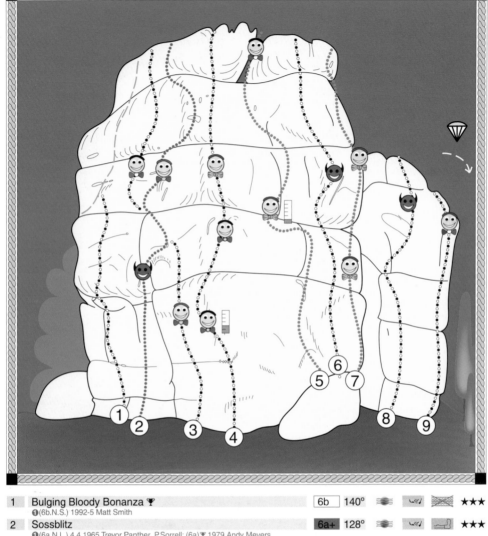

1	Bulging Bloody Bonanza ♈	6b	140°				★★★
	❶(6b.N.S.) 1992-5 Matt Smith						
2	Sossblitz	6a+	128°				★★★
	❶(6a.N.L.) 4.4.1965 Trevor Panther, P.Sorrell: (6a) ♈ 1979 Andy Meyers						
3	What the Butler Saw ♈	6b	128°				★★★
	❶(6b.N.S.) 6.2000 Ian Butler						
4	Republic	6b	87°				★★★
	❶(6b.N.L.) 9.6.1983 Dan Lewis: (6b) 6.8.1992 ♈ Steve Quinton						
5	Niblick	5b	83°				★★★
	❶(5c) Pre-1956						
6	Pincenib ♈	6b+	100°				★★★
	❶(5c.N.L.) 8.1966 Tony Bartlett, T.Panther: (6b) 7.1982 ♈ D.Atchison-Jones						
7	Pinch Arête	5b+	90°				★★★
	❶(5b) Pre-1956						
8	Wellington's Boot ♈	6b	107°				★★
	❶(6b.N.L.) 28.6.1970 Gordon Somerville, T.Panther						
9	Kicks ♈	6b	99°				★★
	❶(6a/b.N.S.) 14.10.1992 Alan Grigg						

Niblick 5b+, Joanna Smyth

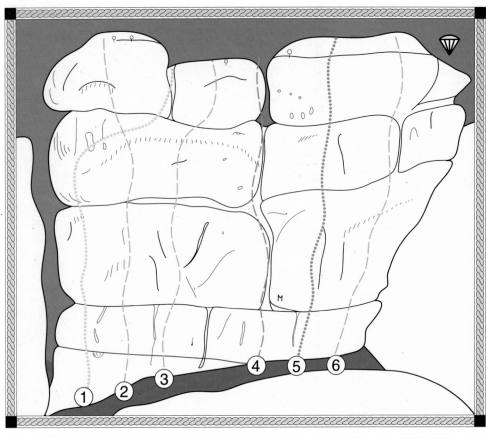

1	Wellington's Chimney	3b	83°				★★★
	❶(3a) Pre-1956						
2	Hitchcock's Horror ♈	5c	87°				★
	❶(5c.N.S.) 27.9.1997 Rob Hitchcock, Dave Verters, Steve Micham						
3	Lady Jane	5c	88°				★
	❶(5c.N.L.) 1969-81 Tim Daniells: (5c) 1992-5 ♈						
4	Sabre Crack	4b	87°				★
	❶(4b) Pre-1956						
5	Caroline	5b	88°				★
	❶(5b) 1980 ♈ David Atchison-Jones						
6	Pete's Reach	5c	98°				★
	❶(6a.N.S.) 12.8.1990 Peter Atkinson: (5c) 1992-5♈						

Republic 6b, Guy McLelland

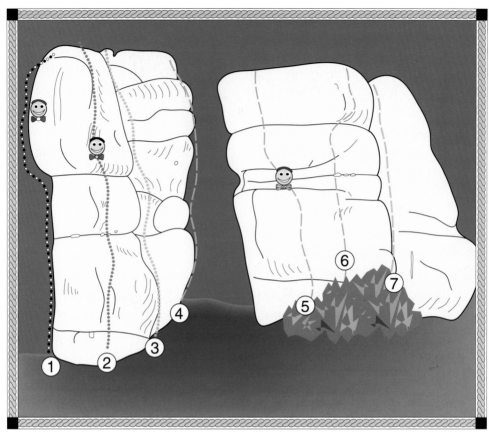

1	**Kicks** 🏆		6b	90°				★★
	❶(6a/b.N.S.) 14.10.1992 Alan Grigg							
2	**Belts and Braces**		5b	90°				★★
	❶(5b.N.L.) 1978-91 Guy McLelland, Tim Daniells: (5b) 1981-9 🏆							
3	**Jetsam**		3b	78°				★★
	❶(2b) Pre-1956							
4	**Flotsam**		2b	77°				★★
	❶(2b) Pre-1956							
5	**Soft Cock**		5c	75°				🗑
	❶(5c.N.S.) 30.11.1991 Doug Reid, Frank Shannon: (5c) 5.8.1993 🏆 Tim Skinner							
6	**Bootless Buzzard**		5c	75°				★
	❶(5c.N.S.) 24.11.1991 Doug Reid, Mike Vetterlein: (5c) 26.4.1993 🏆 Tim Skinner							
7	**Boxing Day Cracker**		1b	68°				
	❶(1b) 26.12.1995 Christine Eades, Steve Durkin, Teresa Hill, Robin Mazinke							

Woodside Blossom 5c+, Tony Forward

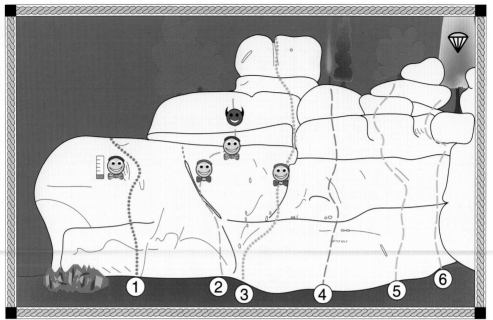

1	**Wildcat Wall**	5b+	55°				★★★
	❶(5a) Pre-1956						
2	**Woodside Blossom**	5c+	85°				★★
	❶(5c) 1974 ♈ Mick Fowler						
3	**Deadwood Crack**	4c	84°				★★
	❶(4a) Pre-1956						
4	**Toeing the Line**	4a	75°				★
	❶(4a) 1999 Jan Cholawo, Martin Cooper						
5	**Tame Variant**	2b	67°				★
	❶(2b) Pre-1956						
6	**Tame Diedre**	2a	67°				★
	❶(2a) Pre-1956						

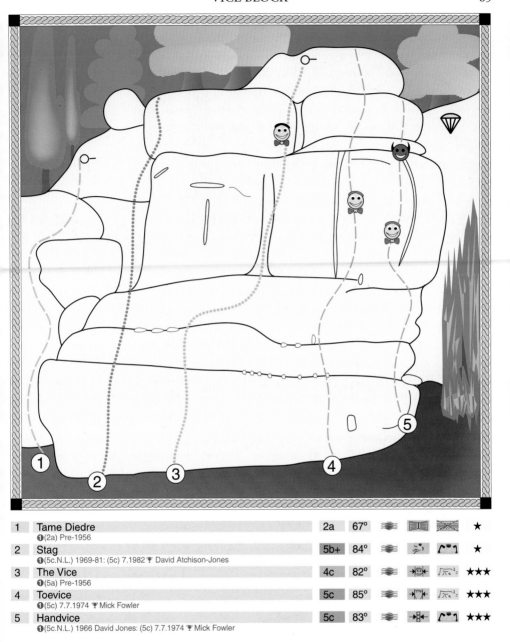

1	Tame Diedre	2a	67°				★
	❶(2a) Pre-1956						
2	Stag	5b+	84°				★
	❶(5c.N.L.) 1969-81: (5c) 7.1982 ♥ David Atchison-Jones						
3	The Vice	4c	82°				★★★
	❶(5a) Pre-1956						
4	Toevice	5c	85°				★★★
	❶(5c) 7.7.1974 ♥ Mick Fowler						
5	Handvice	5c	83°				★★★
	❶(5c.N.L.) 1966 David Jones: (5c) 7.7.1974 ♥ Mick Fowler						

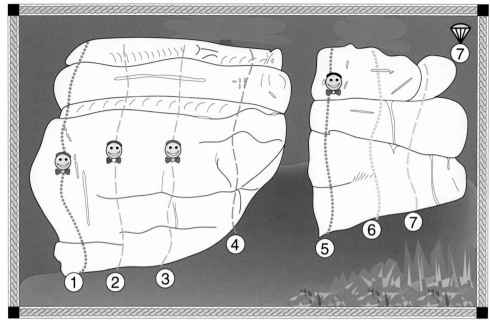

1	Birch Nose		5b	95°				★★
	❶(5b) Pre-1956							
2	Victoria		5c	108°				★
	❶(6a/5c) 11.1989 Tim Skinner							
3	The Clamp		5c	98°				★
	❶(5a) 1969-81 Tim Daniells							
4	Corridor Route		4a	93°				★
	❶(4a) Pre-1956							
5	Rhapsody Inside a Satsuma		5a+	84°				★
	❶(5a) 8.1982 David Atchison-Jones, John Edwards, Matt Saunders							
6	Pickled Pogo Stick		3c	84°				
	❶(33) 8.1982 David Atchison-Jones							
7	Cracking Up		1a	70°				
	❶(1a) Pre-1956							

Tame Variant 2b, Melissa Snaith

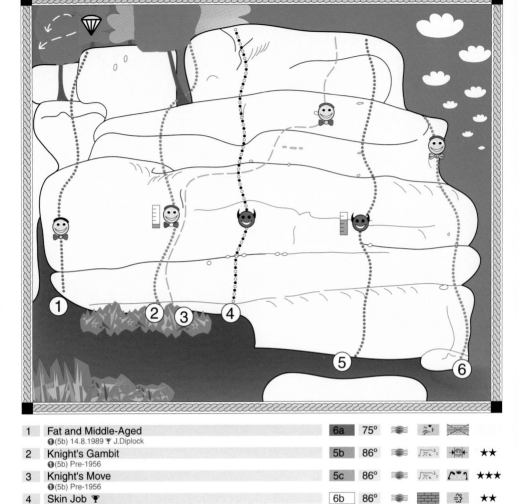

1	Fat and Middle-Aged		6a	75°			
	❶(5b) 14.8.1989 ⚑ J.Diplock						
2	Knight's Gambit		5b	86°			★★
	❶(5b) Pre-1956						
3	Knight's Move		5c	86°			★★★
	❶(5b) Pre-1956						
4	Skin Job ⚑		6b	86°			★★
	❶(6b.N.S.) 11.8.1991 Tim Skinner						
5	Reach for the Sky		6a	86°			★★★
	❶(5c.N.L.) Doug Chase, Trevor Panther: (6a) 4.1992 ⚑Tim Skinner						
6	Set Square Arête		5b	90°			★★
	❶(N.L.) Pre-1956: (5c) 1969-81 ⚑						

The Knam 6a+, Gerry Gilmartin & Theseus Gerard

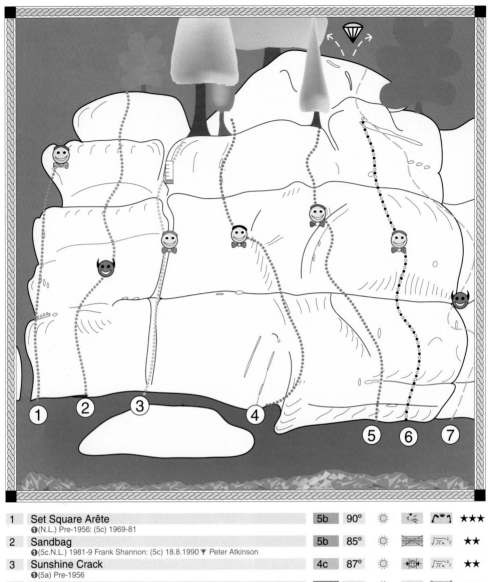

1	Set Square Arête		5b	90°				★★★
	❶(N.L.) Pre-1956: (5c) 1969-81							
2	Sandbag		5b	85°				★★
	❶(5c.N.L.) 1981-9 Frank Shannon: (5c) 18.8.1990 ♈ Peter Atkinson							
3	Sunshine Crack		4c	87°				★★
	❶(5a) Pre-1956							
4	The Knam		6a+	87°				★★★
	❶(6a.N.L.) Trevor Panther, D.Chase, G.Sommerville: (6a) 1981-9 ♈							
5	The Mank		6a	82°				★★★
	❶(6a.N.L.) Barry Wyborough, T.Panther: (6a) 1982 ♈ Dan Lewis							
6	Dr. Pepper ♈		6b	107°				★★★
	❶(6b.N.S.) 21.4.1992 Steve Quinton, Ian Stronghill							
7	Piecemeal Wall		5c	105°				★★★
	❶(5c) Pre-1956 ♈ Arthur Dolphin							

Smooth and Slippery Chimney 3b, Remus Gerard

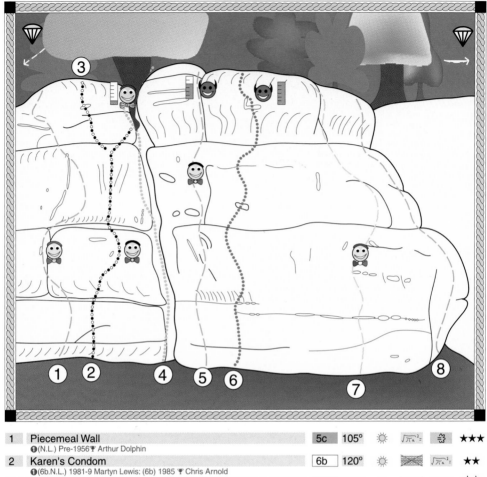

1	Piecemeal Wall	5c	105°	☀	〰	≌	★★★
	❶(N.L.) Pre-1956 ⚑ Arthur Dolphin						
2	Karen's Condom	6b	120°	☀	〰	〰	★★
	❶(6b.N.L.) 1981-9 Martyn Lewis: (6b) 1985 ⚑ Chris Arnold						
3	Hard Condom	6b	120°	☀	〰	〰	★★
	❶(6b) 10.8.1992 ⚑ Steve Quinton						
4	Smooth and Slippery Chimney	3b	72°	☀	▦	⌐	★★★
	❶(3a) Pre-1956						
5	Reverse Traverse	5c+	103°	☀	▦	⌐	★★
	❶(5b) Pre-1956						
6	Eric	6b	140°	☀	▦	⌐	
	❶(5c.N.L.) 1969-81: (5c) 5.1992 ⚑ John Patterson						
7	Two Toed Sloth	5a	84°	☀	▦	〰	★★★
	❶(5a) Pre-1956						
8	Soft Rock'er	5c	92°	☀	⠶	〰	★
	❶(5c) 1992-5						

Two Toed Sloth 5a, Sarah Crane (who of course is neither two toed - or a sloth; assuredly - Mr. Wobbly)

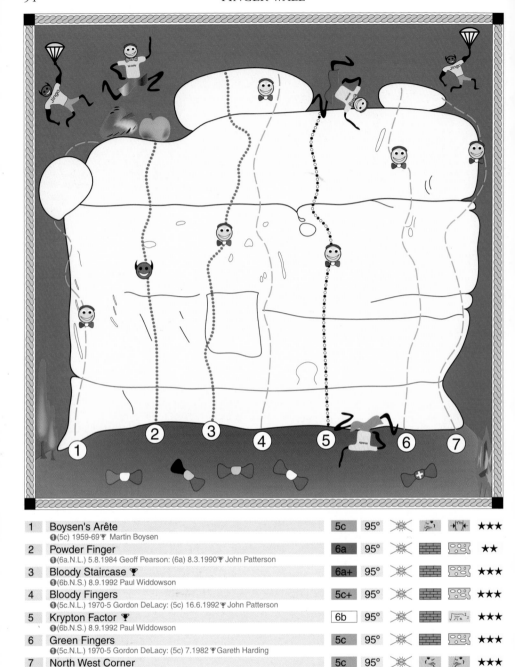

1	Boysen's Arête	5c	95°				★★★
	❶(5c) 1959-69 ♈ Martin Boysen						
2	Powder Finger	6a	95°				★★
	❶(6a.N.L.) 5.8.1984 Geoff Pearson: (6a) 8.3.1990♈ John Patterson						
3	Bloody Staircase ♈	6a+	95°				★★★
	❶(6b.N.S.) 8.9.1992 Paul Widdowson						
4	Bloody Fingers	5c+	95°				★★★
	❶(5c.N.L.) 1970-5 Gordon DeLacy: (5c) 16.6.1992♈ John Patterson						
5	Krypton Factor ♈	6b	95°				★★★
	❶(6b.N.S.) 8.9.1992 Paul Widdowson						
6	Green Fingers	5c	95°				★★★
	❶(5c.N.L.) 1970-5 Gordon DeLacy: (5c) 7.1982 ♈Gareth Harding						
7	North West Corner	5c	95°				★★★
	❶(N.L.) Pre-1956: (5c) 1956-63 ♈						

South West Corner 6a, Malcolm McPherson

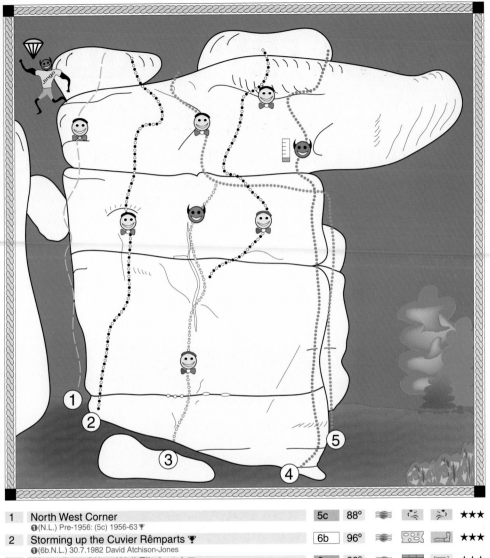

1	North West Corner	5c	88°	≋			★★★
	❶(N.L.) Pre-1956: (5c) 1956-63 ⛾						
2	Storming up the Cuvier Rêmparts ⛾	6b	96°	≋			★★★
	❶(6b.N.L.) 30.7.1982 David Atchison-Jones						
3	Wooly Bear (West Wall Eliminate) ⛾	6c	99°	≋			★★★
	❶(6a.N.L.) 6.1967 Ben Wintringham; 6b,1979 M.Fowler; 6c,1981 J.Sharpe						
4	South West Corner	6a	99°	≋			★★★
	❶(N.L.) Pre-1956: (5c) 1968 ⛾ Terry Tullis						
5	West Wall	5b	88°	≋			★★★
	❶(5b) Pre-1956						

Wooly Bear 6c

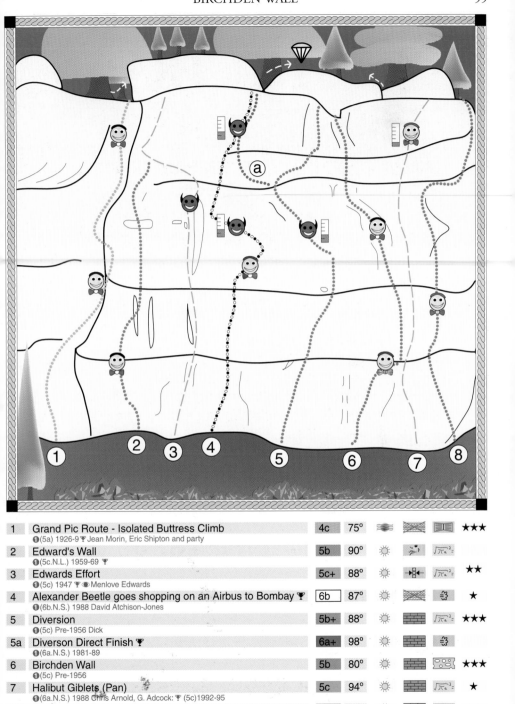

1	Grand Pic Route - Isolated Buttress Climb	4c	75°				★★★
	❶(5a) 1926-9 ⚑ Jean Morin, Eric Shipton and party						
2	Edward's Wall	5b	90°				
	❶(5c.N.L.) 1959-69 ⚑						
3	Edwards Effort	5c+	88°				★★
	❶(5c) 1947 ⚑ ◉ Menlove Edwards						
4	Alexander Beetle goes shopping on an Airbus to Bombay ⚑	6b	87°				★
	❶(6b.N.S.) 1988 David Atchison-Jones						
5	Diversion	5b+	88°				★★★
	❶(5c) Pre-1956 Dick						
5a	Diverson Direct Finish ⚑	6a+	98°				
	❶(6a.N.S.) 1981-89						
6	Birchden Wall	5b	80°				★★★
	❶(5c) Pre-1956						
7	Halibut Giblets (Pan)	5c	94°				★
	❶(6a.N.S.) 1988 Chris Arnold, G. Adcock: ⚑ (5c)1992-95						
8	Birchden Corner	5b+	95°				★★
	❶(5c) 1940's ⚑ Johnnie Lees						

Diversion 5b+, Alison Brewin

Wailing Wall 5c, Frank Shannon

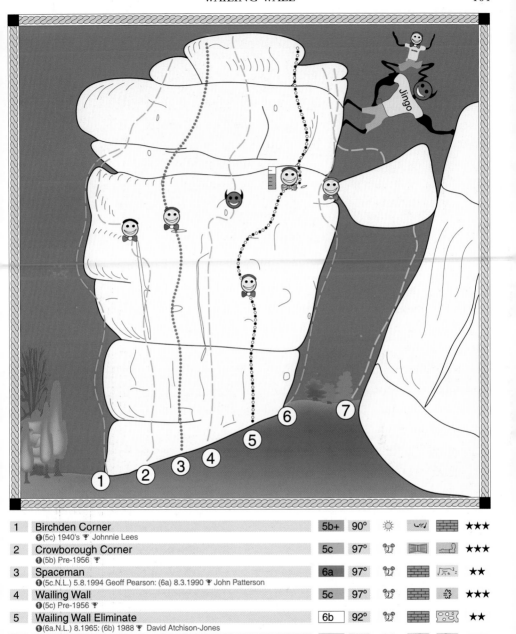

1	Birchden Corner			5b+	90°	☀			★★★
	❶(5c) 1940's ⚑ Johnnie Lees								
2	Crowborough Corner			5c	97°				★★★
	❶(5b) Pre-1956 ⚑								
3	Spaceman			6a	97°				★★
	❶(5c.N.L.) 5.8.1994 Geoff Pearson: (6a) 8.3.1990 ⚑ John Patterson								
4	Wailing Wall			5c	97°				★★★
	❶(5c) Pre-1956 ⚑								
5	Wailing Wall Eliminate			6b	92°				★★
	❶(6a.N.L.) 8.1965: (6b) 1988 ⚑ David Atchison-Jones								
6	Boysen's Arête			5c	98°				★★★
	❶(5c) 1959-69 ⚑ Martin Boysen								
7	Boulder Bridge Route			2b	90°				★★★
	❶(3a) Pre-1956								

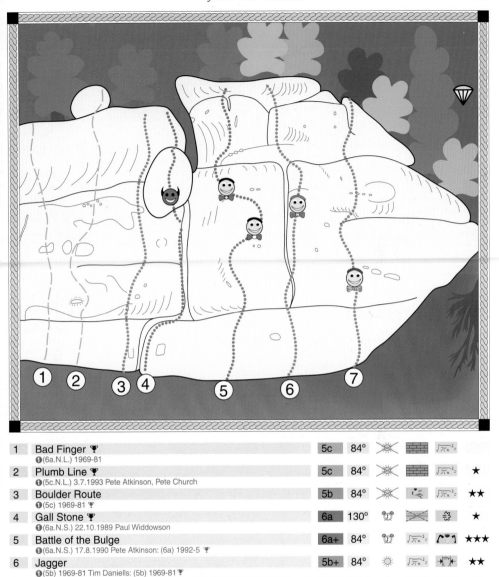

1	Bad Finger ♟		5c	84°				
	❶(6a.N.L.) 1969-81							
2	Plumb Line ♟		5c	84°				★
	❶(5c.N.L.) 3.7.1993 Pete Atkinson, Pete Church							
3	Boulder Route		5b	84°				★★
	❶(5c) 1969-81 ♟							
4	Gall Stone ♟		6a	130°				★
	❶(6a.N.S.) 22.10.1989 Paul Widdowson							
5	Battle of the Bulge		6a+	84°				★★★
	❶(6a.N.S.) 17.8.1990 Pete Atkinson: (6a) 1992-5 ♟							
6	Jagger		5b+	84°				★★
	❶(5b) 1969-81 Tim Daniells: (5b) 1969-81 ♟							
7	Ear-ring		5b	84°				★★
	❶(6a.N.S.) 21.6.1992 Pete Atkinson, Bob Russell: (6a) 1992-5							

Birchden Wall 5b, Malcolm McPherson

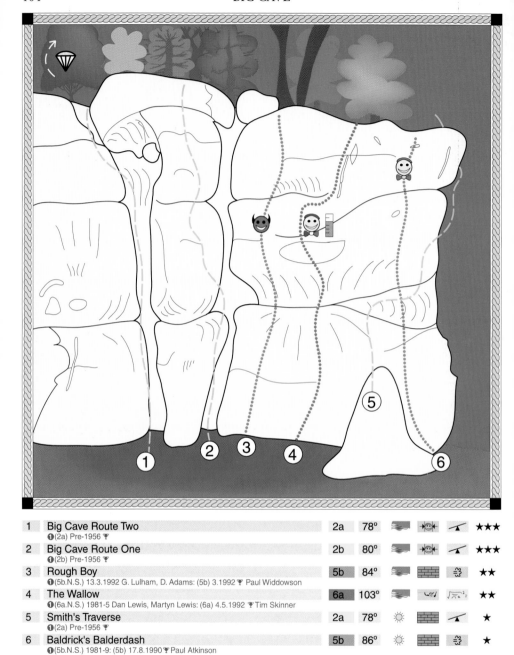

1	Big Cave Route Two	2a	78°				★★★
	❶(2a) Pre-1956 ⚑						
2	Big Cave Route One	2b	80°				★★★
	❶(2b) Pre-1956 ⚑						
3	Rough Boy	5b	84°				★★
	❶(5b.N.S.) 13.3.1992 G. Lulham, D. Adams: (5b) 3.1992 ⚑ Paul Widdowson						
4	The Wallow	6a	103°				★★
	❶(6a.N.S.) 1981-5 Dan Lewis, Martyn Lewis: (6a) 4.5.1992 ⚑ Tim Skinner						
5	Smith's Traverse	2a	78°				★
	❶(2a) Pre-1956 ⚑						
6	Baldrick's Balderdash	5b	86°				★
	❶(5b.N.S.) 1981-9: (5b) 17.8.1990 ⚑ Paul Atkinson						

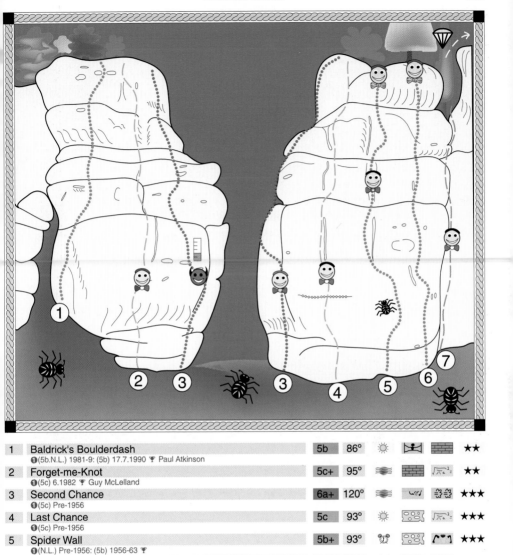

1	Baldrick's Boulderdash	5b	86°				★★
	❶(5b.N.L.) 1981-9: (5b) 17.7.1990 ⚑ Paul Atkinson						
2	Forget-me-Knot	5c+	95°				★★
	❶(5c) 6.1982 ⚑ Guy McLelland						
3	Second Chance	6a+	120°				★★★
	❶(5c) Pre-1956						
4	Last Chance	5c	93°				★★★
	❶(5c) Pre-1956						
5	Spider Wall	5b+	93°				★★★
	❶(N.L.) Pre-1956: (5b) 1956-63 ⚑						
6	Big Cave Wall	5b	87°				★★★
	❶(5b) Pre-1956						
7	Grand Morin - (Crack and Cave)	4a	90°				★★★
	❶(5a) 1926-9 Jean Morin, Eric Shipton and Party						

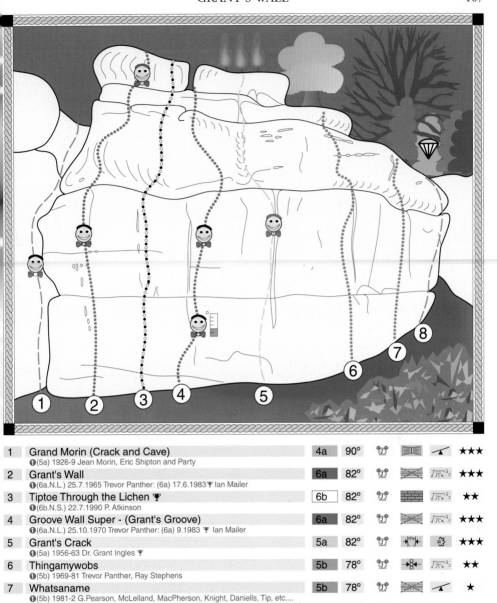

1	Grand Morin (Crack and Cave)	4a	90°				★★★
	❶(5a) 1926-9 Jean Morin, Eric Shipton and Party						
2	Grant's Wall	6a	82°				★★★
	❶(6a.N.L.) 25.7.1965 Trevor Panther: (6a) 17.6.1983 ♈ Ian Mailer						
3	Tiptoe Through the Lichen ♈	6b	82°				★★
	❶(6b.N.S.) 22.7.1990 P. Atkinson						
4	Groove Wall Super - (Grant's Groove)	6a	82°				★★★
	❶(6a.N.L.) 25.10.1970 Trevor Panther: (6a) 9.1983 ♈ Ian Mailer						
5	Grant's Crack	5a	82°				★★★
	❶(5a) 1956-63 Dr. Grant Ingles ♈						
6	Thingamywobs	5b	78°				★★
	❶(5b) 1969-81 Trevor Panther, Ray Stephens						
7	Whatsaname	5b	78°				★
	❶(5b) 1981-2 G.Pearson, McLelland, MacPherson, Knight, Daniells, Tip, etc....						
8	Thingy	4b	85°				★
	❶(4b) 1969-81						

Last Chance 5c, Frank 'Cool River' Shannon

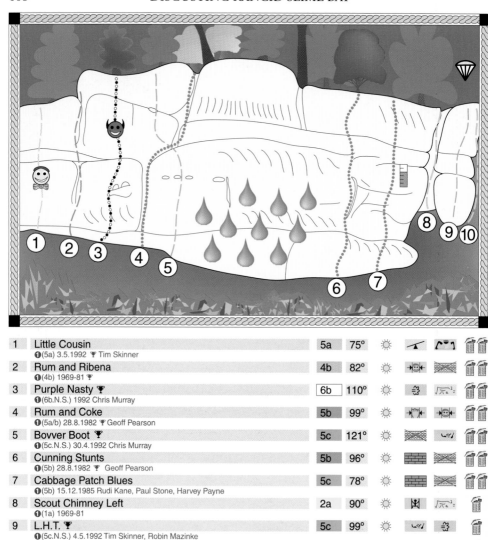

1	Little Cousin		5a	75°	☀				
	❶(5a) 3.5.1992 ♈ Tim Skinner								
2	Rum and Ribena		4b	82°	☀				
	❶(4b) 1969-81 ♈								
3	Purple Nasty ♈		6b	110°	☀				
	❶(6b.N.S.) 1992 Chris Murray								
4	Rum and Coke		5b	99°	☀				
	❶(5a/b) 28.8.1982 ♈ Geoff Pearson								
5	Bovver Boot ♈		5c	121°	☀				
	❶(5c.N.S.) 30.4.1992 Chris Murray								
6	Cunning Stunts		5b	96°	☀				
	❶(5b) 28.8.1982 ♈ Geoff Pearson								
7	Cabbage Patch Blues		5c	78°	☀				
	❶(5b) 15.12.1985 Rudi Kane, Paul Stone, Harvey Payne								
8	Scout Chimney Left		2a	90°	☀				
	❶(1a) 1969-81								
9	L.H.T. ♈		5c	99°	☀				
	❶(5c.N.S.) 4.5.1992 Tim Skinner, Robin Mazinke								
10	Scout Chimney Right		1a	60°	☀				
	❶(1a) 1969-81								

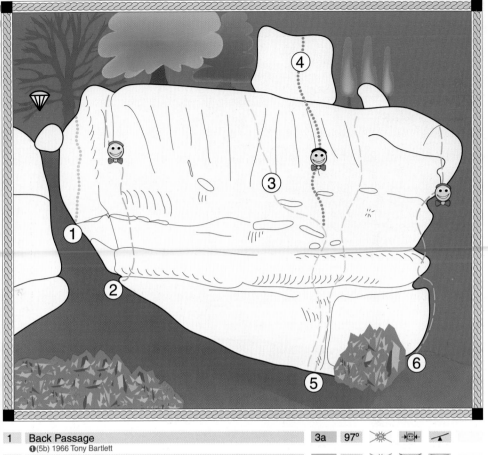

1	Back Passage	3a	97°			
	❶(5b) 1966 Tony Bartlett					
2	Araldite Wall	5c	97°			
	❶(5c) 7.11.1965 ☗ Peter(Soss) Sorrell, Mike Mansfield, Trevor Panther					
3	Garden Slab Left	5a	79°			
	❶(5a) 1959-69					
4	Tiptoe thru the Tulips	5b	79°			
	❶(5a) 1982 M. Barrett, R. Nossiter					
5	Garden Slab Right	5a	79°			
	❶(5b) 1969-69					
6	Biceps Buttress	5c	99°			★★
	❶(N.L.) Pre-1956: (5b) 1959-69					

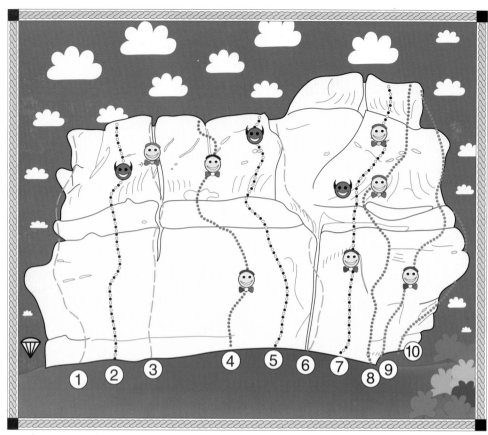

1	**Biceps Buttress**	5c	99°				★★
	❶(N.L.) Pre-1956: (5b) 1959-69						
2	**Finger Popper** ♈	6b	99°				★
	❶(6b.N.S.) 1985 Ian Mailer						
3	**Muscle Crack**	5c+	98°				★
	❶(5c.N.L.) 1956-63: (6a) 1969-81 ♈						
4	**Crucifix**	6a	99°				★★
	❶(6a.N.L.) 1968 T.Panther,D.Chase,G.Somerville: (6a) 28.5.1992 ♈ Tim Skinner						
5	**Hector's House** ♈	6b	99°				★★
	❶(6a.N.L.) 8.1982 Barry Knight, Guy McLelland, David Atchison-Jones						
6	**Corner**	5c	93°				★★
	❶(5c) 1959-69 ♈						
7	**Magic Wall** ♈	6b	110°				★★★
	❶(6b.N.L.) 1981-9 Guy McLelland						
8	**Phillipa**	6a+	112°				★★★
	❶(5c.N.L.) 7.1982 Guy McLelland, Barry Knight: (6a) ♈						
9	**Shodan**	5b+	95°				★★★
	❶(5c) 1956-63						
10	**Half Crown Corner**	5b	120°				★★
	❶(5b) Jean Morin and Party						

Phillipa 6a+, Chris Harrison

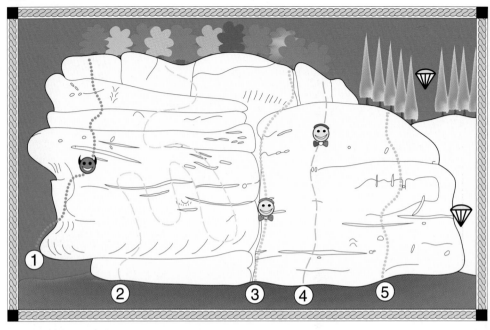

1	Half Crown Corner		5b	120°				★★★
	❶(5b) 1926-9 Jean Morin and Party							
2	Wander at Leisure		5a	80°				★★★
	❶(5a) 1956-63							
3	Birch Tree Crack		3c	90°				★★
	❶(3b) Pre-1956							
4	Birch Tree Variations		5c+	87°				★★
	❶(4a) 1959-69							
5	Birch Tree Wall		4c	82°				★★
	❶(5a) 1926-9 Jean Morin and Party							

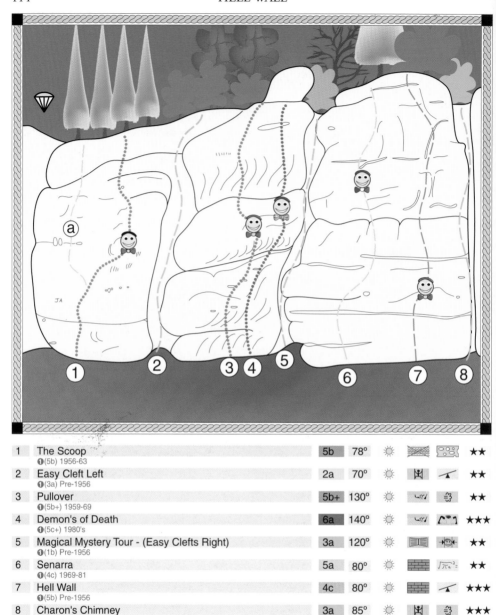

1	The Scoop	5b	78°	☼			★★
	❶(5b) 1956-63						
2	Easy Cleft Left	2a	70°	☼			★★
	❶(3a) Pre-1956						
3	Pullover	5b+	130°	☼			★★
	❶(5b+) 1959-69						
4	Demon's of Death	6a	140°	☼			★★★
	❶(5c+) 1980's						
5	Magical Mystery Tour - (Easy Clefts Right)	3a	120°	☼			★★
	❶(1b) Pre-1956						
6	Senarra	5a	80°	☼			★★
	❶(4c) 1969-81						
7	Hell Wall	4c	80°	☼			★★★
	❶(5b) Pre-1956						
8	Charon's Chimney	3a	85°	☼			★★★
	❶(2b) Pre-1956						

Far Left 5b+, Malcolm McPherson

Right Unclimbed 6a, Martin Randall

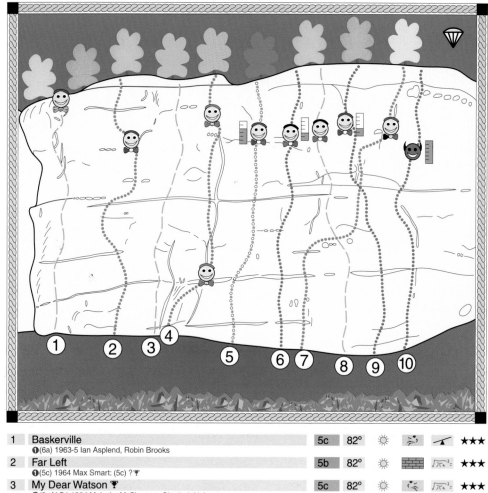

1	Baskerville		5c	82°	☀			★★★
	❶(6a) 1963-5 Ian Asplend, Robin Brooks							
2	Far Left		5b	82°	☀			★★★
	❶(5c) 1964 Max Smart: (5c) ?♈							
3	My Dear Watson ♈		5c	82°	☀			★★★
	❶(5c.N.S.) 1994 Malcolm McPherson, Sherlock Holmes							
4	Elementary		5b+	82°	☀			★★★
	❶(5c) Max Smart: (5c) ? ♈							
5	Dennis the Menace ♈		6c	82°	☀			★★★
	❶(6a) 1980's							
6	Desperate Dan		6a	82°	☀			★★★
	❶(6a.N.L.) 8.1982 Dan Lewis: (6a) 8.3.1990 ♈ John Patterson							
7	Unclimbed Wall - (The Hoarding)		5b	82°	☀			★★★
	❶(N.L.) 1926-9 Jean Morin and Party: (5c) 1956-63							
8	Wizzard's Progress		5c+	82°	☀			★★★
	❶(6a.N.L.) 2.5.1965 Mike Mansfield: (6a) 9.1982 ♈ David Atchison-Jones							
9	Wizzard's Shuffle		6a	82°	☀			★★★
	❶(6a.N.L.) 1981 A team of Wizzards: (6a) 1982 ♈ Dan Lewis							
10	Jingo Wobbly - (Django Wobbly)		6a+	82°	☀			★★★
	❶(6b.N.L.) 1983-9 Dan Lewis: (6b) 8.3.1990 ♈ John Patterson							

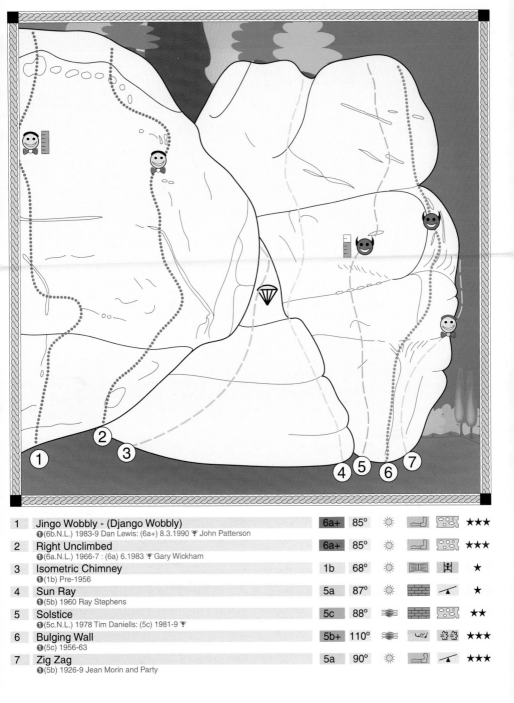

1	Jingo Wobbly - (Django Wobbly)	6a+	85°	☀			★★★
	❶(6b.N.L.) 1983-9 Dan Lewis: (6a+) 8.3.1990 ⚑ John Patterson						
2	Right Unclimbed	6a+	85°	☀			★★★
	❶(6a.N.L.) 1966-7 : (6a) 6.1983 ⚑ Gary Wickham						
3	Isometric Chimney	1b	68°	☀			★
	❶(1b) Pre-1956						
4	Sun Ray	5a	87°	☀			★
	❶(5b) 1960 Ray Stephens						
5	Solstice	5c	88°	≋			★★
	❶(5c.N.L.) 1978 Tim Daniells: (5c) 1981-9 ⚑						
6	Bulging Wall	5b+	110°	≋			★★★
	❶(5c) 1956-63						
7	Zig Zag	5a	90°	☀			★★★
	❶(5b) 1926-9 Jean Morin and Party						

Solstice 5c, Alice in Wonderland

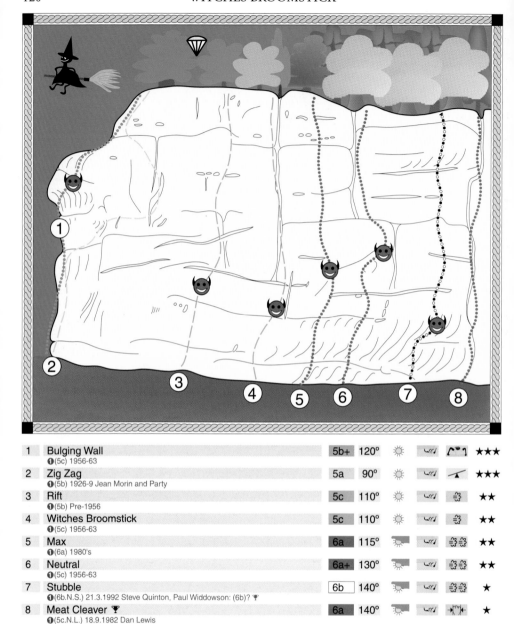

1	Bulging Wall	5b+	120°	☀	⌇	⌐*⌐	★★★
	❶(5c) 1956-63						
2	Zig Zag	5a	90°	☀	⌇	⌐	★★★
	❶(5b) 1926-9 Jean Morin and Party						
3	Rift	5c	110°	☀	⌇	彐	★★
	❶(5b) Pre-1956						
4	Witches Broomstick	5c	110°	☀	⌇	彐	★★
	❶(5c) 1956-63						
5	Max	6a	115°	☁	⌇	彐彐	★★
	❶(6a) 1980's						
6	Neutral	6a+	130°	☁	⌇	彐彐	★★
	❶(5c) 1956-63						
7	Stubble	6b	140°	☁	⌇	彐彐	★
	❶(6b.N.S.) 21.3.1992 Steve Quinton, Paul Widdowson: (6b)? ♟						
8	Meat Cleaver ♟	6a	140°	☁	⌇	⊁ᵐ⊁	★
	❶(5c.N.L.) 18.9.1982 Dan Lewis						

Desperate Dan 6a, Malcolm (the Wizzard) McPherson

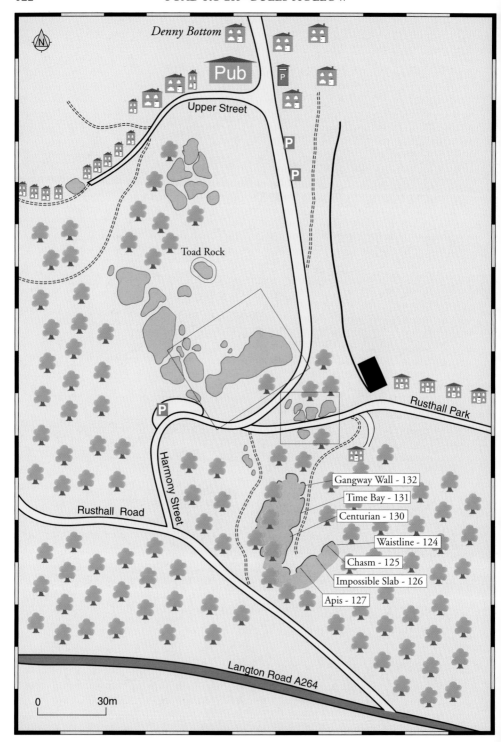

RUSTHALL MAP

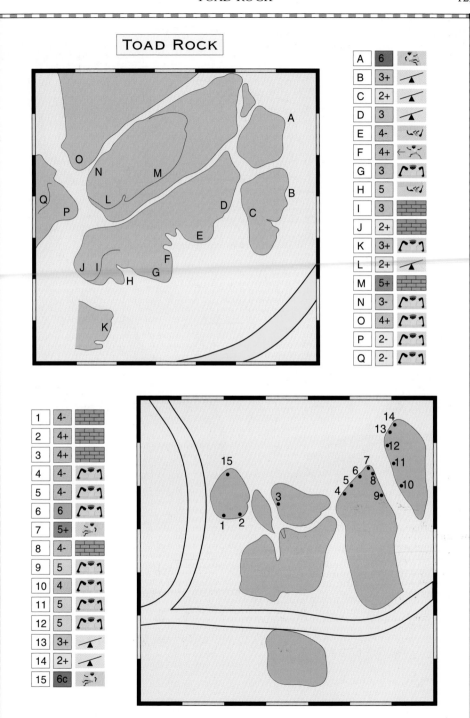

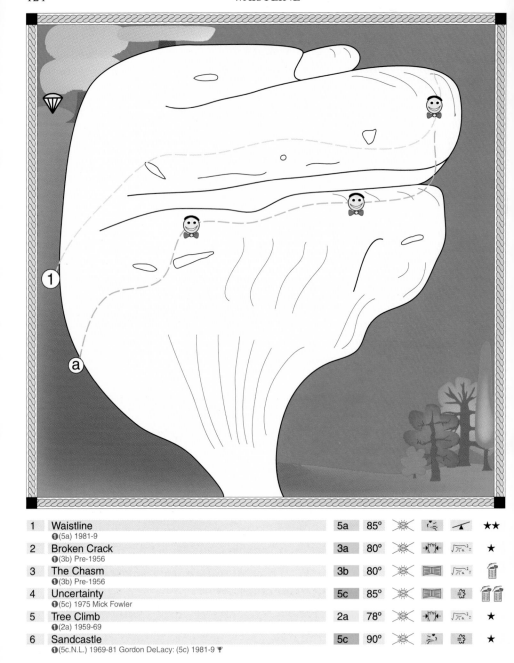

1	Waistline	5a	85°	☼			★★
	❶(5a) 1981-9						
2	Broken Crack	3a	80°	☼			★
	❶(3b) Pre-1956						
3	The Chasm	3b	80°	☼			🗑
	❶(3b) Pre-1956						
4	Uncertainty	5c	85°	☼			🗑🗑
	❶(5c) 1975 Mick Fowler						
5	Tree Climb	2a	78°	☼			★
	❶(2a) 1959-69						
6	Sandcastle	5c	90°	☼			★
	❶(5c.N.L.) 1969-81 Gordon DeLacy: (5c) 1981-9 ♟						

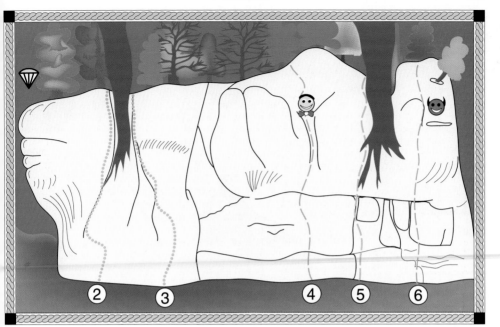

The Toad Rock Retreat
Harmony St, Rusthall, Tunbridge Wells

Climbing Bull's Hollow and the Rocks in Rusthall this week?

Why not work up an appetite then visit us? We offer an extensive home-cooked menu, including vegetarian meals and also coffee or hot chocolate for those in need of a warm-up!

The Toad Rock Retreat is a real ale pub right next to the Toad Rock and prides itself on its ambient atmosphere for those in need of a rest

We also have live music on Thursday nights from 9pm and welcome party bookings

telephone 01892 520818

or see the website at www.toadrock.net

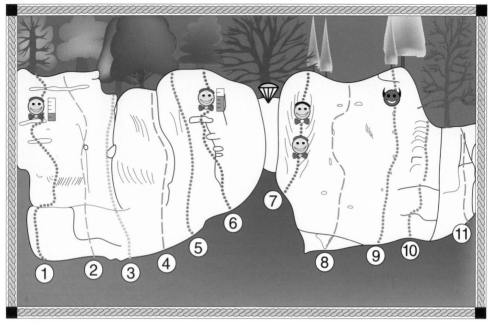

1	Yew Wall	5b	85°				★★
	❶(5a.N.L.) 1969-81: (5a) 1981-9 ⚑						
2	Poltergeist	5c	90°				★★
	❶(5c.N.L.) 1969-81: (5c) 1981-9 ⚑						
3	Yellowstone Wall	3b	78°				
	❶(4b) Pre-1956						
4	Yellowstone Crack	4b	87°				
	❶(4a) 1959-69						
5	Taurus	5b	88°				★
	❶(5b) 1969-81						
6	Minotaur ⚑	6a	98°				★★
	❶(A1) 1969-74: (6a.N.L.) 10.8.1975 Mick Fowler						
7	The Scoop ⚑	6a	87°				★
	❶(6a.N.L.) 1974 Mick Fowler						
8	Possibility Wall	4b	74°				★★
	❶(5b) 1956-63						
9	Impossibility	5b	75°				★★
	❶(5b) 1969-81						
10	Sentry Box Arête	5b	90°				★
	❶(5a) 1959-69						
11	Sentry Box	4b	85°				★
	❶(4b) Pre-1956						

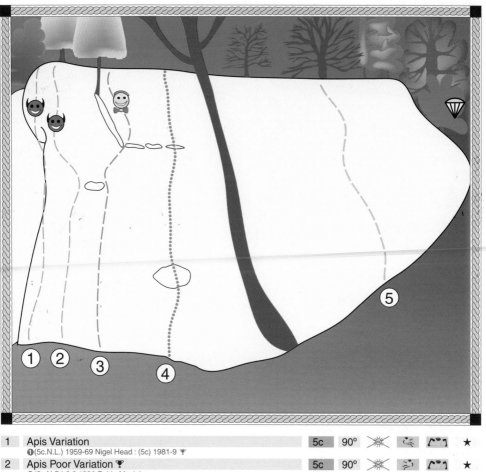

1	Apis Variation		5c	90°				★

1 Apis Variation
❶(5c.N.L.) 1959-69 Nigel Head : (5c) 1981-9 🍸 — 5c — 90° — ⚔ — 🏃 — ⌐¹ — ★

2 Apis Poor Variation 🍸
❶(5c.N.S.) 8.8.1996 Robin Mazinke — 5c — 90° — ⚔ — 🏃 — ⌐¹ — ★

3 Apis
❶(4b) 1956-63 — 4b — 78° — ⚔ — 🧱 — ⌐¹ — ★

4 Moss
❶(5b) 1961-81 — 5b — 87° — ⚔ — 🧱 — ▨ — ★

5 Cellar Wall
❶(3b) Pre-1956 — 2a — 68° — ⚔ — 🧱 — ◣ — 🗑

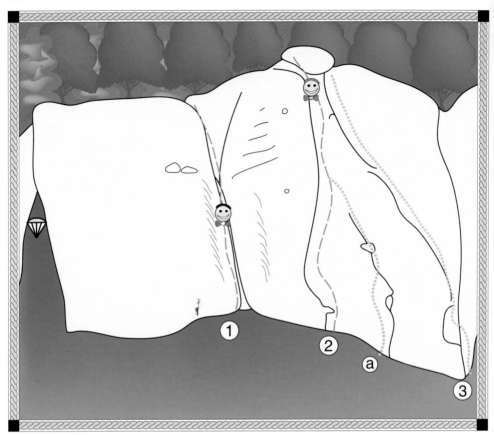

1	Blasphemy	4a	82°			
	❶(4a) 1959-69					
2	Solo	4b	100°			
	❶(4b) 1959-69					
3	Conway's Variation	3b	60°			★★
	❶(3b) 1959-69					

BULLS HOLLOW - TOPO 5

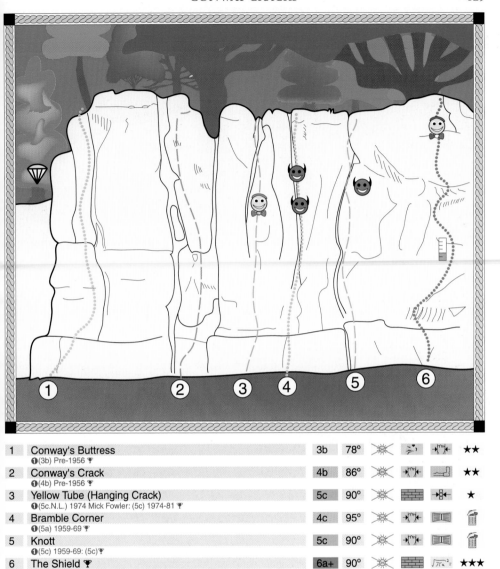

1	Conway's Buttress	3b	78°				★★
	❶(3b) Pre-1956						
2	Conway's Crack	4b	86°				★★
	❶(4b) Pre-1956						
3	Yellow Tube (Hanging Crack)	5c	90°				★
	❶(5c.N.L.) 1974 Mick Fowler: (5c) 1974-81						
4	Bramble Corner	4c	95°				
	❶(5a) 1959-69						
5	Knott	5c	90°				
	❶(5c) 1959-69: (5c)						
6	The Shield	6a+	90°				★★★
	❶(6a.N.L.) 6.4.1975 Mick Fowler, John Stevenson, Mike Morrison						

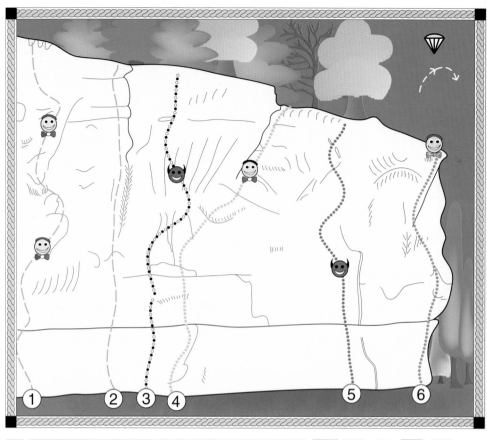

1	The Wall		5c+	90°				★★★
	❶(5c.N.L.) 1959-69: (5c) 17.7.1996 ♛ John Patterson							
2	Caesar		5c	96°				★★
	❶(5c.N.L.) 1969-81: (5c) 1981-9 ♛							
3	Squeak ya Heel Cups ♛		6b	102°				★
	❶(6a/b.N.S.) 8.7.1993 James Dunlop, Rob Kennard							
4	Centurian's Groove		4c	78°				★★★
	❶(4c) Pre-1956 ♛							
5	Pseudonym		5c+	97°				★
	❶(6a.N.L.) 1959-69: (5c) 6.1982 ♛ David Atchison-Jones							
6	Broken Nose		5b	88°				★★
	❶(N.L.) Pre-1956: (5c) 1959-69 ♛							

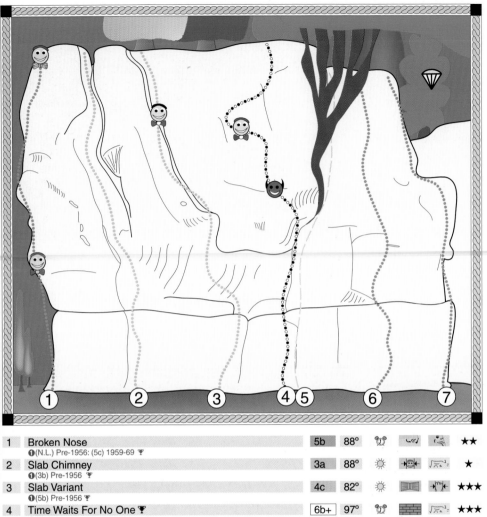

1	Broken Nose	5b	88°				★★

1   Broken Nose •(N.L.) Pre-1956: (5c) 1959-69 ⚑   `5b`   88°   ★★

2   Slab Chimney •(3b) Pre-1956 ⚑   `3a`   88°   ★

3   Slab Variant •(5b) Pre-1956 ⚑   `4c`   82°   ★★★

4   Time Waits For No One ⚑ •(6b.N.L.) 6.1982 David Atchison-Jones   `6b+`   97°   ★★★

5   Full Moon •(5a) 1959-69 ⚑   `5a`   100°

6   Eyewash •(5b.N.L.) 1969-81: (5b) 1981-2 ⚑David Atchison-Jones   `5b`   93°

7   Triangle Arête •(3a) Pre-1956 ⚑   `5b`   95°

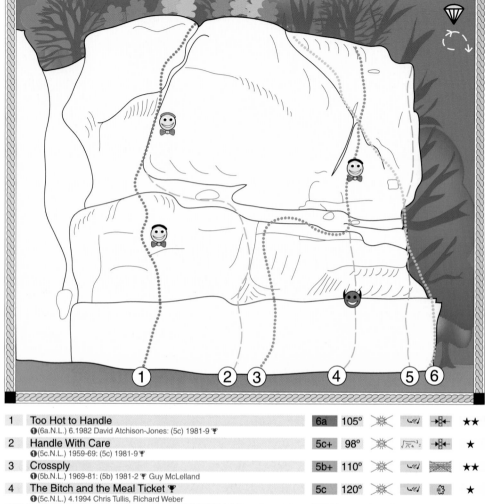

1	Too Hot to Handle		6a	105°				★★
	❶(6a.N.L.) 6.1982 David Atchison-Jones: (5c) 1981-9 ☥							
2	Handle With Care		5c+	98°				★
	❶(5c.N.L.) 1959-69: (5c) 1981-9 ☥							
3	Crossply		5b+	110°				★★
	❶(5b.N.L.) 1969-81: (5b) 1981-2 ☥ Guy McLelland							
4	The Bitch and the Meal Ticket ☥		5c	120°				★
	❶(5c.N.L.) 4.1994 Chris Tullis, Richard Weber							
5	Square Cut		5c	80°				★★
	❶(5c.N.L.) 1975 John Stevenson,M. Fowler: (5c) 6.1982 ☥David Atchison-Jones							
6	Gangway Wall		3a	90°				★★
	❶(3b) Pre-1956 ☥							

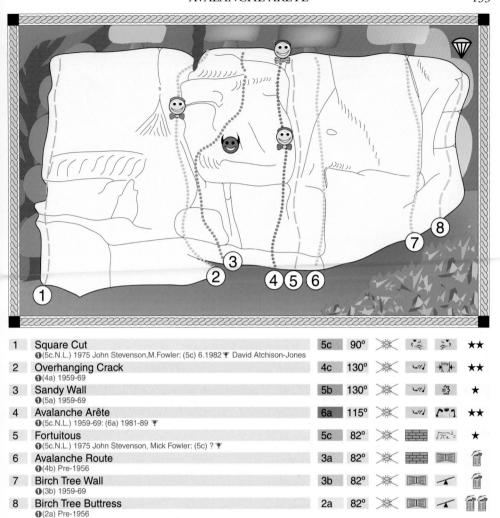

1	Square Cut	5c	90°				★★
	❶(5c.N.L.) 1975 John Stevenson,M.Fowler: (5c) 6.1982 ♈ David Atchison-Jones						
2	Overhanging Crack	4c	130°				★★
	❶(4a) 1959-69						
3	Sandy Wall	5b	130°				★
	❶(5a) 1959-69						
4	Avalanche Arête	6a	115°				★★
	❶(5c.N.L.) 1959-69: (6a) 1981-89 ♈						
5	Fortuitous	5c	82°				★
	❶(5c.N.L.) 1975 John Stevenson, Mick Fowler: (5c) ? ♈						
6	Avalanche Route	3a	82°				
	❶(4b) Pre-1956						
7	Birch Tree Wall	3b	82°				
	❶(3b) 1959-69						
8	Birch Tree Buttress	2a	82°				
	❶(2a) Pre-1956						

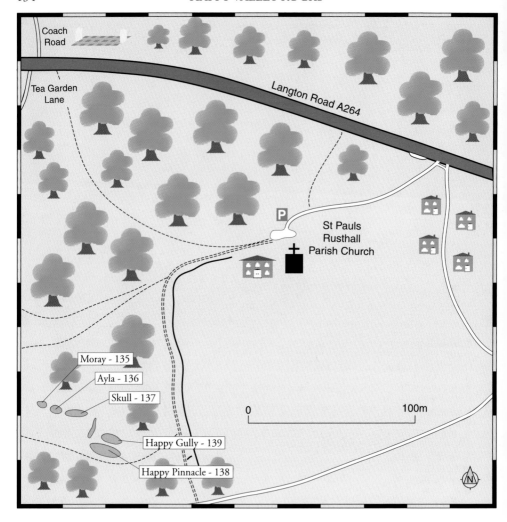

Happy Valley Rocks in recent years have been rescued from the bramble undergrowth of Rusthall common. They are small for the most part – only some 10-12 feet high, but offer excellent bouldering across the mid grades. They get the sun all year round, and have good landings. On the approach you will pass the Happy Valley Pinnacle, which offers a sandy wall with classic, grimy, graunchy and possibly revolting – overhanging cracks. A popular spot for people walking their dogs, so if you fall off – watch out for the gnashing fidos, as you plummet back to planet Earth.

HAPPY VALLEY MAP

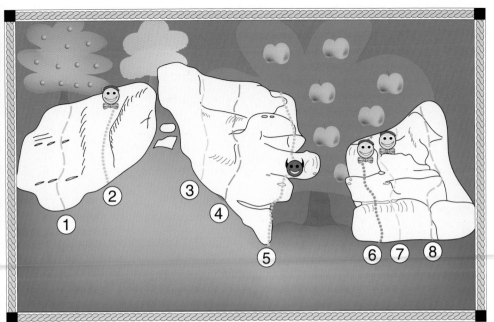

1	Ever so Minnow Minnow	2a	67°				
	❶(2a) 1990's						
2	Minnow	4c	90°				★
	❶(2a) 1990's						
3	Sushi	5a	96°				★
	❶(4b) 12.6.1999 Mike Eden, Robin Mazinke						
4	Stonefish	4b	87°				★
	❶(5a) 1990's						
5	Moray	4a	88°				★★
	❶(4c) 1990's						
6	Red Snapper	5b+	145°				★★
	❶(5b) 1990's						
7	Going Turbot	5a	100°				★★
	❶(5a) 1990's						
8	Kippers	3b	94°				★
	❶(2b) 1990's						

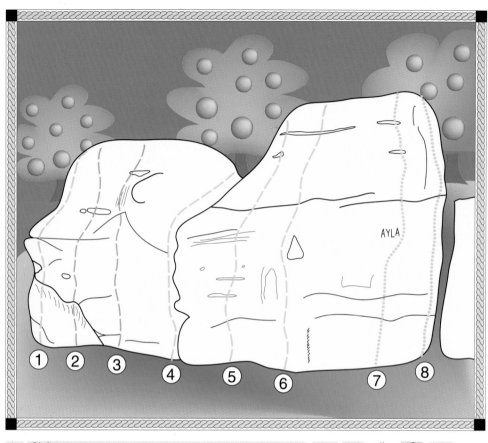

1	Cleft	2b	67°			
	❶(2b) Pre-1995					
2	Cornocopica	4b	83°			★
	❶(4c) 12.6.1999 Robin Mazinke, Mike Eden					
3	Pot Belly	4b	84°			★
	❶(4c) Pre-1995					
4	Mist	2a	66°			
	❶(2a) Pre-1995					
5	Festive	2b	75°			
	❶(2b) 28.12.1995 Steve Durkin, Robin Mazinke					
6	The Short Sharp Cock	2a	75°			
	❶(2a) Pre-1995					
7	Master of Muck	3b	80°			★
	❶(5a) Pre-1995					
8	November Rain	3a	80°			
	❶(3a) 1.8.1996 Robin Mazinke					

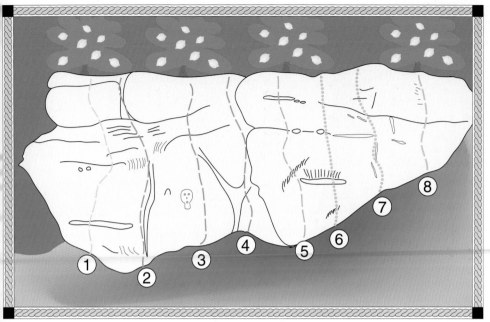

1	Home to Roost	5a	85°				
	❶(5a) 1.8.1996 Robin Mazinke						
2	The Buzzard Years	4a	82°				★
	❶(4a) Pre-1995						
3	And Tigger Too	4b	82°				★★
	❶(4b) 1.8.1996 Robin Mazinke						
4	Corner Crack	4a	82°				★★
	❶(4a) Pre-1995						
5	Pooh's Route	5c+	95°				★
	❶(5c) 18.7.1996 Pete Church						
6	Rotpunkt	4c	80°				★
	❶(4c) Pre-1995						
7	The Deadly Lampshade	3a	78°				
	❶(3a) Pre-1995						
8	Malcolm MacPherson is Fantastic	1a	78°				
	❶(1a) Pre-1995 Henry Nottage						

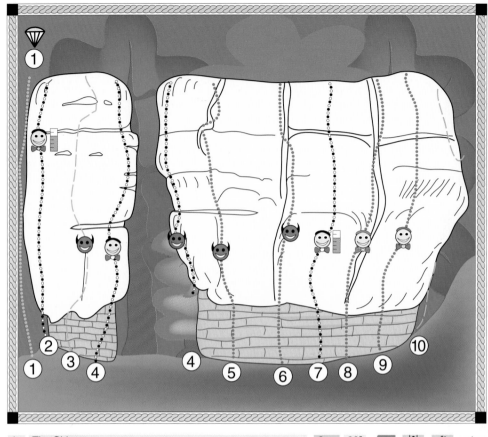

1	**The Chimney**	3a	90°				★
	❶(3a) Pre-1956						
2	**Harvey's** ⚑	6b	92°				★★
	❶(6b.N.S.) 20.6.1999 Robin Mazinke						
3	**Thoroughly Kentish** ⚑	5c	88°				★★★
	❶(5c.N.L.) Pre-1956						
4	**Colour of the Sun** ⚑	6b	105°				★★
	❶(6b.N.S.) 19.5.1996 Ian Stronghill						
5	**Eckpfeiler**	6a	110°				★★★
	❶(6a) 1981-9: (6a) 17.7.1996 ⚑ John Patterson						
6	**Brouillard**	6a	110°				★★★
	❶(6a.N.L.) Pre-1956: (6a) 17.7.1996 ⚑ John Patterson						
7	**Nightrain** ⚑	6b	110°				★
	❶(6b.N.S.) 8.6.1996 Robin Mazinke						
8	**Frêney**	6a	110°				★★★
	❶(6a.N.L) Pre-1956: (6a) 17.7.1996 ⚑ John Patterson						
9	**Sandstone Safari** ⚑	6a	110°				★★
	❶(6a.N.S.) 3.8.1991 Tim Skinner						
10	**Chalybeate**	5c	95°				★
	❶(5c) Pre-1956						

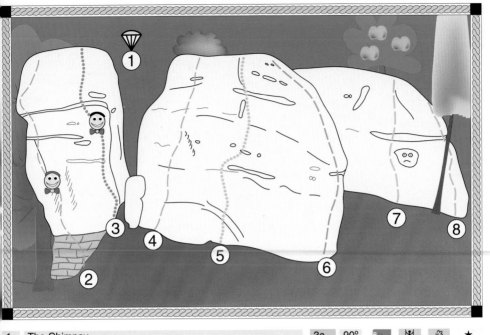

1	The Chimney	3a	90°				★
	❶(3a) Pre-1956						
2	Chalybeate	5c	95°				★
	❶(5c) Pre-1995						
3	From Behind	5b	88°				★
	❶(5b) Pre-1995						
4	Rhody-O ♼	5c	80°				
	❶(5c.N.L.) Pre-1995						
5	Route Minor	4c	80°				★
	❶(4c) Pre-1995						
6	Undercut Rib	4b	80°				
	❶(4b) Pre-1995						
7	Grimace	2a	75°				
	❶(2a) Pre-1995						
8	The Race Home	1b	65°				
	❶(1b) Pre-1995						

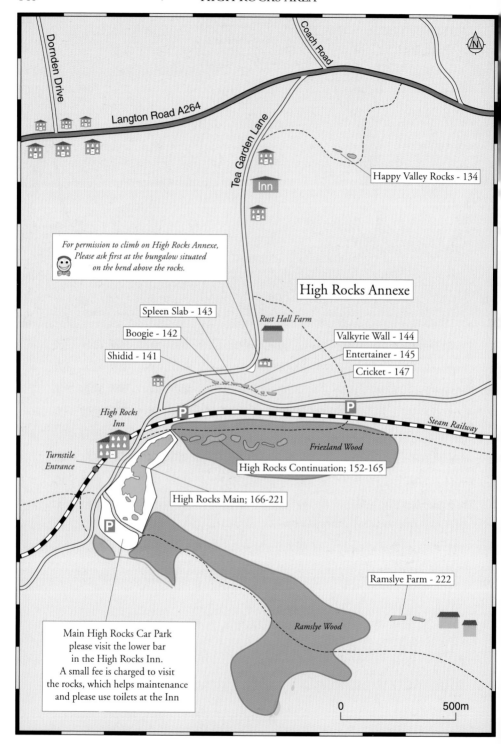

Dornden Drive

Coach Road

Langton Road A264

Tea Garden Lane

Inn

Happy Valley Rocks - 134

For permission to climb on High Rocks Annexe,
Please ask first at the bungalow situated
on the bend above the rocks.

High Rocks Annexe

Spleen Slab - 143

Boogie - 142

Shidid - 141

Rust Hall Farm

Valkyrie Wall - 144

Entertainer - 145

Cricket - 147

High Rocks
Inn

P

P

Steam Railway

Turnstile
Entrance

Friezland Wood

High Rocks Continuation; 152-165

High Rocks Main; 166-221

P

Ramslye Farm - 222

Main High Rocks Car Park
please visit the lower bar
in the High Rocks Inn.
A small fee is charged to visit
the rocks, which helps maintenance
and please use toilets at the Inn

Ramslye Wood

0   500m

HIGH ROCKS MAP

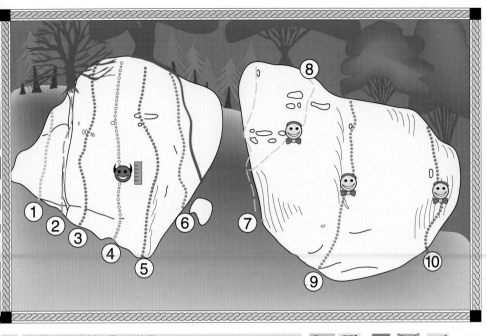

1	Fir Tree Wall (Yew Tree Wall)	3a	75°				
	❶(3a) Pre-1956						
2	Fir Tree Crack (Yew Tree Crack	4b	76°				★
	❶(4b) Pre-1956						
3	It's Only Natural	6a	80°				★★
	❶(6a) 8.7.1999 ⚑ Tim Skinner						
4	Southern Softie	7a	77°				★★
	❶(7a) 25.3.1997 ⚑ Johnny Dawes						
5	Shidid	6a	75°				★★★
	❶(5b) 1969-81						
6	Annexe Slab	5b	75°				
	❶(5b) Pre-1956						
7	Bare Foot Arête (Titch Arête)	5a	90°				★
	❶(5a) 1.9.1957 Chris Morley						
8	Letter Box Wall (Meander)	5a	90°				★★
	❶(N.L.) 1.9.1957 Paul Lebars: (5a) 1959-69 ⚑						
9	Twitch	6a	95°				★★★
	❶(5b) 1956-63						
10	Arnold Thesaanigger	6a	95°				★
	❶(6b.N.S.) 1990 Matt Smith: (6a) ⚑ 1992-5						

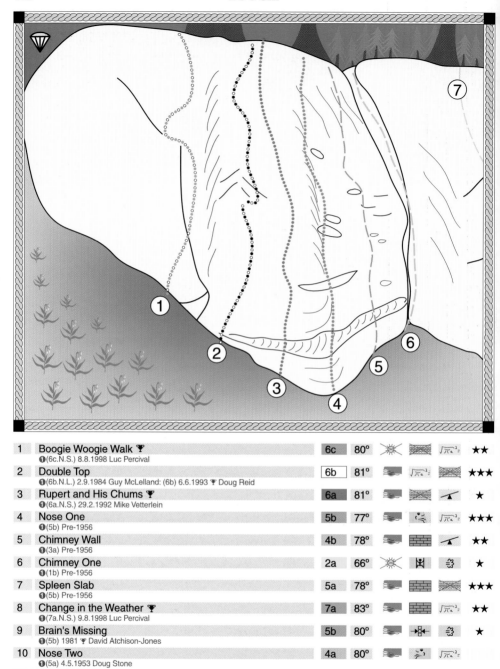

1	Boogie Woogie Walk ♔	6c	80°				★★
	❶(6c.N.S.) 8.8.1998 Luc Percival						
2	Double Top	6b	81°				★★★
	❶(6b.N.L.) 2.9.1984 Guy McLelland: (6b) 6.6.1993 ♔ Doug Reid						
3	Rupert and His Chums ♔	6a	81°				★
	❶(6a.N.S.) 29.2.1992 Mike Vetterlein						
4	Nose One	5b	77°				★★★
	❶(5b) Pre-1956						
5	Chimney Wall	4b	78°				★★
	❶(3a) Pre-1956						
6	Chimney One	2a	66°				★
	❶(1b) Pre-1956						
7	Spleen Slab	5a	78°				★★★
	❶(5b) Pre-1956						
8	Change in the Weather ♔	7a	83°				★★
	❶(7a.N.S.) 9.8.1998 Luc Percival						
9	Brain's Missing	5b	80°				★
	❶(5b) 1981 ♔ David Atchison-Jones						
10	Nose Two	4a	80°				
	❶(5a) 4.5.1953 Doug Stone						
11	Chimney Two	2a	70°				
	❶(1a) Pre-1956						

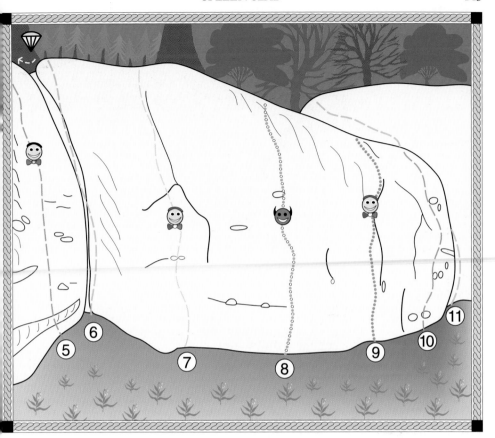

HIGH ROCKS ANNEXE - TOPO 3

1	Chimney Two	2a	70°			
	●(1a) Pre-1956					
2	Fahrenheit	5c	85°			★★
	●(5c.N.S.) 1.3.1992 Paul Widdowson, Mike Vetterlein: (5c) 4.6.1996 ♀ T.Skinner					
3	Green Slab (Thinner)	5a	80°			★
	●(N.L.) 9.6.1957 Salt Sullivan					
4	Nose Three	3b	77°			★★
	●(3a) Pre-1956					
5	Thug	6a	95°			★
	●(6a) 8.3.1992 Paul Widdowson, R. Mazinke, R. Woods					
6	Valkyrie Wall	5c	90°			★★
	●(N.L.) 3.5.1953 Ned Cordery: (5c) 1969-81 ♀					
7	Chute and Chimney	3b	60°			
	●(4a) Pre-1956					
8	Didshi	5c	74°			
	●(5b) 1969-81					
9	Gorilla Wall	5a	70°			★★
	●(5b) Pre-1956					

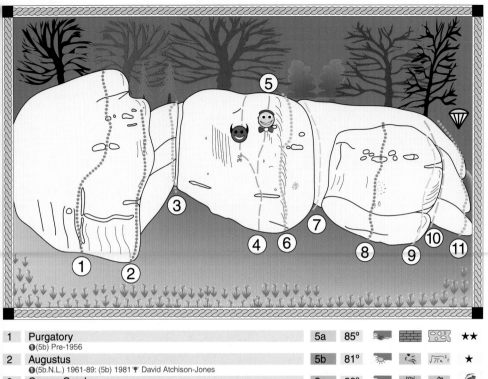

1	Purgatory	5a	85°				★★
	❶(5b) Pre-1956						
2	Augustus	5b	81°				★
	❶(5b.N.L.) 1961-89: (5b) 1981 ❦ David Atchison-Jones						
3	Corner Crack	3a	88°				
	❶(2b) Pre-1956						
4	The Entertainer	5c+	81°	☀			★★★
	❶(5c.N.L.) 1980 David Atchison-Jones: (6a) 1981-9 ❦David Atchison-Jones						
5	Billy the Bong ❦	5c	81°	☀			★★★
	❶(5c.N.S.) 1990 Matt Smith, Tip' Tipton						
6	Valhalla Wall	4c	78°	☀			★★★
	❶(5b) Pre-1956						
7	Fig Roll	5a	90°				★
	❶(5a) 8.8.1995 Tim Skinner, R. Mazinke						
8	Patrick's Wall	5b	99°				★
	❶(5b) 1956-63						
9	Dumpy	5a	90°				
	❶(4b) 1959-69						
10	Flatus Groove	1a	75°				
	❶(1b) Pre-1956						
11	Quickset	3b	75°				
	❶(3a) Pre-1956						

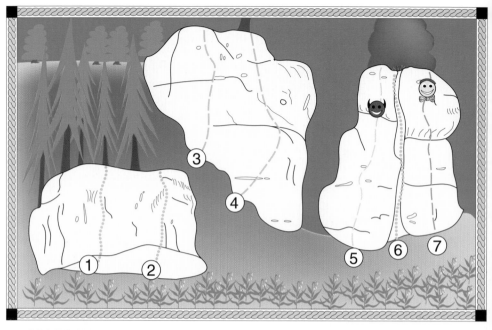

1	Horizon Crack	3a	78°	☀	➡️◀	√▭²	★
	❶(2b) 2000						
2	Horizon Wall	3b	78°	☀	🧱	√▭²	★
	❶(2b) Pre-1956						
3	Wonderwall	2b	77°	☀	🧱	⚊	★
	❶(3a) Pre-1956						
4	Wonderwall Ramp	2b	77°	☀	🖼	⚊	★
	❶(3a) Pre-1956						
5	Monolith Left Buttress	5a	85°	☁	🖼	√▭²	★★
	❶(4b) Pre-1956						
6	Monolith Crack	3a	88°	☁	🚪	≋	
	❶(2a) Pre-1956						
7	Monolith Right Buttress	4a	85°	☁	🖼	⌐¹	★
	❶(N.L.) Pre-1956: (3a)1959-69						

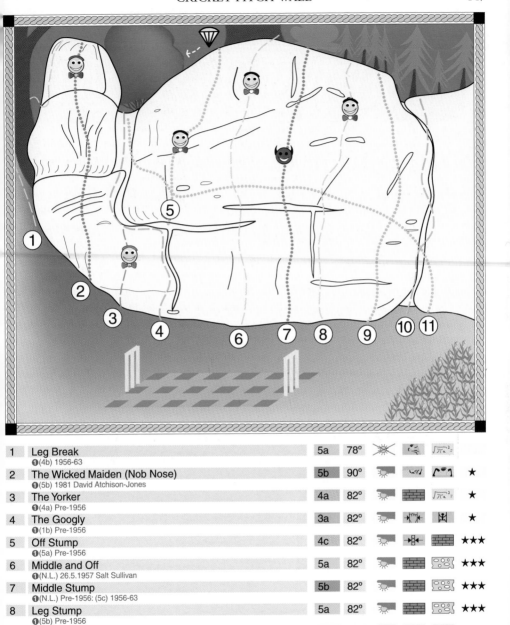

1	Leg Break	5a	78°				
	❶(4b) 1956-63						
2	The Wicked Maiden (Nob Nose)	5b	90°				★
	❶(5b) 1981 David Atchison-Jones						
3	The Yorker	4a	82°				★
	❶(4a) Pre-1956						
4	The Googly	3a	82°				★
	❶(1b) Pre-1956						
5	Off Stump	4c	82°				★★★
	❶(5a) Pre-1956						
6	Middle and Off	5a	82°				★★★
	❶(N.L.) 26.5.1957 Salt Sullivan						
7	Middle Stump	5b	82°				★★★
	❶(N.L.) Pre-1956: (5c) 1956-63						
8	Leg Stump	5a	82°				★★★
	❶(5b) Pre-1956						
9	Out	3b	82°				★★
	❶(3b) Pre-1956						
10	Boundary Gully	2b	82°				
	❶(1b) Pre-1956						
11	A Line of Coke	4c	82°				★★★
	❶(4c) 1990's tours, An assortment of particularly fine English cricketers						

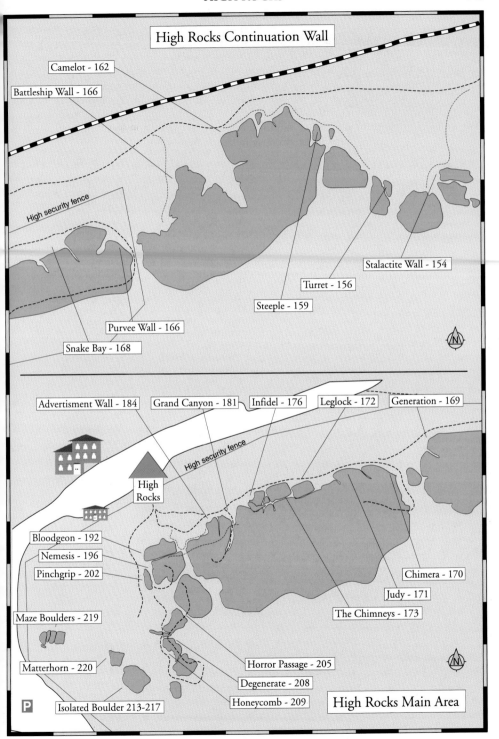

High Rocks Continuation Wall

Camelot - 162

Battleship Wall - 166

High security fence

Stalactite Wall - 154

Turret - 156

Steeple - 159

Purvee Wall - 166

Snake Bay - 168

Advertisment Wall - 184

Grand Canyon - 181

Infidel - 176

Leglock - 172

Generation - 169

High security fence

High Rocks

Bloodgeon - 192

Nemesis - 196

Pinchgrip - 202

Chimera - 170

Judy - 171

The Chimneys - 173

Maze Boulders - 219

Matterhorn - 220

Horror Passage - 205

Degenerate - 208

Honeycomb - 209

Isolated Boulder 213-217

High Rocks Main Area

A quick glance at the graded list, very heavy with 6b routes and ample 7a's. Not a crag for beginners or sunseekers. The rocks are high – up to 30 feet, and very overhanging. The holds are in short supply, generally good, but miles apart. The harder routes tend to be long reaches, or dynamic lunges up slippery, damp overhangs. In a dry and very hot summer, most of the outcrop will dry out, to give excellent hard climbing. To the southern end, a lot of trees have been cleared in the past 10 years and it is quite open and dry. To the north; it is a wet, dank, mosquito ridden, jungleiffied, snake infested! climbing nightmare - hopefully this may change in years to come. If you are prepared for dampish greasy rock, you will not be disappointed. However, most people realise that there is surprising fun to be had climbing in such conditions – it is the same for everyone, even the first ascentionists.

GRADED LIST

7a
Chimaera
The Snowdrop
Pet Cemetary

6c+
Bone Machine
The Gob
Kranked
Mocasyn
Continuing Adventures of
Porg
The Second Generation

6c
Porg's Progress
Cool Bananas
Kinda Lingers Direct
Bad Blood
Kinda Lingers
Unforgettable
I'll be Back
Gentle Giant

Punch
Renascence
6b+
Judy
Powerpull Pearson
Krait Arête
Very Steep M-Staircase
Lamp Light
Boonoonoonoos
Jug of Flowers
Smoke
Honeycomb Direct

6b
Salad Days
Whiff Whaff
Look Sharp
Dyno-Sore
Leglock
Slowhand
The First Crack
Cheetah
Mervin Direct

Plantaganet
Mysteries of the Orgasm
Early Breakfast
Educating Airlie
Tubby Fats Waller
White Rabbit
Death Cap
Fungal Smear
Pegasus
Telegram Sam
Rag Trade
Moving Staircase
The Purvee
Malcolm's Codpiece
Designer Label
Monkey's Sphincter
Crossing the Rubicon
Peapod
Strangler Direct Finish
Prangster
Roofus
Nemesis
Kraken

Barracuda
Missing Link
Penis Door Slam
Senile Walk
Civil War
Natterjack
Too Hard for Dave
So What
Beer Gut Shuffle
Touch too Much
Rattlesnake II
Firefly
Shattered
Honeycomb

6a+
Adder
Devastator
Robin's Route
Too Tall for Tim
Roobarb
Infidel
Genevieve
Metaphysical Poets Come
Visiting

6a
Ragged Trade
Boysen's Crack
Conchita
P.M.A.
Id
Gibbons Progress
Sombrero Wall
Independence
Parrot's Parasol
Camelot
The Dragon
The Prang
The Oligarchy
Scimitar
Ockendon Slab
Lobster
Something Crack

Tilley Lamp Crack
Rum, Bum and Biscuits
Dagger Crack
Champagne Celebration
Mike's Left Knee
Vingt-et-un
Tool Wall
Oven Ready Freddy
Dri Martini III
Crack and Wall Front
All That Meat - Veg
The Diver
Marathon Man
Ides of March
Lunge'n'shelf
Firebird
Craig-Y-Blanco

5c+
Woofus Weejects
Temple of Doom
The Sphinx
Sputnik
Bloodgeon
Tequila Marquita
Coronation Crack Direct
Cut Steps Crack
Jaws
Graveyard Groove

5c
Mulligan's Wall
Effie RH Finish
Slant Eyes
Effie Left Fork
Canyon Crack
Dysentery
Pinchgrip
Dinner Plate
Sweaty Pussy
Orca
Rockney
Celebration
Lucita
Travellin' Man
Drunkard's Dilemma
Amnesia Variation
Shelter Arête
Sequins of Cosmic
Seaman's Wall
Long Stretch
Bludnok Wall
Navy Way
Profiterole
Climbers behaving Badly
Engagement Wall
Breakfast
Rubber Panty

Going to the Pub
Orion Arête
Paul Skinback
Coronation Crack
Lady of the Light-bulb
Peace on Earth
Co-Co
Rake's Progress
Elephant's Umbrella
Nigg Nogg Variation
Twinkle Toe Slab
Fork
Knife
Simian Crack Direct
Odin's Wall
Simian Mistake
Hangman's Wall
Prickle Corner

5b+
Brenva
Orrer Crack
Simian Face
Monkey Nut
Pussyfoot
Swing Face
Beanstalk
Steps Crack
Krankenkopf Crack
Boa-Constrictor

5b
Pure Arête
Battleship Nose
Sorrow
Geoff's Bald Patch
Hidden Arête
The Gibbet
Henry the Ninth
Python Crack
Bright Eyes
Anaconda Chimney
Mamba Crack
Wishful Thinking
Lady of the Lake
Shalot
Taurus
Whiplash
Viper Crack
Advertisment Wall
Cough Drop
Shelter Slabs
Open Groove
Awkward Corner
Poacher Corner
Something Different
Finger Wall
Green Slab

Yom Kippa
Left Edge
Limpet Wall
Awkward
Effie

5a+
Z'mutt
Birthday Arête
Motza

5a
Solo
Degenerate
Bow Crack
Greasy Crack
Rhino's Eyebrow
Simian Progress
North Wall
Roof Route
Stalactite Wall Direct
Yer Greet Narthern
Windy Wall
Nosh
Steeple Direct
Barefoot Crack
Birthday Buttress
Strangler
Issingdown
Bell Rock Route II
Bell Rock Route I
Bold Finish
Hut Transverse Arête

4c
Anchor Chain
Quirkus
Crack Route
Puzzle Corner
Bell Rock Route III
Orion Crack
Obverse Route
I'm a Dutchman

4b
Rattlesnake
Bush Arête
Shelter Passage
Dirty Dick
Balcony Direct
Crack and Wall
Overboard
Pot-Hole Crack
Turret Face
Port Crack

4a
Boa by the Back

Crypt Crack
Ordinary Route
Bell Rock Passage
The Chute
Wye Chimney
Smooth Chimney
Cobra Chimney
Limpet Crack
Two Bit

3b/c
Stalactite Wall
Labyrinth
P.E. Traverse
Hut Passage - C Route
Outside Edge Route
Rhododendron Route
Jug Arête
Bottle Chimney
Spider's Chimney
Warning Rock Buttress
One Bit
Steeple Back

3a
Central Route
Hut- Rufrock route
Giant's Stride
Parrot's Wing
Two Mantleshelves
E Chimney
Recess Wall
Starboard Chimney

2b
Rake Buttress
Turret Wall
Tunnel Chimney
Chimneys are Missing
Insinuation Crack
Chockstone Chimney
Colorado Crack
Slab Chimney
Hut Transverse Passage
Deadwood Chimney
Ordinary Route
Midway Chimney
Shelter Chimney

2a
Easy Crack
Icicle Passage
Warning Rock Chimney
Short Chimney II
Short Chimney
Stepped Buttress

1
Scotland Slab

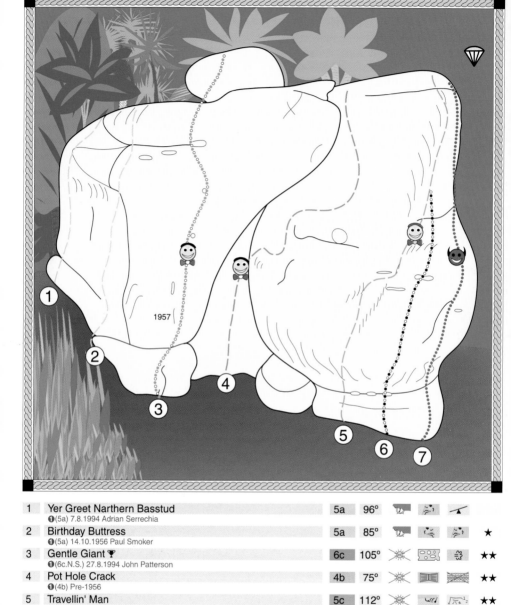

1	Yer Greet Narthern Basstud ❶(5a) 7.8.1994 Adrian Serrechia	5a	96°				
2	Birthday Buttress ❶(5a) 14.10.1956 Paul Smoker	5a	85°				★
3	Gentle Giant ♈ ❶(6c.N.S.) 27.8.1994 John Patterson	6c	105°				★★
4	Pot Hole Crack ❶(4b) Pre-1956	4b	75°				★★
5	Travellin' Man ❶(5c) 7.8.1994 Tim Skinner	5c	112°				★★
6	White Rabbit ♈ ❶(6b.N.S.) 22.9.1996 Robin Mazinke	6b	120°				★★
7	Gibbons Progress ❶(5b) 5.5.1957 John Smoker	6a	116°				★★

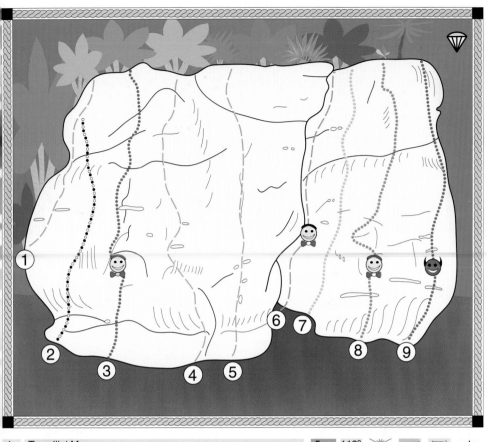

1	Travellin' Man		5c	112°	☀	⌐	√π⁻²	★
	➊(5c) 7.8.1994 Tim Skinner							
2	White Rabbit		6b	120°	☀	⌐	⧈	★
	➊(6b.N.S.) 22.9.1996 Robin Mazinke							
3	Gibbons Progress		6a	116°	☀	⌐	✍	★
	➊(5b) 5.5.1957 John Smoker							
4	Co-Co		5c	113°	☀	⧈	√π⁻²	★
	➊(5c.N.S.) 5.8.1994 Alan Rean: (5c) 7.8.1994 ♟ Tim Skinner							
5	Rake's Progress		5c	89°	☀	⧈	▨	★★
	➊(N.L.) 5.5.1957 Geoff Mulligan							
6	Limpet Crack		4a	80°	☀	⊡	▦	★★★
	➊(4b) Pre-1956							
7	Ziehen		4b	84°	☀	▤	⚖	★
	➊(5a) 1956-58							
8	Finger Wall		5b	84°	☀	▤	√π⁻²	★★
	➊(5a) 1956-63							
9	Sombrero Wall ♟		6a	118°	☀	⌐	⧈	★★
	➊(5b) 5.4.1957 John Smoker: (6a.N.S.) 25.6.1993 Doug Reid							

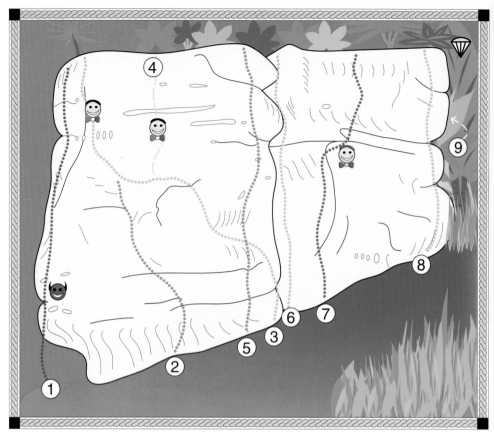

1	Sombrero Wall	6a	118°				★★
	❶(5b) 5.4.1957 John Smoker: (6a.N.S.) 25.6.1993 Doug Reid						
2	Something Different	5b	118°				★
	❶(5b) 8.1958 John Smoker						
3	Stalactite Wall	3b	84°				★★★
	❶(5b) Pre-1956						
4	Stalactite Wall Direct	5a	92°				★★
	❶(N.L.) 6.1958 Pat Maher: (5c) ☙ 1969-81						
5	Poacher Corner	5b	96°				★
	❶(5a-Hard) 8.6.1958 Pat Maher						
6	Bottle Chimney	3b	120°				★★
	❶(2b) Pre-1956						
7	Independence	6a	150°				★★
	❶(5b.N.L.) 17.3.1974 M.Fowler, John Stevenson: (5b) 1981-2 ☙ D.A-Jones						
8	Jug Arête	3b	86°				★
	❶(3b) Pre-1956						
9	Wobbler Wall	4c	86°				
	❶(4c) 1981-9						

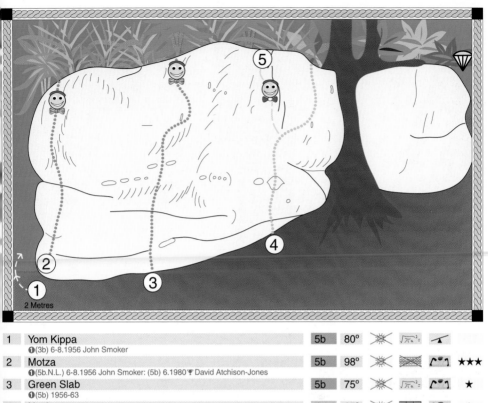

1	Yom Kippa	5b	80°

①(3b) 6-8.1956 John Smoker

2	Motza	5b	98°	★★★

①(5b.N.L.) 6-8.1956 John Smoker: (5b) 6.1980 ♛ David Atchison-Jones

3	Green Slab	5b	75°	★

①(5b) 1956-63

4	Nosh	4c	95°	★

①(4b) 1956-63

5	Super Nosh	5a	95°	★

①(5a) 1960's

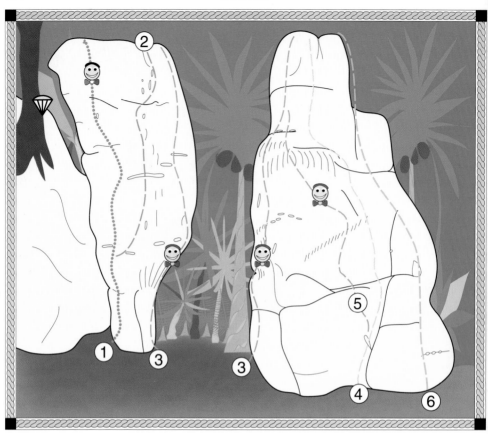

1	Left Edge	5b	89°				★★
	❶(5b) 1956-63						
2	Turret Face	4b	81°				★★★
	❶(5b) Pre-1956						
3	Drunkard's Dilemma	5c	120°				★★★
	❶(N.L.) 10.1956 Paul Smoker: (5a) 26.10.1956 ♟ John Smoker						
4	Windy Wall	5a	95°				★★
	❶(5b) 1.4.1956 Billy Maxwell						
5	Nigg Nogg Variation	5c	106°				★★★
	❶(5b.N.L.) 1956-63: (5b)♟ 1992-5						
6	Turret Wall	2b	68°				★★
	❶(2b) Pre-1956						
7	Twinkle Toe Slab	5c	79°				★
	❶(5b) 1956-63						
8	Limpet Wall	5b	76°				★
	❶(5a) 4.6.1955 Harry Barnes						
9	Awkward	5b	87°				★
	❶(5b) 1992-5						

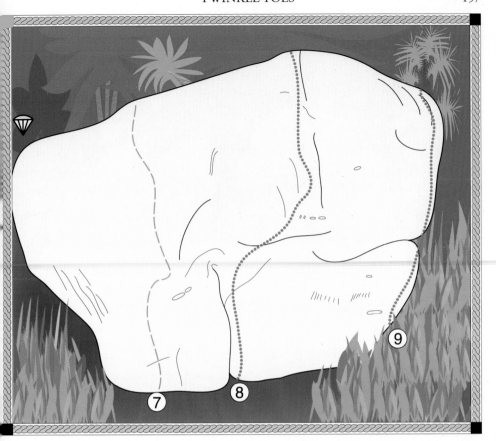

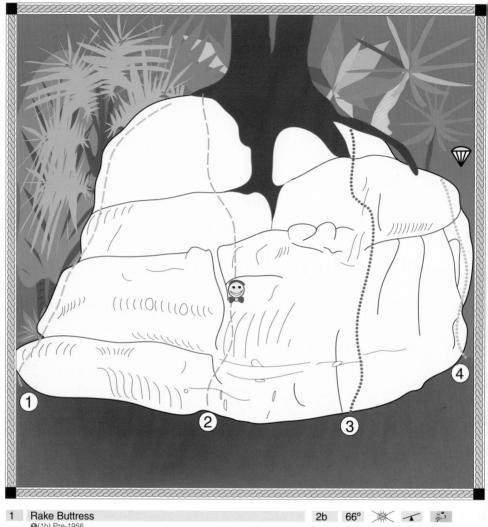

1	Rake Buttress	2b	66°				
	❶(1b) Pre-1956						
2	Elephant's Umbrella	5c	138°				★★
	❶(5b) 7.1956 Philip Gordon						
3	Parrot's Parasol	6a	115°				★★
	❶(5c) 1956-63						
4	Parrot's Wing	3a	84°				
	❶(3a) 1969-81						

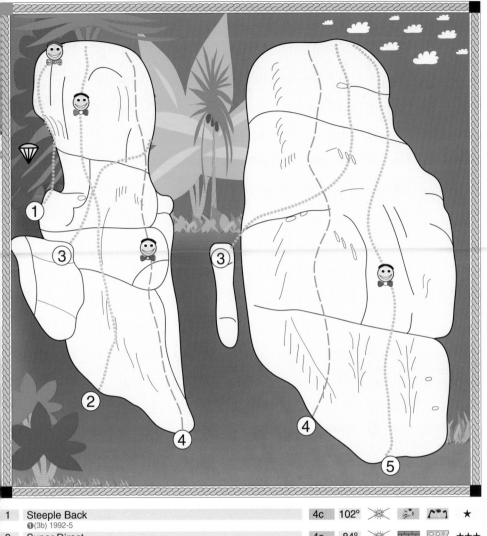

1	Steeple Back	4c	102°				★
	①(3b) 1992-5						
2	Super Direct	4c	84°				★★★
	①(N.L.) 21.4.1956 John Smoker						
3	Steeplejack	3c	80°				★★
	①(4b) 21.4.1956 John Smoker						
4	I'm a Dutchman	4b	84°				★★
	①(4c) 1992-5						
5	Steeple (Obverse Route)	4c	92°				★★★
	①(3b) 21.4.1956 John Smoker						

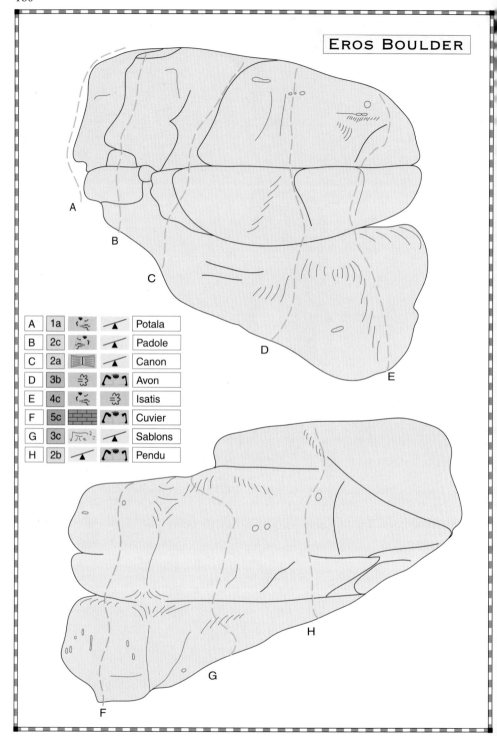

EROS BOULDER

A	1a			Potala
B	2c			Padole
C	2a			Canon
D	3b			Avon
E	4c			Isatis
F	5c			Cuvier
G	3c	$\sqrt{\pi a^2}=$		Sablons
H	2b			Pendu

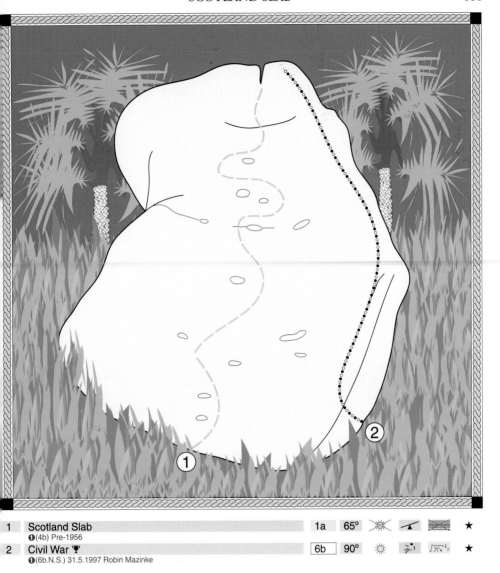

1	Scotland Slab		1a	65°	☀	◤	≋	★
	❶(4b) Pre-1956							
2	Civil War ⟡		6b	90°	☀	⇲	√⏢²	★
	❶(6b.N.S.) 31.5.1997 Robin Mazinke							

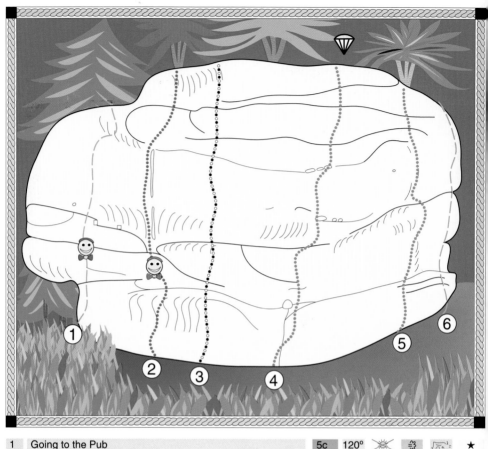

1	Going to the Pub	5c	120°	☀	⇄	√⚄	★
	❶(5c) 7-8.1984 Paul Hayes						
2	Camelot	6a	112°	☀	⇥◄	⇄	★★
	❶(N.L.) 20.9.58 J.Smoker: (6a.N.L.) 5.10.75 M.Fowler: (6a) 🏆 9.1982 D.Wajzner						
3	Penis Door Slam 🏆	6b	112°	☀	⤳	√⚄	★
	❶(6b.N.S.) 7.1991 Matt Smith						
4	The Greyphion (Lady of the Lake)	5b	114°	☀	▦	⇄	★★
	❶(5b) 21.8.1958 Don Ingrey, Direct start - John Smoker						
5	Shalot	5b	104°	☀	▦	⋔	★★
	❶(5b.N.L.) 4.6.1955 Derek Salter						
6	Lost in Paris 🏆	5c	90°	☀	▦	√⚄	★★
	❶(5c.N.S.) 4.9.1997 R. Mazinke, Mike Eden						

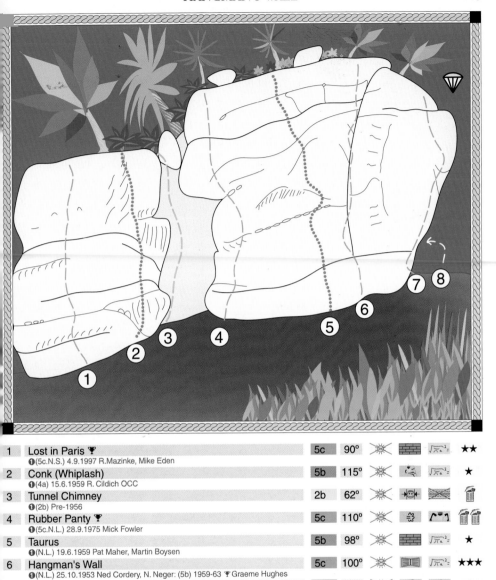

1	**Lost in Paris** ♈	5c	90°				★★
	❶(5c.N.S.) 4.9.1997 R.Mazinke, Mike Eden						
2	**Conk (Whiplash)**	5b	115°				★
	❶(4a) 15.6.1959 R. Cildich OCC						
3	**Tunnel Chimney**	2b	62°				
	❶(2b) Pre-1956						
4	**Rubber Panty** ♈	5c	110°				
	❶(5c.N.L.) 28.9.1975 Mick Fowler						
5	**Taurus**	5b	98°				★
	❶(N.L.) 19.6.1959 Pat Maher, Martin Boysen						
6	**Hangman's Wall**	5c	100°				★★★
	❶(N.L.) 25.10.1953 Ned Cordery, N. Neger: (5b) 1959-63 ♈ Graeme Hughes						
7	**Prickle Corner**	5c	108°				★
	❶(5c.N.L.) 12.2.1975 Mick Fowler: (5c) 7-8.1989 ♈ Dave Turner						
8	**Icicle Passage**	2a	78°				
	❶(2a) Pre-1956						

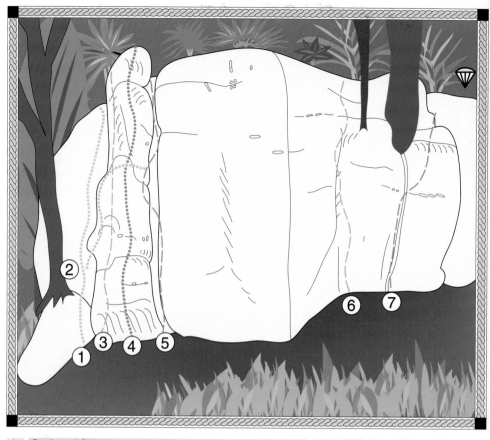

1	Starboard Chimney	3a	74°				★
	❶(3a) Pre-1956						
2	Anchor Chain	4c	86°				★★
	❶(N.L.) Pre-1956: (4c) ⚑1956-63						
3	Nasal Nightmare ⚑	5c	86°				★★
	❶(5c.N.S.) 20.9.1997 R. Mazinke						
4	Battleship Nose	5b	85°				★★★
	❶(5b) 1956-63						
5	Port Crack	4b	85°				★★★
	❶(5a) Pre-1956						
6	Paul Skinback	5c	99°				
	❶(5c) 1975 Mick Fowler						
7	Overboard	4b	102°				★
	❶(?) Pre-1956						

THE LOCKER

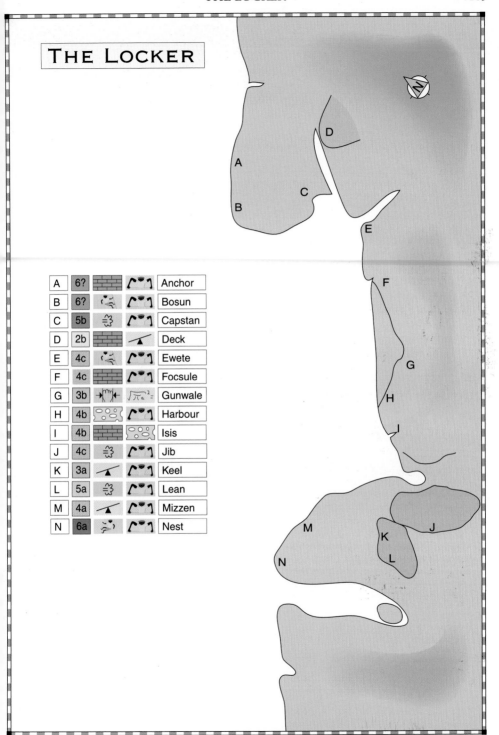

A	6?			Anchor
B	6?			Bosun
C	5b			Capstan
D	2b			Deck
E	4c			Ewete
F	4c			Focsule
G	3b			Gunwale
H	4b			Harbour
I	4b			Isis
J	4c			Jib
K	3a			Keel
L	5a			Lean
M	4a			Mizzen
N	6a			Nest

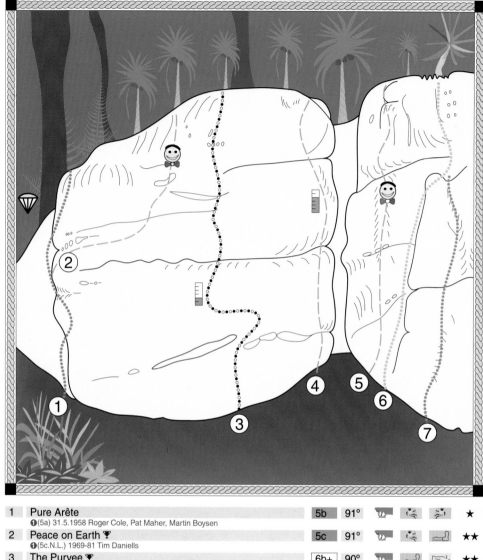

1	**Pure Arête**			**5b**	91°				★
	❶(5a) 31.5.1958 Roger Cole, Pat Maher, Martin Boysen								
2	**Peace on Earth** ♆			**5c**	91°				★★
	❶(5c.N.L.) 1969-81 Tim Daniells								
3	**The Purvee** ♆			**6b+**	90°				★★
	❶(6b.N.S.) 15.7.1990 Gary Wickham, Jasper Sharpe								
4	**Lady of the Light Bulb** ♆			**5c**	95°				★★
	❶(5c.N.S.) 16.2.1992 Doug Reid, Mike Vetterlein								
5	**Orion Arête** ♆			**5c**	94°				★★
	❶(5c.N.L.) 1969-81								
6	**Orion Crack**			**4c**	82°				★★
	❶(5a) Pre-1956								
7	**Brian Arête**			**5b**	80°				★
	❶(5c) 1998 Chris Arnold, Mike Eden								

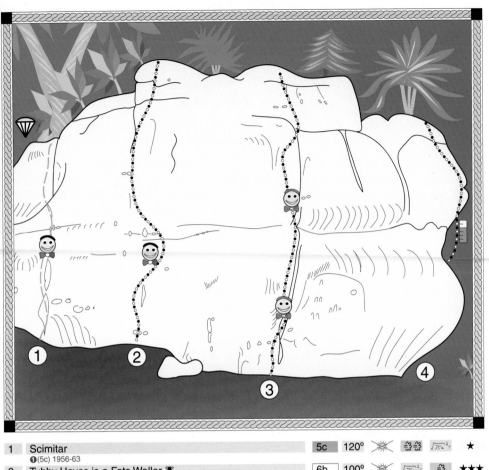

1	Scimitar	5c	120°				★
	❶(5c) 1956-63						
2	Tubby Hayes is a Fats Waller ♟	6b	100°				★★★
	❶(6b.N.S.) 12.8.1990 Dave Turner, Gary Wickham						
3	First Crack ♟	6b	130°				★★
	❶(6b.N.L.) 9.7.1978 Mick Fowler						
4	Missing Link ♟	6b	134°				★★★
	❶(6b.N.S.) 12.8.1990 Gary Wickham, Paul Hayes						

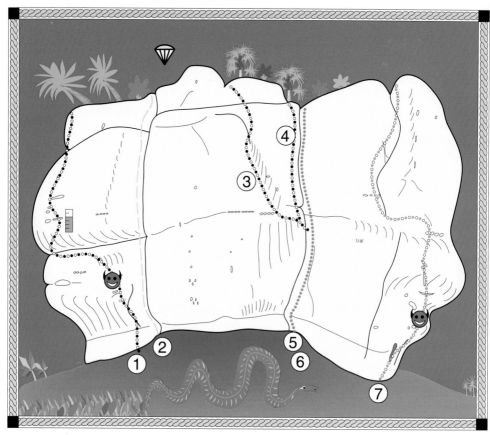

1	Missing Link ♈		6b	134°				★★★
	❶(6b.N.S.) 12.8.1990 Gary Wickham, Paul Hayes							
2	Anaconda Chimney		5a	90°				★
	❶(4b) Pre-1956							
3	Fungal Smear ♈		6b	79°				★★
	❶(6b.N.S.) 15.7.1990 Gary Wickham							
4	Rattlesnake 2 ♈		6b	80°				★★★
	❶(6a.N.L.) 6.1986 Ian Mailer							
5	Boa-Constrictor Chimney		5b	90°				★
	❶(4b) Pre-1956							
6	Boa by the Back		4c	90°				★★
	❶(4a) Pre-1956							
7	Bone Machine ♈		6c+	157°				★★★
	❶(6c/7a.N.S.) 25.7.1993 Gary Wickham							

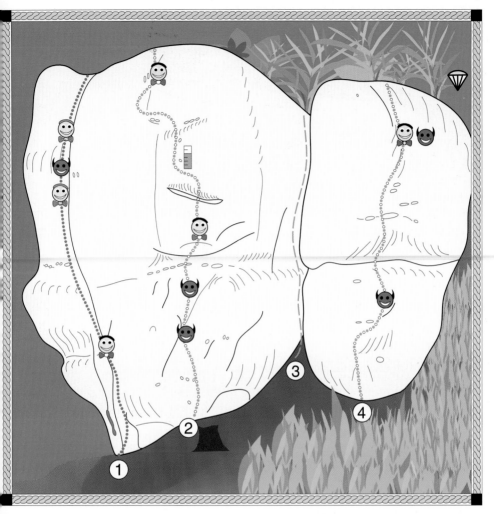

1	Adder ♈		6a+	112°				★★
	❶(6a.N.L) 5.1976 Gordon DeLacy							
2	The Second Generation ♈		6c+	117°				★★★
	❶(6c.N.S.) 24.6.1990 Jasper Sharpe							
3	Cobra Chimney		4a	90°				★★
	❶(4a) 1959-69							
4	Renascence ♈		6c	129°				★★★
	❶(6b.N.S.) 14.7.1990 Dave Turner, G. Wickham, P. Hayes							

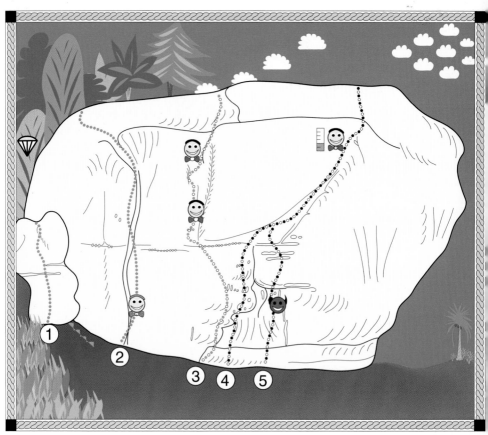

1	Sorrow	5b	73°			

(5b) 1969-81 Tim Daniells

2	Steps Crack	5b+	98°			★★★

(5b) 1926-9 Jean Morin, Nea Morin

3	Chimaera ♈	7a	96°			★★★

(6c+.N.S.) 14.7.1990 Dave Turner

4	Moving Staircase ♈	6b	128°			★★★

(6b.N.L.) 6.1986 Martin Boysen

5	Very Steep Moving Staircase ♈	6b+	140°			★★★

(6b.N.S.) 1986-9 Guy McLelland

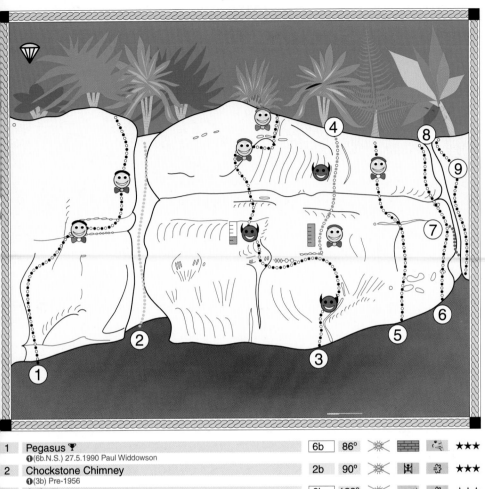

1	**Pegasus** ⚑ ❶(6b.N.S.) 27.5.1990 Paul Widdowson	6b	86°	☀	🧱	🤸	★★★
2	**Chockstone Chimney** ❶(3b) Pre-1956	2b	90°	☀	🏚	〰	★★★
3	**Judy** ⚑ ❶(6b.N.L.) 6.1982 Guy McLelland	6b+	138°	☀	〰	〰	★★★
4	**Punch** ⚑ ❶(6c.N.S.) 6.8.1995 Luc Percival	6c	122°	☀	〰	〰〰	★★
5	**Telegram Sam** ⚑ ❶(6b.N.S.) 24.7.1990 Paul Widdowson	6b	109°	☀	〰	〰	★★★
6	**Rag Trade** ⚑ ❶(5c.N.L.) 6.1980 Mick Fowler	6b	100°	〰	〰	〰	★★
7	**Ragged Trade** ⚑ ❶(6a.N.S.) 1992-5 Paul Widdowson	6a	100°	〰	🔺	🤸	★★
8	**E Chimney** ❶(3a) Pre-1956	3b	84°	☀	🏚	🛝	★
9	**Designer Label** ⚑ ❶(6a.N.L.) 23.4.1987 Ian Mailer, Martin Boysen	6b	100°	☀	🔺	√π⁻¹=	★★★

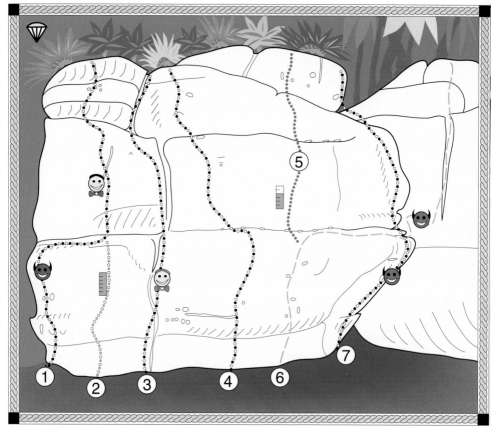

1	Salad Days Ⓨ	6b+	140°	☀	⚡⚡	▓▓	★★★
	❶(6a/b.N.L.) 7.1982 Guy McLelland						
2	Pet Cemetary Ⓨ	7a	130°	☀	⌐	⚡	★★
	❶(7a.N.S.) 28.8.1995 Luc Percival						
3	Leglock Ⓨ	6b	128°	☀	✛	▓▓	
	❶(N.L.) 14.9.1954 B.Maxwell: (6a.N.L.) 1980 Andy Meyers						
4	Crossing the Rubicon Ⓨ	6b	90°	☀	▨	√π²	★★★
	❶(6b.N.S.) 19.7.1990 Mike Vetterlein						
5	Too Tall for Tim Ⓨ	6a	87°	≈	▨	√π²	★★★
	❶(6a.N.L.) 7-8.1984 Chris Arnold, Gary Wickham						
6	Cut Steps Crack Ⓨ	5c+	96°	≈	⌐	✛	★★★
	❶(5c.N.L.) 1969-81 Gordon DeLacy						
7	Too Hard for Dave (Turner) Ⓨ	6b	135°	☀	⌐	⌐	★★★
	❶(6b.N.S.) 14.7.1990 Paul Widdowson, Mike Vetterlein						

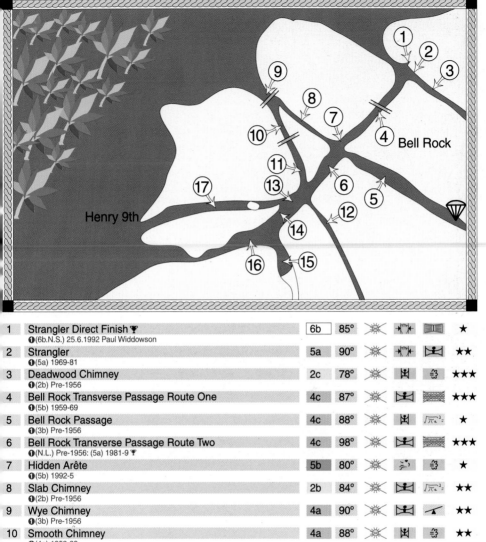

1	Strangler Direct Finish ⚘	6b	85°				★
	❶(6b.N.S.) 25.6.1992 Paul Widdowson						
2	Strangler	5a	90°				★★
	❶(5a) 1969-81						
3	Deadwood Chimney	2c	78°				★★★
	❶(2b) Pre-1956						
4	Bell Rock Transverse Passage Route One	4c	87°				★★★
	❶(5b) 1959-69						
5	Bell Rock Passage	4c	88°				★
	❶(3b) Pre-1956						
6	Bell Rock Transverse Passage Route Two	4c	98°				★★★
	❶(N.L.) Pre-1956: (5a) 1981-9 ⚘						
7	Hidden Arête	5b	80°				★
	❶(5b) 1992-5						
8	Slab Chimney	2b	84°				★★
	❶(2b) Pre-1956						
9	Wye Chimney	4a	90°				★★
	❶(3b) Pre-1956						
10	Smooth Chimney	4a	88°				★★
	❶(4a) 1959-69						
11	One of Our Chimney's is Missing	3b	95°				★★
	❶(2b) 19.6.1994 R. Mazinke, M.Vetterlein, I.Stronghill						
12	Spider's Chimney	3b	90°				★★
	❶(3b) Pre-1956						
13	Bell Rock Transverse Passage Route Three	4c	90°				★★★
	❶(N.L.) Pre-1956: (4c) 1969-81 ⚘						
14	Senile Walk ⚘	6b	95°				★
	❶(6b.N.S.) 25.7.1992 Martin Boysen						
15	Serpent Chimney	4b	95°				★
	❶(4b) 1969-81						
16	Giant's Stride	4a	95°				★
	❶(3a) Pre-1956						
17	Warning Rock Chimney	2a	85°				★★
	❶(1b) 1959-69						

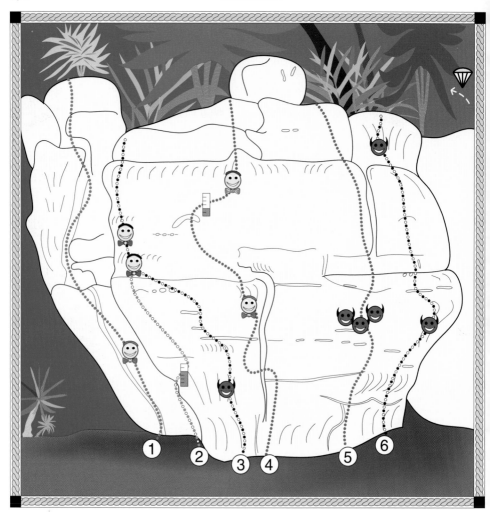

1	Krankenkopf Crack	5b	135°				★
	❶(A1.N.L.) 18.7.1954 B.Maxwell, Les Entwhistle: (5b) ⚑ 1969-81						
2	Kranked ⚑	6c+	154°				★★
	❶(6c.N.S.) 28.7.1995 Luc Percival						
3	Kraken ⚑	6b	154°				★★★
	❶(6b.N.S.) 7.4.1990 Paul Widdowson						
4	The Dragon	6a	130°				★★★
	❶(6a.N.L.) 6.9.1959 John Smoker: (6a) ⚑ 1981-9						
5	Robin's Route	6a+	136°				★★★
	❶(6a.N.L.) 1959-69 Robin Harper: (6a)14.5.1980 ⚑ Mick Fowler						
6	So What ⚑	6b	136°				★★★
	❶(6b.N.S.) 15.7.1990 Paul Hayes						

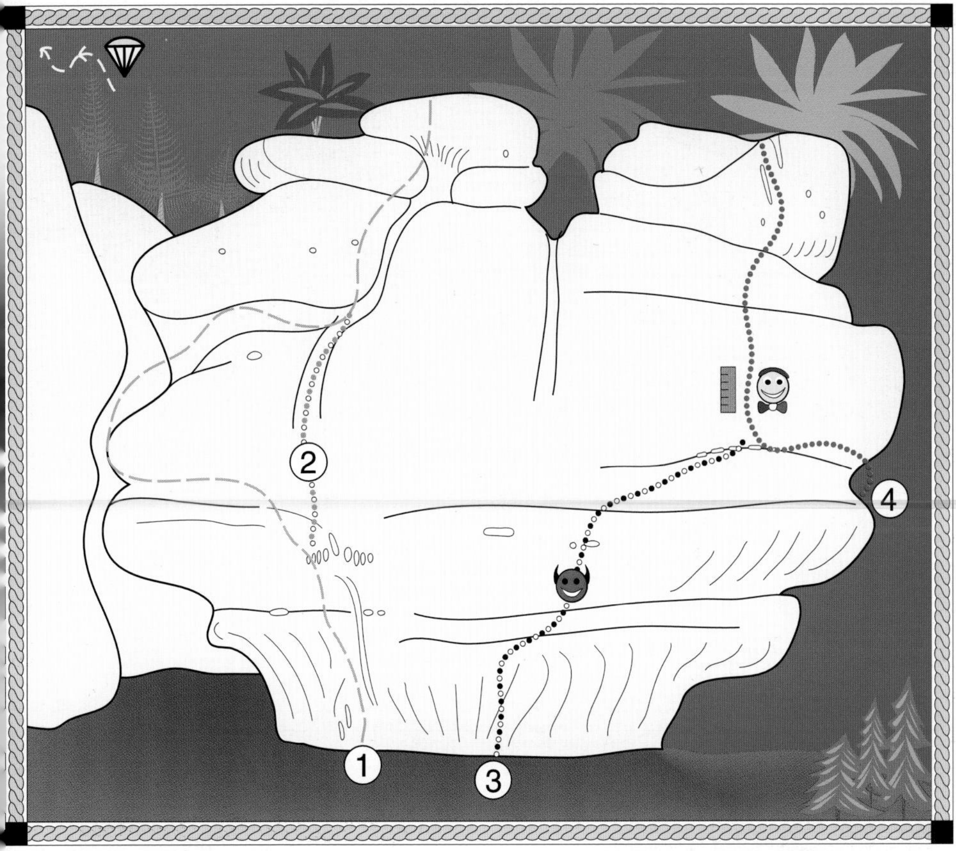

1	Dysentry 🏆 ❶(5c.N.L.) 1969-81 Nigel Head	5c	120°				
2	Snowdrop ❶(7a.N.S.) 3-4.1997 Johnny Dawes	7a	120°				★★
3	The Prangster 🏆 ❶(6a+.N.S.) 26.5.1992 Steve Quinton	6b	130°				★★
4	The Prang 🏆 ❶(5c.N.L.) 1969-81 Nigel Head	6a	120°				★★

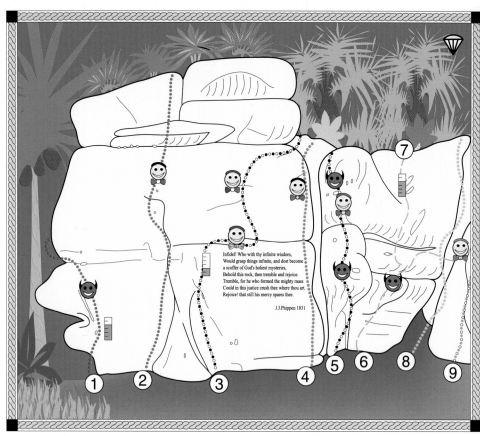

1	**The Prang** ♛		6b	118°				★★
	❶(5c.N.L.) 1969-81 Nigel Head							
2	**Lobster** ♛		6a	116°				★★
	❶(6a.N.L.) 27.5.1959 John Smoker, Martin Boysen							
3	**Infidel**		6a+	84°				★★★
	❶(6b.N.L.) 13.3.1977 Mick Fowler: (6a) 16.7.1985 ♛ Mick Fowler							
4	**Henry the Ninth**		5b	80°				★★★
	❶(5c.N.L.) 1959-69: (5c) 1977 ♛ Mick Fowler							
5	**Slowhand** ♛		6b	160°				★★
	❶(6b.N.S.) 5.4.1990 Paul Widdowson							
6	**Jaws**		5c+	130°				★★★
	❶(5b.N.L.) 1969-81 Tim Daniells: (5c) ♛ 1981-9							
7	**Orca** ♛		5c+	140°				★★★
	❶(5c.N.S.) 1.4.1990 Paul Widdowson, M. Vetterlein, R. Alexandre							
8	**Balcony direct**		4b	90°				★★★
	❶(4b) 1959-69							
9	**Fat Start**		7a	90°				★★
	❶(7a.Solo) 3-4.1997 ♛ Johnny Dawes							

Henry the Ninth 5b, Kim Tullett

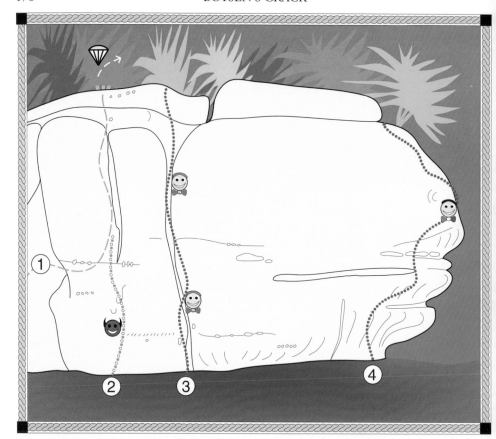

HIGH ROCKS - TOPO 26

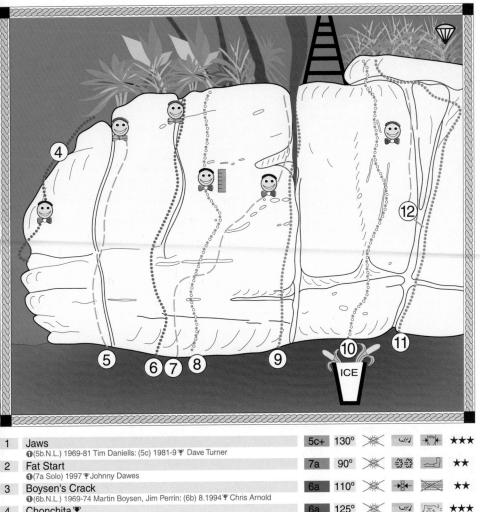

1	Jaws	5c+	130°				★★★
	❶(5b.N.L.) 1969-81 Tim Daniells: (5c) 1981-9 ♈ Dave Turner						
2	Fat Start	7a	90°				★★
	❶(7a Solo) 1997 ♈Johnny Dawes						
3	Boysen's Crack	6a	110°				★★
	❶(6b.N.L.) 1969-74 Martin Boysen, Jim Perrin: (6b) 8.1994 ♈ Chris Arnold						
4	Chonchita ♈	6a	125°				★★★
	❶(N.L.A1.) 14.6.1958 John Smoker: (6a.N.L.) 1969-81						
5	Tequila Marquita	5c+	87°				★★
	❶(5c) 14.6.1958 John Smoker, Paul Smoker, Martin Boysen						
6	Lucita	5c	87°				★★★
	❶(5c) 28.6.1958 John Smoker, Paul Smoker, Martin Boysen						
7	Slant Eyes	5c	87°				★★★
	❶(5c.N.L.) 12.8.1978 Mick Fowler: (5c) ♈1981-9						
8	Mocasyn ♈	6c+	87°				★★★
	❶(6c.N.S.) 5.8.1995 Luc Percival						
9	The Gibbet	5b	109°				★★
	❶(5b) 2-4.1957 Philip Gordon						
10	Cool Bananas ♈	6c	95°				★★★
	❶(6c.N.L.) 28.8.1987 Dave Turner						
11	Effie	5c	95°				★★★
	❶(5b) 1956-63 George Clark						
12	Effie Left Fork ♈	5c	85°				★★★
	❶(5c.N.L.) 26.1.1975 Mick Fowler, John Stevenson						

Advertisment Wall 5b, Gerry Porter

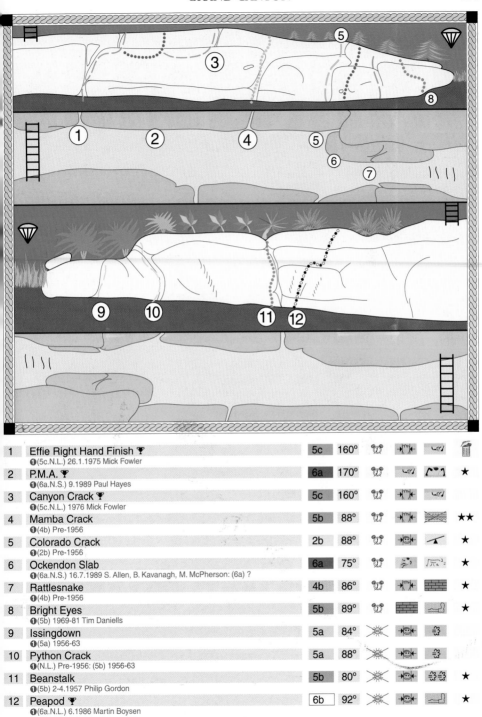

1	Effie Right Hand Finish ♆		5c	160°				
	❶(5c.N.L.) 26.1.1975 Mick Fowler							
2	P.M.A. ♆		6a	170°				★
	❶(6a.N.S.) 9.1989 Paul Hayes							
3	Canyon Crack ♆		5c	160°				
	❶(5c.N.L.) 1976 Mick Fowler							
4	Mamba Crack		5b	88°				★★
	❶(4b) Pre-1956							
5	Colorado Crack		2b	88°				★
	❶(2b) Pre-1956							
6	Ockendon Slab		6a	75°				★
	❶(6a.N.S.) 16.7.1989 S. Allen, B. Kavanagh, M. McPherson: (6a) ?							
7	Rattlesnake		4b	86°				★
	❶(4b) Pre-1956							
8	Bright Eyes		5b	89°				★
	❶(5b) 1969-81 Tim Daniells							
9	Issingdown		5a	84°				
	❶(5a) 1956-63							
10	Python Crack		5a	88°				
	❶(N.L.) Pre-1956: (5b) 1956-63							
11	Beanstalk		5b	80°				★
	❶(5b) 2-4.1957 Philip Gordon							
12	Peapod ♆		6b	92°				★
	❶(6a.N.L.) 6.1986 Martin Boysen							

Effie 5b, Glyn Williams

HIGH ROCKS - TOPO 28

Mile End

Climbing Wall

Haverfield Road, Bow, E3 5BE

020 8980 0289

Photo: James Avery Cunliffe

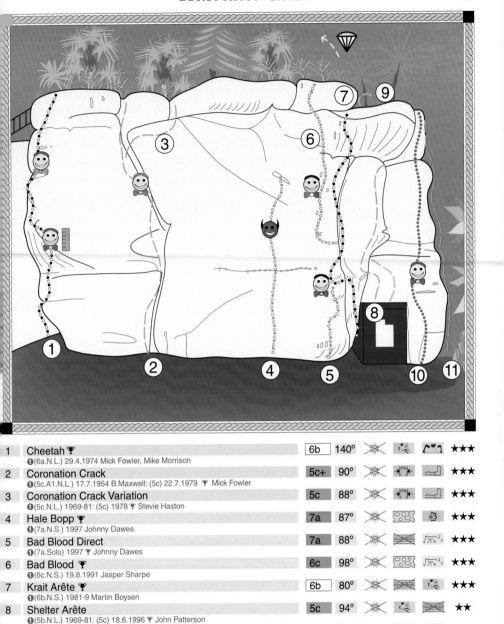

1	**Cheetah** ❦ ❶(6a.N.L.) 29.4.1974 Mick Fowler, Mike Morrison	6b	140°	※			★★★
2	**Coronation Crack** ❶(5c.A1.N.L.) 17.7.1954 B.Maxwell: (5c) 22.7.1979 ❦ Mick Fowler	5c+	90°	※			★★★
3	**Coronation Crack Variation** ❶(5c.N.L.) 1969-81: (5c) 1978 ❦ Stevie Haston	5c	88°	※			★★★
4	**Hale Bopp** ❦ ❶(7a.N.S.) 1997 Johnny Dawes	7a	87°	※			★★★
5	**Bad Blood Direct** ❶(7a.Solo) 1997 ❦ Johnny Dawes	7a	88°	※			★★★
6	**Bad Blood** ❦ ❶(6c.N.S.) 19.8.1991 Jasper Sharpe	6c	98°	※			★★★
7	**Krait Arête** ❦ ❶(6b.N.S.) 1981-9 Martin Boysen	6b	80°	※			★★★
8	**Shelter Arête** ❶(5b.N.L.) 1969-81: (5c) 18.6.1996 ❦ John Patterson	5c	94°	※			★★
9	**Shelter Chimney** ❶(2b) Pre-1956	2c	95°	※			★★
10	**The Oligarchy** ❦ ❶(6a.N.S.) 19.5.1991 Mike Vetterlein, Paul Widdowson, Oliver Hill	6a	95°	※			
11	**Advertisement Arête** ❶(5c.N.L.) 1956-69: (5b) ❦ 1960's	5c	95°				★★★

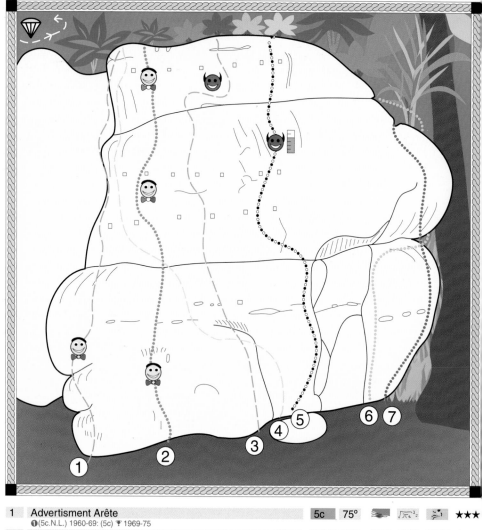

1	**Advertisment Arête** ❶(5c.N.L.) 1960-69: (5c) ♛ 1969-75	5c	75°	★★★
2	**Advertisment Wall Direct** ❶(N.L.) 1969-75: (5c) ♛ 1969-75	5b	90°	★★★
3	**Engagement Wall (Paul Lebars to Beryl Osborne)** ❶(5c.N.L.) 7.1958 Paul Smoker: (5c) 1990 ♛ John Godding	5c	88°	★★★
4	**Advertisment Wall** ❶(N.L.) 11.3.1956 Paul Smoker: (5b) ♛ 1956-63	5a+	87°	★★★
5	**Dyno-Sore ♛** ❶(6b.N.L.) 16.8.1987 Dave Turner	6b+	88°	★★★
6	**Quirkus** ❶(5a) 1956-63	4c	98°	★
7	**Genevieve ♛** ❶(6a.N.S.) 18.3.1990 Paul Widdowson	6a	80°	★★★

Engagement Wall 5c, Tony Forward

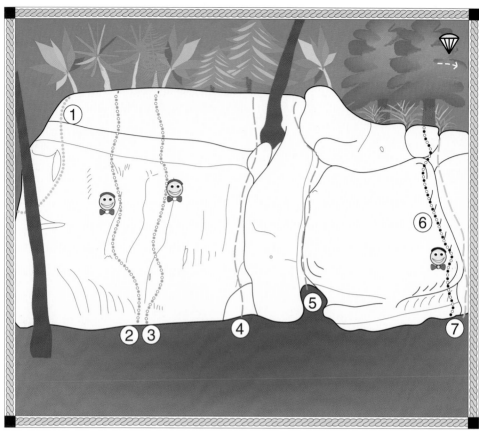

1	Quirkus	4c	95°				★
	❶(5a) 1956-63						
2	Continuing Adventures of Porg 🏆	6c+	82°				★★
	❶(6c+.N.S.) 26.8.1995 Luc Percival						
3	Porg's Progress 🏆	6c	82°				★★
	❶(6c.N.S.) 17.5.1992 Paul Widdowson						
4	Dirty Dick	4b	82°				
	❶(4b) Pre-1956						
5	Crypt Crack	4a	83°				
	❶(4a) Pre-1956						
6	Look Sharp	6b	81°				★★
	❶(6b.N.L.) 1.9.1984 Guy McLelland: (6b) 1985 🏆 Barry Knight						
7	Short Chimney	2a	77°				
	❶(2a) Pre-1956						
8	Natterjack 🏆	6b	81°				★
	❶(6b.N.S.) 1.4.1990 Mike Vetterlein, Paul Widdowson						
9	Death Cap 🏆	6b	89°				★
	❶(6b.N.S.) 13.5.1991 Mike Vetterlein						
10	Mervin Direct 🏆	6b	101°				★★
	❶(6a/b) 1985 Gary Wickham						
11	Crack and Wall - With Tree	5a	95°				★
	❶(4b) Pre-1956						

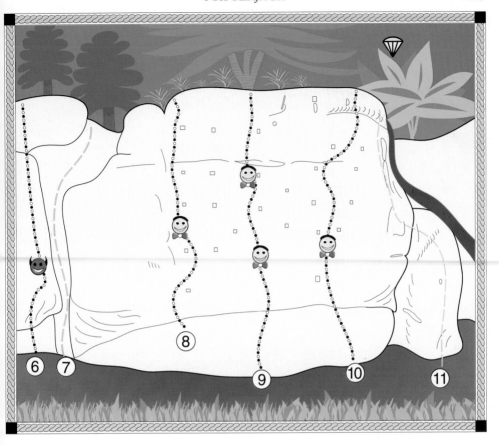

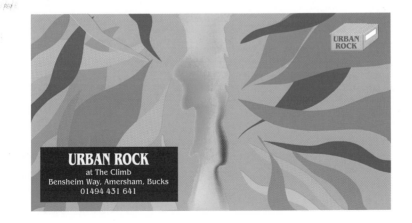

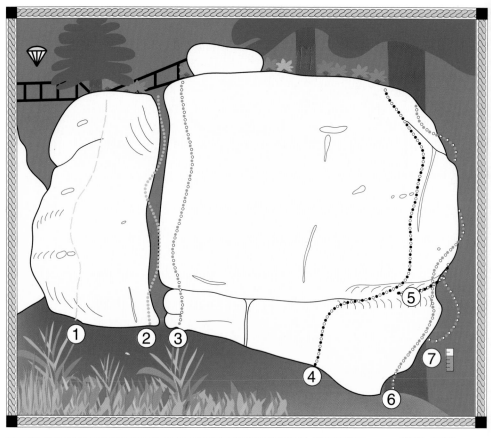

1	Hut Passage Arête		5a	82°				★
	❶(5b) 18.8.1958 Pat Maher							
2	Brushwood Chimney		3a	90°				★★★
	❶(3a) Pre-1956							
3	I'll Be Back ♈		6c	90°				★★★
	❶(6c.N.S.) 26.8.1991 Jasper Sharpe							
4	Educating Airlie ♈		6b	90°				★★
	❶(6b.N.S.) 10.8.1991 Mike Vetterlein							
5	Kinda Wanders ♈		6b+	93°				★★★
	❶(6b+.N.S.) 1981-9 Gary Wickham							
6	Kinda Direct Start ♈		6c	107°				★★★
	❶(6c) 13.5.1980 Jasper Sharpe, Gary Wickham							
7	Kinda Lingers ♈		6c	99°				★★★
	❶(6c.N.S.) 1981-9 Gary Wickham							

Boonoonoonoonous 6b, Barry Knight

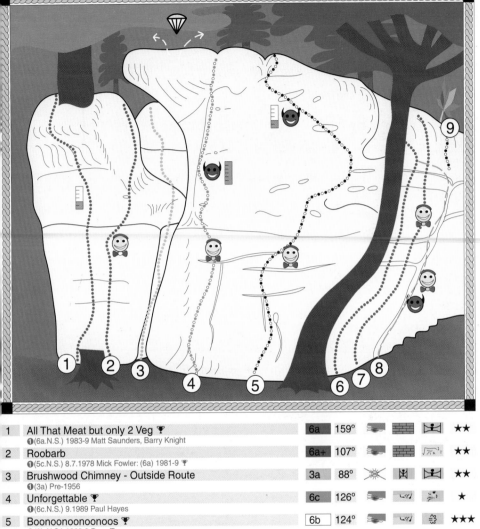

1	All That Meat but only 2 Veg ♈	6a	159°				★★
	➊(6a.N.S.) 1983-9 Matt Saunders, Barry Knight						
2	Roobarb	6a+	107°				★★
	➊(5c.N.S.) 8.7.1978 Mick Fowler: (6a) 1981-9 ♈						
3	Brushwood Chimney - Outside Route	3a	88°				★★
	➊(3a) Pre-1956						
4	Unforgettable ♈	6c	126°				★
	➊(6c.N.S.) 9.1989 Paul Hayes						
5	Boonoonoonoonoos ♈	6b	124°				★★★
	➊(6b.N.S.) 1983-9 Dave Turner						
6	Dry Martini III ♈	6a	122°				★★★
	➊(5c.N.L.) 1980 David Atchison-Jones						
7	Firebird ♈	6a	122°				★★★
	➊(5c.N.L.) 1969-81 Tim Daniells						
8	Mulligan's Wall	5c	128°				★★★
	➊(N.L.) 3.5.1959 Don Ingrey: (5c) 1969-81 ♈						
9	Smoke ♈	6b+	130°				★
	➊(6a/b.N.S.) 11.9.1992 Alan Grigg						

Boonoonoonoonous 6b, 'The' Barry Knight

1	**Dry Martini III** ⚑		6a	122°				★★★
	❶(5c.N.L.) 1980 David Atchison-Jones							
2	**Firebird** ⚑		6a	122°				★★★
	❶(5c.N.L.) 1969-81 Tim Daniells							
3	**Mulligan's Wall**		5c	128°				★★★
	❶(N.L.) 3.5.1959 Don Ingrey: (5c) 1969-81 ⚑							
4	**Bloodgeon (Mulligan's Blood Variant)** ⚑		5c+	128°				★★★
	❶(5c.N.L.) 9.5.1959 Martin Boysen							
5	**Smoke** ⚑		6b+	130°				★
	❶(6a/b.N.S.) 11.9.1992 Alan Grigg							
6	**Firefly** ⚑		6b	142°				★★
	❶(6a.N.L.) 13.3.1977							
7	**Celebration**		5c	108°				★★★
	❶(5b.N.L.) 4.1959 Paul Smoker: (5c) 1969-81 ⚑							

Bloodgeon 5c+, Ray

Celebration 5c, Paul Smith

A Touch Too Much 6b, Dave Potts

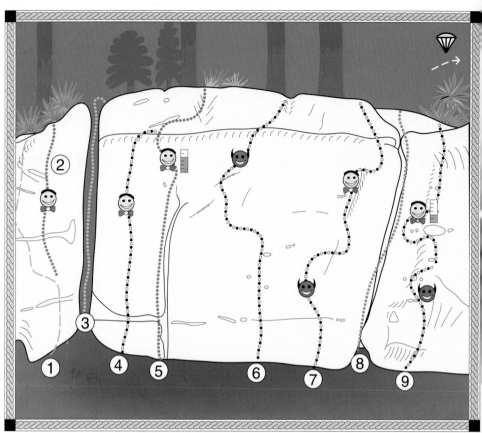

1	Celebration	5c	108°	★★★
	❶(5b.N.L.) 4.1959 Paul Smoker: (5c) 1969-81 ⚐			
2	Champagne Celebration	6a	108°	★★★
	❶(6a.N.L.) 1981 Guy McLelland, David Atchison-Jones: (6a) 1983 ⚐ D.A-Jones			
3	Brushwood Chimney	3a	90°	★★★
	❶(3a) Pre-1956			
4	Lamplight ⚐	6b	88°	★★★
	❶(6b.N.S.) 1996 Barry Knight			
5	Tilley Lamp Crack	6a	87°	★★★
	❶(6a.N.L.) 1956-63 George Clark: (6a) 25.6.1996 ⚐ John Patterson			
6	Nemesis ⚐	6b+	87°	★★★
	❶(6b.N.L.) 3.7.1986 Gary Wickham			
7	A Touch Too Much	6b	85°	★★★
	❶(6b.N.L.) 14.10.1985 Matt Saunders: (6b) 28.7.1986 ⚐ Gary Wickham			
8	Viper Crack	5b	82°	★★
	❶(5b) 1959-69			
9	Shattered	6b	110°	★★★
	❶(6c.N.L.) 8.1982 David Atchison-Jones: (6c) 9.1982 ⚐ D. Atchison-Jones			

Nemesis 6b+, Pat King

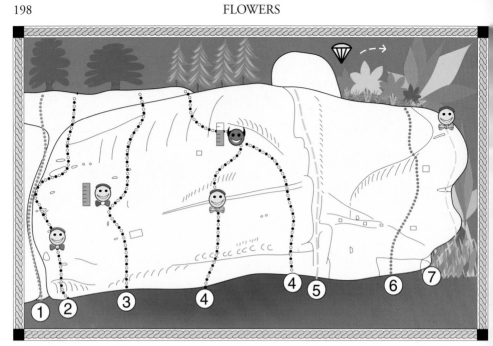

1	Viper Crack	5b	82°				★★
	❶(5b) 1959-69						
2	Shattered	6b	120°				★★★
	❶(6c.N.L.) 8.1982 David Atchison-Jones: (6c) 9.1982 ⚑ D. Atchison-Jones						
3	Powerpull Pearson (and the shorts of Death) ⚑	6b+	96°				★★
	❶(6b+.N.S.) 28.4.1991 Jasper Sharpe						
4	Jug of Flowers ⚑	6b+	81°				★★
	❶(6b.N.S.) 1981-9 Guy McLelland						
5	Easy Crack	2a	78°				★★★
	❶(1b) Pre-1956						
6	Mike's Left Knee ⚑	6a	98°				★
	❶(6a.N.S.) 7.4.1990 Paul Widdowson, M.Vetterlein, Brian Kavanagh						
7	Bold Finish	5a	90°				★★
	❶(5b) 1956-63						

Shattered 6b, Bazzer Knight

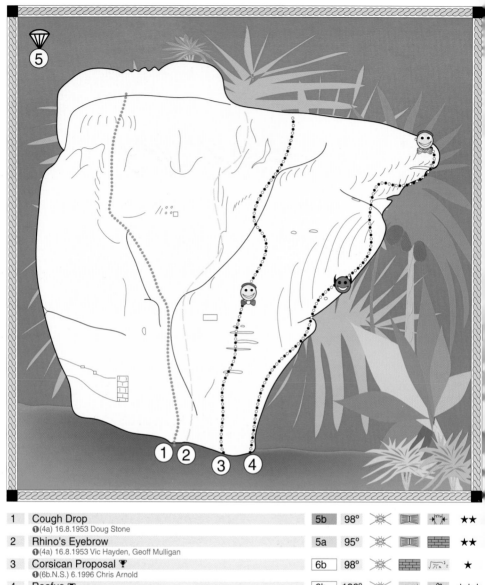

1	**Cough Drop**		5b	98°				★★
	❶(4a) 16.8.1953 Doug Stone							
2	**Rhino's Eyebrow**		5a	95°				★★
	❶(4a) 16.8.1953 Vic Hayden, Geoff Mulligan							
3	**Corsican Proposal** 🏆		6b	98°				★
	❶(6b.N.S.) 6.1996 Chris Arnold							
4	**Roofus** 🏆		6b	136°				★★★
	❶(6a.N.L.) 19.8.1993 Guy McLelland							
5	**Crack Route**		4c	82°				★★★
	❶(5b) 1936-7 Oxford University Climbers							

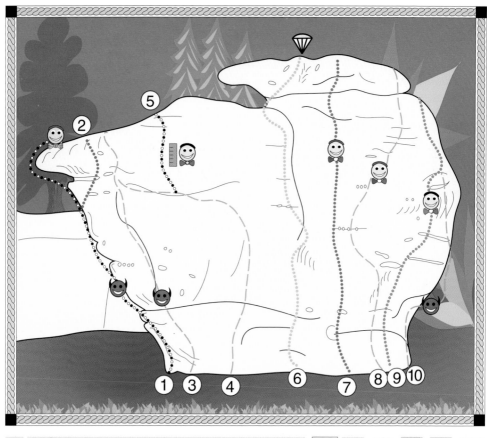

1	Roofus ♛ ❶(6a.N.L.) 19.8.1993 Guy McLelland	6b+	136°	≋			★★★
2	Id ♛ ❶(6a.N.L.) 1956-63	6a	130°	☼			★★
3	Long Stretch ❶(5b) 17.5.1958 John Smoker ♛	5c	82°	☼			★★★
4	Bludnok Wall ❶(5c) 24.8.1957 John Smoker: (5c) 6.6.1969 ♛ Martin Boysen	5c	82°	☼			★
5	Knock On Blood ♛ ❶(6b.N.S.) 6.4.1977 Robin Mazinke	6b	82°	☼			★
6	Crack Route ❶(5b) 1936-7 Oxford University Climbers ♛	4c	82°	☼			★★★
7	Metaphysical Poets ♛ ❶(6a+.N.S.) 1988 David & Carrie Atchison-Jones	6a+	87°	☼			★★★
8	Pinchgrip ❶(5c.N.L.) 1.4.1956 Bill Maxwell: (5c) 7-8.1984 ♛ Chris Arnold	5c	86°	☼			★★★
9	Pussyfoot ❶(N.L.) 15.8.1953 Kevin Day, Geoff Mulligan: (5b) 1956-63 ♛	5b+	113°				★★★
10	Sweaty Pussy ❶(N.L.) 12.9.1958 John Smoker: (5c+) 1982 ♛ Various Hot Panting Climbers	5c+	130°				★★★

Id 6a, Gwynfor Jones

Pinchgrip 5c, Sarah Robards

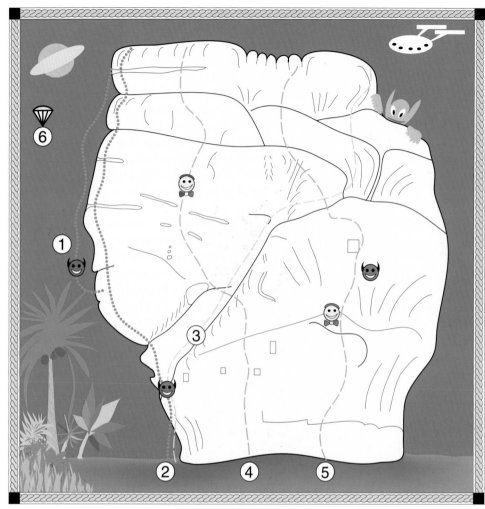

1	Swing Face	5b+	124°	★★★
	❶(5b) Pre-1956			
2	Birthday Arête	5a+	106°	★★★
	❶(N.L.) 15.8.1953 Doug Stone: (5a) 1956-63 ⚑			
3	Roof Route	5a	106°	★★★
	❶(4a) Pre-1956			
4	Sequins of Cosmic Turbulence	5c	89°	★★★
	❶(6a.N.L.) 8.1982 David Atchison-Jones: (5c) 1.7.1993 ⚑ Tim Skinner			
5	Rockney	5c+	116°	★★★
	❶(5c.N.L.) 1981-2 Barry Franklin: (5c) 1981-9 ⚑			
6	Crack Route	4c	82°	★★★
	❶(5b) 1936-7 Oxford University Climbers			

HIGH ROCKS - TOPO 40

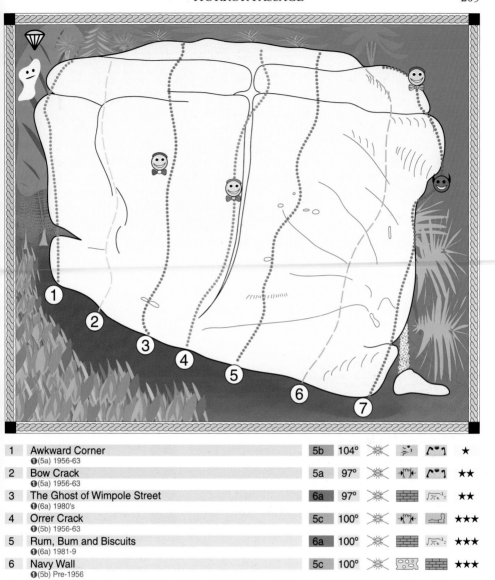

1	Awkward Corner	5b	104°				★
	❶(5a) 1956-63						
2	Bow Crack	5a	97°				★★
	❶(5a) 1956-63						
3	The Ghost of Wimpole Street	6a	97°				★★
	❶(6a) 1980's						
4	Orrer Crack	5c	100°				★★★
	❶(5b) 1956-63						
5	Rum, Bum and Biscuits	6a	100°				★★★
	❶(6a) 1981-9						
6	Navy Wall	5c	100°				★★★
	❶(5b) Pre-1956						
7	Bow Spirit	6a	110°				★★★
	❶(6a) 1980's						

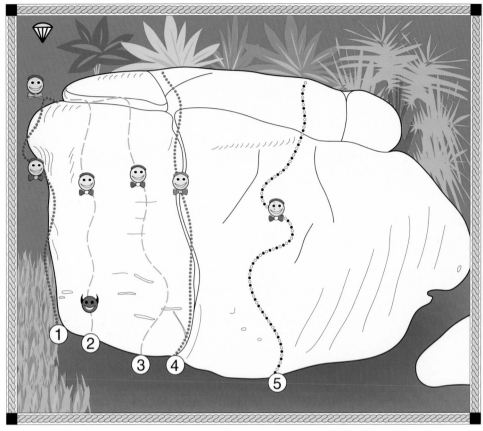

1	Bow Spirit	6a	110°	☀			★★★
	❶(6a) 1980's						
2	Climbers Behaving Badly - In Spain	5c+	108°	☀			★★★
	❶(5c+) 3.2000 Martin the Vandal						
3	Odin's Wall	5c	108°	☀			★★★
	❶(N.L.) 23.5.1959 Martin Boysen: (5c) 14.5.1980 ⚘ Mick Fowler						
4	Something Crack	6a	111°	☀			★★★
	❶(5c.N.L.) 1956-63: (6a) 7.1995 ⚘ Tim Skinner						
5	Whiff Whaff ⚘	6b+	84°	☀			★★
	❶(6b.N.S.) 9.1989 Paul Hayes						

Odin's Wall 5c, Carrie Atchison-Jones

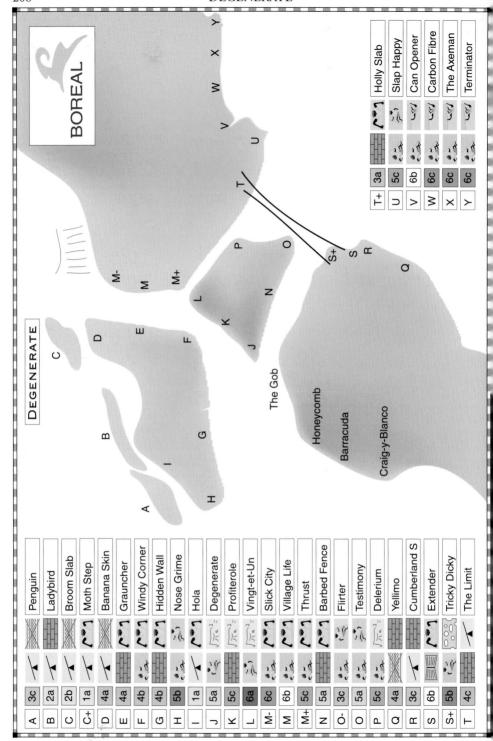

BOREAL

DEGENERATE

The Gob

Honeycomb

Barracuda

Craig-y-Blanco

			Holly Slab
		T+	Slap Happy
		U	3a
		V	5c
		W	6b
		X	Can Opener
		Y	Carbon Fibre

		6c	The Axeman
		6c	Terminator

			Penguin		3c	A
			Ladybird		2a	B
			Broom Slab		2b	C
			Moth Step		1a	C+
			Banana Skin		4a	D
			Grauncher		4a	E
			Windy Corner		4b	F
			Hidden Wall		4b	G
			Nose Grime		5b	H
			Hola		1a	I
			Degenerate		5a	J
			Profiterole		5c	K
			Vingt-et-Un		6a	L
			Slick City		6c	M-
			Village Life		6b	M
			Thrust		5c	M+
			Barbed Fence		5a	N
			Flirter		3c	O-
			Testimony		5a	O
			Delerium		5c	P
			Yellimo		4a	Q
			Cumberland S		3c	R
			Extender		6b	S
			Tricky Dicky		5b	S+
			The Limit		4c	T

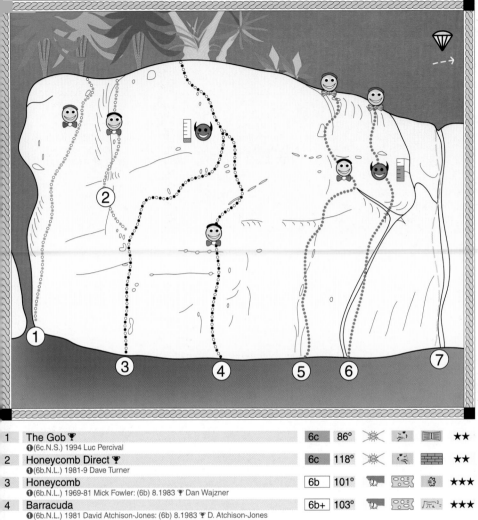

1	**The Gob** ♈ ❶(6c.N.S.) 1994 Luc Percival	6c	86°				★★
2	**Honeycomb Direct** ♈ ❶(6b.N.L.) 1981-9 Dave Turner	6c	118°				★★
3	**Honeycomb** ❶(6b.N.L.) 1969-81 Mick Fowler: (6b) 8.1983 ♈ Dan Wajzner	6b	101°				★★★
4	**Barracuda** ❶(6b.N.L.) 1981 David Atchison-Jones: (6b) 8.1983 ♈ D. Atchison-Jones	6b+	103°				★★★
5	**Craig-Y-Blanco** ❶(N.L.) 1956-63 P. S. Maher: (5c) 28.4.1976 ♈ Mick Fowler	6a	116°				★★★
6	**Dagger Crack** ❶(6a.N.L.) 14.5.1980 Mick Fowler: (6a) 1981 ♈ David Atchison-Jones	6a+	117°				★★★
7	**Greasy Crack** ❶(5a) 1956-63	5a	96°				

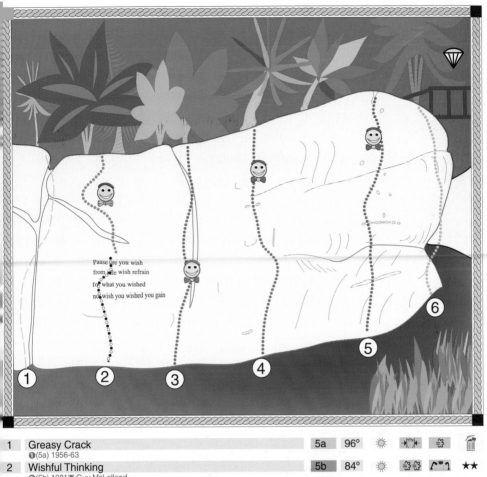

Pause ere you wish
from the wish refrain
for what you wished
not wish you wished you gain

1	Greasy Crack	5a	96°	☀	➹	⧉	🗑
	❶(5a) 1956-63						
2	Wishful Thinking	5b	84°	☀	⧉⧉	⌒	★★
	❶(5b) 1981 ♛ Guy McLelland						
3	Woofus Weejects ♛	6a	84°	☀	➹	√	★
	❶(5c.N.L.) 20.8.1993 Chris Arnold, Tim Daniells						
4	Ides of March ♛	6a	113°	☀	▦	√	★★
	❶(6a.N.L.) 26.3.1983 Guy McLelland						
5	Lunge'n'Shelf ♛	6a	113°	☀	⌣	⧉⧉	★★
	❶(6a.N.L.) 23.10.1983 Guy McLelland						
6	Puzzle Corner	4c	105°	☀	⌣	▦	★
	❶(4b) 1956-63						

Wishfull Thinking 6b, Guy McLelland

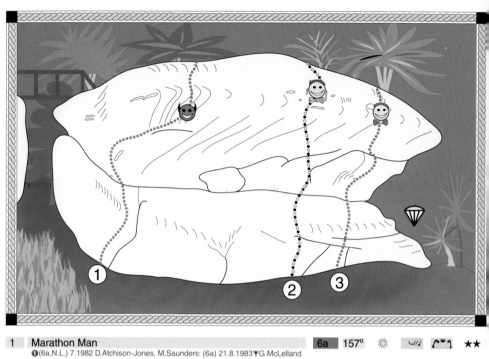

1	Marathon Man		6a	157°	☀	◡◡/	⌐▞	★★
	❶(6a.N.L.) 7.1982 D.Atchison-Jones, M.Saunders: (6a) 21.8.1983🍷G.McLelland							
2	Beer Gut Shuffle		6b	143°	☀	◡◡/	√π²=	★★
	❶(6a) 1982 Barry Knight, Guy McLelland 🍷							
3	The Diver 🍷		6a	137°	☀	◡◡/	≡3	★
	❶(6a.N.S.) 13.9.1992 Alan Grigg							

Dinner Crack 5c, David Atchison-Jones

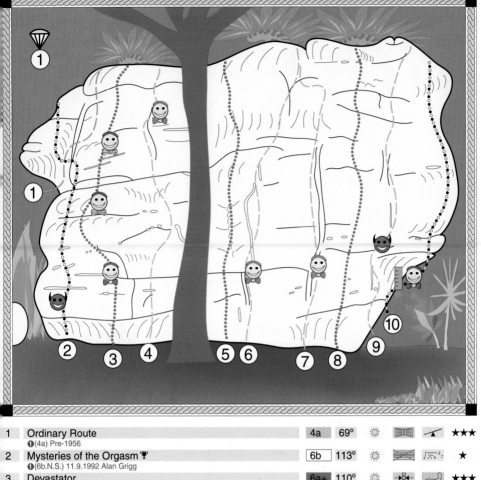

1	Ordinary Route ❶(4a) Pre-1956	4a	69°	☀				★★★
2	Mysteries of the Orgasm ❦ ❶(6b.N.S.) 11.9.1992 Alan Grigg	6b	113°	☀				★
3	Devastator ❶(6a.N.L.) 1959-69: (6a) 1981-9 ❦	6a+	110°	☀				★★★
4	Graveyard Groove ❶(5c.N.L.) 27.9.1958 John Smoker, Don Ingrey: (5c) 1981 ❦ D. Atchison-Jones	5c	99°	☀				★★★
5	Tool Wall ❦ ❶(6a.N.S.) 11.9.1992 Alan Grigg	6a	112°	☀				★★
6	Fork ❶(5c) 1956-63 ❦	5c	109°	☀				★★★
7	Knife ❶(5c) 1956-63 ❦	5c	118°	☀				★★★
8	David Jones and the Temple of Doom ❦ ❶(6a.N.L.) 1987 David Atchison-Jones, Fliss Butler	6a	112°	☀				★★
9	Dinner Crack ❶(A1) 11.12.1954 Nick Nicholls: (5b) 1963-79 ❦	5c+	118°	☀				★★★
10	Early Breakfast ❶(6a.N.L.) 1980 David Atchison-Jones: (6b) 1992-5 ❦	6b	146°	☀				★

FOX'S

ADVENTURE CLOTHING AND EQUIPMENT

PERFORMANCE CLOTHING
LOWE ALPINE, ROHAN, COLUMBIA, EX-OFFICIO, ROYAL ROBBINS, BERGHAUS, TILLEY, SCANDA, SPRAYWAY, SALEWA, ODLO & REGATTA.

PERFORMANCE FOOTWEAR
SALOMON, BRASHER, SCARPA, MEINDL, ZAMBERLAN, BOREAL, LINE 7, HAWKINS, AIGLE, MEPHISTO, TEVA, TIMBERLAND & ECCO

PERFORMANCE EQUIPMENT
KARRIMOR, VANGO, SNUGPAK, LEKI, THERMAREST, BLOC, LEATHERMAN, MAGLITE, PETZL, WILD COUNTRY, LIFESYSTEMS, SIGG, AZTEC, BEAL, MAGELLAN, PLATYPUS & HIGH 5

ADJACENT TO TESCO (OLD AMERSHAM)
1 LONDON ROAD, AMERSHAM, BUCKS.
01494 431 431

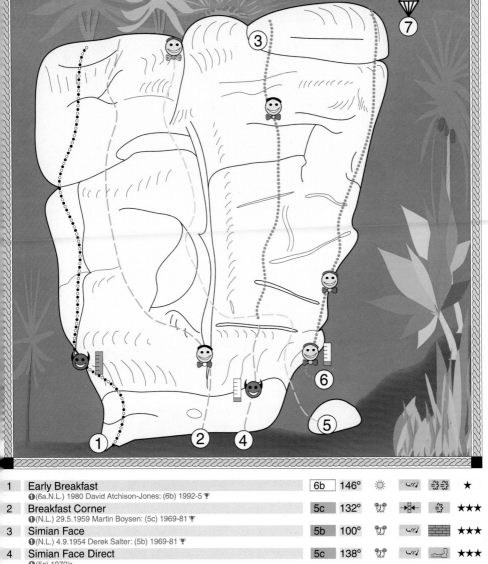

1	**Early Breakfast** ❶(6a.N.L.) 1980 David Atchison-Jones: (6b) 1992-5 ⚘	6b	146°	☀	〜⚷	⚘⚘	★
2	**Breakfast Corner** ❶(N.L.) 29.5.1959 Martin Boysen: (5c) 1969-81 ⚘	5c	132°	⚇	→▣←	⚘	★★★
3	**Simian Face** ❶(N.L.) 4.9.1954 Derek Salter: (5b) 1969-81 ⚘	5b	100°	⚇	〜⚷	▦	★★★
4	**Simian Face Direct** ❶(5c) 1970's	5c	138°	⚇	〜⚷	⌣	★★★
5	**Simian Progress** ❶(5a) 1936-7 Oxford University Climbers	5a	130°	⚇	〜⚷	⌐⚫⌐	★★★
6	**Monkey Nut** ❶(5b) 19.6.1965 H. Barnes	5b+	121°	⚇	⋗	⚫	★★★
7	**Ordinary Route** ❶(4a) Pre-1956	4a	67°	☀	▤	⚓	★★★

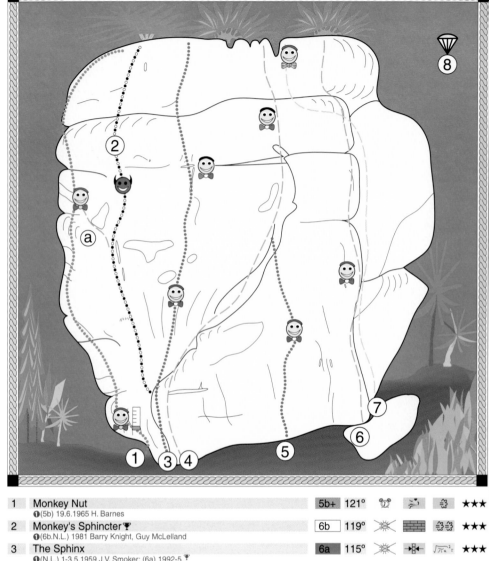

1	**Monkey Nut** ❶(5b) 19.6.1965 H. Barnes	5b+	121°				★★★
2	**Monkey's Sphincter**🏆 ❶(6b.N.L.) 1981 Barry Knight, Guy McLelland	6b	119°				★★★
3	**The Sphinx** ❶(N.L.) 1-3.5.1959 J.V. Smoker: (6a) 1992-5 🏆	6a	115°				★★★
4	**Simian Mistake** ❶(N.L.) Pre-1956: (5b) 1959-69 🏆	5c	115°				★★★
5	**Simian Direct** ❶(6a) 8.1983 🏆 Dan Wazjner	6a	100°				★★
6	**Sputnik** ❶(5c.N.L.) 2.11.1956 John Smaker: (5c) 17.5.1992 🏆 Tim Skinner	5c+	110°				★★★
7	**North Wall** ❶(5b) Oxford University Climbers: (5a) Pre-1956 🏆	5a	90°				★★★
8	**Ordinary Route** ❶(4a) Pre-1956	4a	69°				★★★

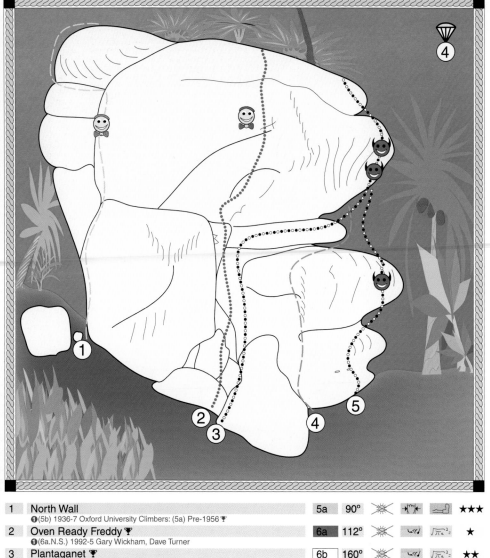

1	**North Wall**		5a	90°				★★★
	❶(5b) 1936-7 Oxford University Climbers: (5a) Pre-1956 ♈							
2	**Oven Ready Freddy** ♈		6a	112°				★
	❶(6a.N.S.) 1992-5 Gary Wickham, Dave Turner							
3	**Plantaganet** ♈		6b	160°				★★
	❶(6b.N.S.) 11.4.1992 Paul Widdowson							
4	**Ordinary Route**		4a	69°				★★★
	❶(4a) Pre-1956							
5	**Mysteries of the Orgasm** ♈		6b	113°				★★
	❶(6b.N.S.) 11.9.1992 Alan Grigg							

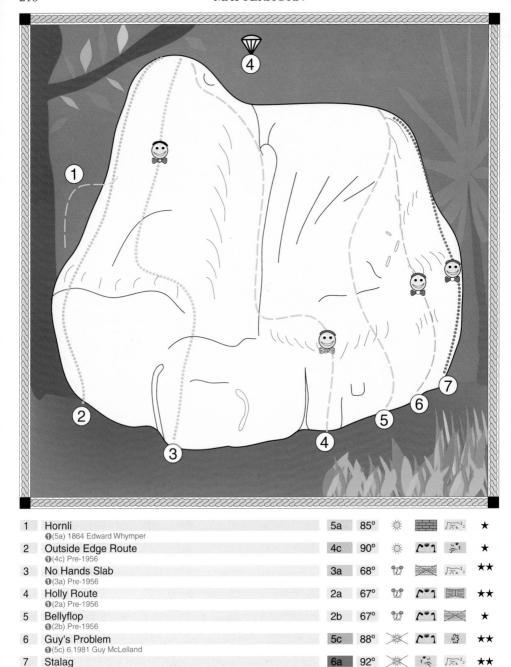

1	Hornli	5a	85°				★
	❶(5a) 1864 Edward Whymper						
2	Outside Edge Route	4c	90°				★
	❶(4c) Pre-1956						
3	No Hands Slab	3a	68°				★★
	❶(3a) Pre-1956						
4	Holly Route	2a	67°				★★
	❶(2a) Pre-1956						
5	Bellyflop	2b	67°				★
	❶(2b) Pre-1956						
6	Guy's Problem	5c	88°				★★
	❶(5c) 6.1981 Guy McLelland						
7	Stalag	6a	92°				★★
	❶(N.L.) 1956-63 Paul Smoker, Martin Boysen, R. Maher						

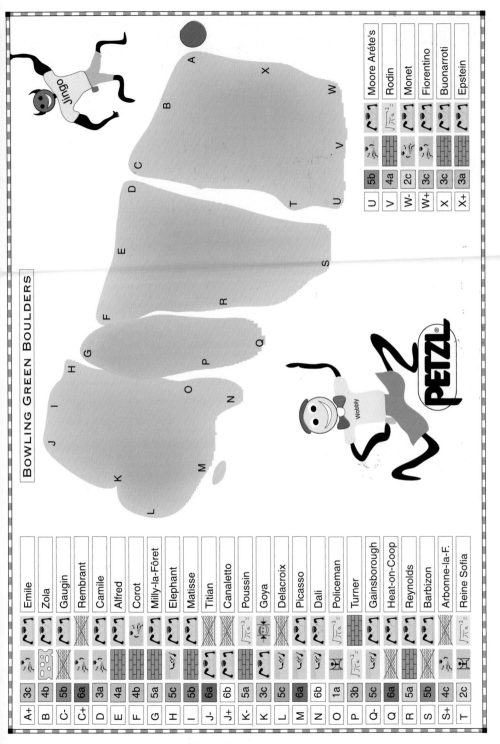

BOWLING GREEN BOULDERS

5b				U	Moore Aréte's
4a				V	Rodin
2c				W-	Monet
3c				W+	Fiorentino
3c				X	Buonarroti
3a				X+	Epstein

A+	3c		Emile
B	4b		Zola
C-	5b		Gaugin
C+	6a		Rembrant
D	3a		Camile
E	4a		Alfred
F	4b		Corot
G	5a		Milly-la-Fôret
H	5c		Elephant
I	5b		Matisse
J-	6a		Titian
J+	6b		Canaletto
K-	5a		Poussin
K	3c		Goya
L	5c		Delacroix
M	6a		Picasso
N	6b		Dali
O	1a		Policeman
P	3b		Turner
Q-	5c		Gainsborough
Q	6a		Heat-on-Coop
R	5a		Reynolds
S	5b		Barbizon
S+	4c		Arbonne-la-F.
T	2c		Reine Sofia

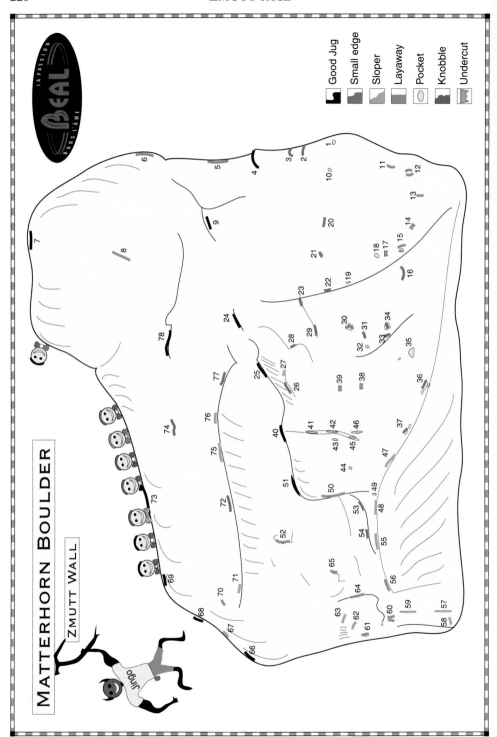

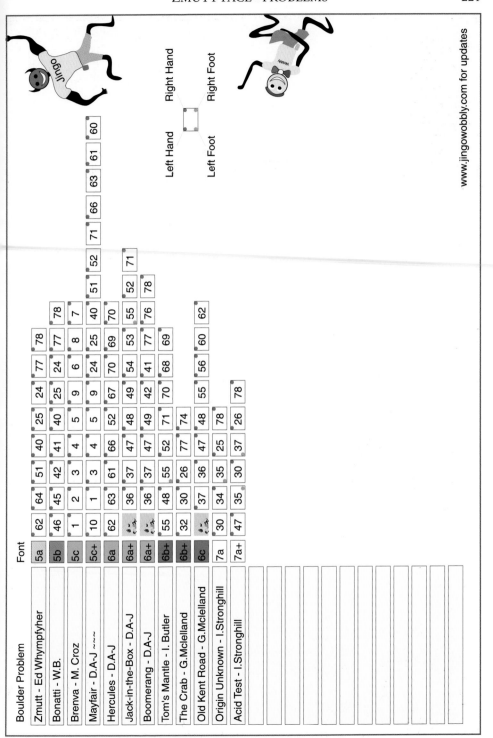

Boulder Problem	Font										
Zmutt - Ed Whympfyher	5a	62	64	51	40	25	24	77	78		
Bonatti - W.B.	5b	46	45	42	41	40	25	24	77	78	
Brenva - M. Croz	5c	1	2	3	4	5	9	6	8	7	
Mayfair - D.A-J ~~~	5c+	10	1	3	4	5	9	24	25	40	51 / 52
Hercules - D.A-J	6a	62	63	61	66	52	67	70	69	70	
Jack-in-the-Box - D.A-J	6a+	36	37	47	48	49	54	53	55	52	71
Boomerang - D.A-J	6a+	36	37	47	49	42	41	77	76	78	
Tom's Mantle - I. Butler	6b+	55	48	55	52	71	70	68	69		
The Crab - G.Mclelland	6b+	32	30	26	77	74					
Old Kent Road - G.Mclelland	6c	37	36	47	48	55	56	60	62		
Origin Unknown - I.Stronghill	7a	30	34	35	25	78					
Acid Test - I.Stronghill	7a+	47	35	30	37	26	78				

jingo

wobbly

Left Hand — Right Hand

Left Foot — Right Foot

www.jingowobbly.com for updates

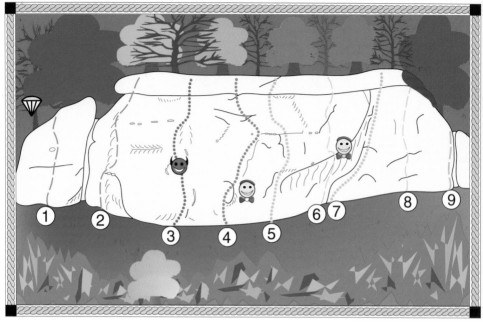

1	**Stinging Nettle**		4b	87°				🗑
	❶(4b) 8.10.1994 Robin Mazinke							
2	**Tumble**		4b	82°				★★
	❶(4a) Pre-1969							
3	**Tequile Mockingbird**		6a	90°				★★★
	❶(6a) 6.1982 David Atchison-Jones, Guy McLelland							
4	**Entwhistle's Effort**		5b	79°				★★★
	❶(5a) 5.1953 Les Entwhistle							
5	**Cut Holds**		3b	79°				★★
	❶(2b) Pre-1969							
6	**Overlap Centre**		5a	93°				★★
	❶(5a) 1969-81							
7	**Bishop's Move**		3b	75°				★
	❶(3a) 2.5.1953 Ned Cordery, Ken Cross							
8	**Slapper**		4c	78°				★
	❶(4c) 8.10.1994 Tim Skinner							
9	**Jamber**		2b	78°				🗑
	❶(2a) Pre-1969							

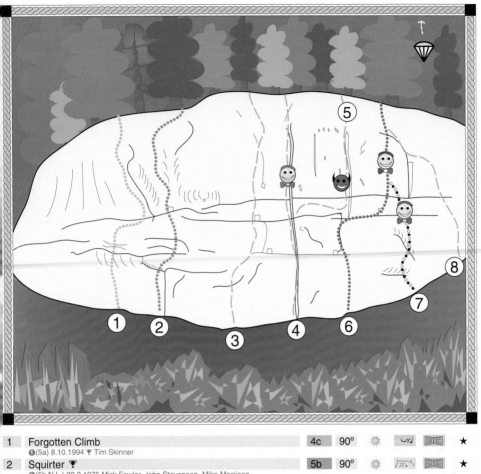

1	**Forgotten Climb**	4c	90°				★
	❶(5a) 8.10.1994 ⚑ Tim Skinner						
2	**Squirter** ⚑	5b	90°				★
	❶(5b.N.L.) 23.2.1975 Mick Fowler, John Stevenson, Mike Morrison						
3	**Doing the Dirty** ⚑	5c	94°				★★
	❶(5c.N.L.) 7.8.1984 Chris Arnold, Paul Hayes						
4	**Headhunter** ⚑	5c	93°				★★
	❶(5c.N.L.) 23.2.1975 Mick Fowler, John Stevenson, Mike Morrison						
5	**Hanging Crack** ⚑	5c	93°				★★
	❶(5c.N.L.) 23.2.1975 Mick Fowler, John Stevenson, Mike Morrison						
6	**Equinox** ⚑	6a	97°				★★★
	❶(5c.N.L.) 26.2.1983 David Atchison-Jones, Guy McLelland						
7	**Pheonix** ⚑	6b	97°				★★
	❶(6b.N.L.) 26.2.1983 David Atchison-Jones						
8	**Chez Moi** ⚑	5c	97°				
	❶(5c.N.L.) 26.2.1983 Guy McLelland, David Atchison-Jones						

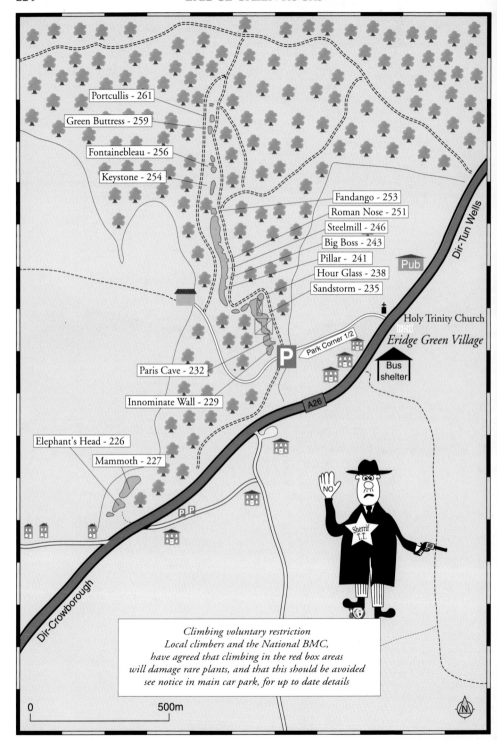

Question? Do you like mosquito's! need we comment any further. If you are prepared to take your chances with malaria and other infestical tropicallizing dizzeseasses, then visit Eridge on a warm, still, summers evening. But on the more positive side, the climbing is excellent, varied, and rewards those who are prepared to try something different. Finding the ways up to the belays, can require your deepest, soul searching, amazonian intuition – quite simply, a must.

GRADED LIST

5c
Nonpareil
5b+
The Beguiled
The Crunch
5b
Zugzwang
Evoloution
Enigma
Oliver Amazing Under-
pants
Higher Purchase
Lou
Lazy Chive
Ken Clean Air System
Scirocco
The Nail
Tortoise on a Spin Out
Condom Corner
Fernkop Crack
Kinetix
Diagonal
Meaty Thighs
Snail Trail
Achilles Last Stand
Roman Nose Direct
Waffer Thin
6a+
More Cake for Me
Big Boss
Hottie
Prowess
Sandstorm
6a
Scorpion
Triceratops
Nigel Mantel
Touchdown
Steamroller
Yellow Soot
Getafix
Higher Purchase Direct
More Monkey - Funky
Brighton Rock
Nododedendron
5.11 Crack
Snap, Crackle, Pop
Sandstone Hell
Thrutch

Poofy Finger's Revenge
Touchdown
Fly by Knight
Iron Man Tyson
Mellow Toot
Stem Son
Revelations
Appetite for Destruction
Close to You
Emerald
Mein Herr
Good Route-Poor Line
Aero
Elephant's Arse
Afterburner
Life in the Old Dog Yet
Earthrise
Safe Sex
Dr. Kemp's Cure
Hyphenated Jones
Too Short to Mention
Too Short Direct
Empty Vee
Parisian Affair
5c+
Dilemma
Steelmill
Obelisk
Stirling Moss
Genesis
5c
Locust
Finance
Fandango
The Pillar
Portcullis
Innominate Buttress
Fontainebleau
Tusk Direct Start
Impacted Stool
Asterix
Great Bald Turkey
Communist
Extinct Mammoth
Big Fat Tart
Polly Ticks
Antoninus
Middleclass Ponce
Last of the Summer Wine

Trainer Drainer
Eric
Scooped Slab Eliminate
Tweedle Dum
Short Work
Good Route Good Line
Viking Line
Too Short
Wet Bank Holiday
Brian's Corner
Fruits
Elephant's Head
5b+
Nuthin'Fancy
Libra
5b
Mammoth Wall
Siesta Wall
Tusk
Innominate Crack
Concorde
Sonny Dribble Chops
Romulus
Paisley
Just Ice
Optical Racer
Hipposuction
The Pink Pengster
Wobble
Elastic Headbands
Keystone Kops
Just CIA
Tweedle Dee
Layaway
Misty Wall
Hadrian's Wall
Green Bollard Chimney
Long Man's Slab
Eridge Tower Route
Hour Glass
5a+
Equilibrium Wall
Scooped Slab
Fernkop Crack
5a
Battlements Crack
Why not go Right
Hanging Crack
Roman Nose

Bugbear Buttress
Shanty Wall
4c
Y Crack
Backyard
Dust Crack
Remus
Primrose
Keystone Face
Beginner's Wall
4b
Barbican Buttress
Crackpot
Long Man's Neighbour
Just Cause
6.00a.m. Route
Geronimo
Flutings
Spot the Dog
Hartleys
Pedestal Wall
4a
Slanting Crack
Toadstool Crack
Capstan Wall
3b
Black Crack
Yew Crack
Embarkation Crack
Elephant's Tail
Greasy Slab
Keystone Wall
3a
Flake Crack
Truncate
2b
London Wall
Boulder Chimney
London Corner
2a
Giant step for Mankind
Heffalump
Flake Crack R-Side
Jug Handle Route
1
Bivouac Chimney
Keystone Crack

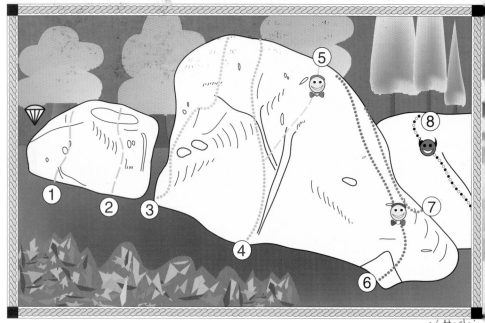

Vetterlein

1	A Giant Step for Mankind	2a	68°			
	❶(2a) Pre-1956					
2	Heffalump	2b	65°			
	❶(4a) 5.8.1984 Geoff Pearsons: (4a) 1984 ❦ Ben Pritchard					
3	Elephant's Tail	3b	65°			
	❶(1b) Pre-1956					
4	Y Crack	4c	85°			★
	❶(3b) Pre-1956					
5	Why not go Right	5a	80°			★
	❶(5a) 2000					
6	Elephant's Arse	6a	67°			
	❶(6a) 15.4.1997 ❦ Robin Mazinke, Mike Eden					
7	Elephant's Head	5c	88°			★
	❶(N.L.) Pre-1956: (5c)1981-99 ❦					
8	Diagonal	6b	87°			★★
	❶(6b.N.S.) 1981-87 Guy Mclelland: (6b) 16.6.1994 ❦ John Patterson					
9	Mammoth Wall	5b	88°			★★
	❶(5b) 1969-81					
10	Wall of the Extinct Mammoth ❦	5c	88°			★★
	❶(5c.N.S.) 1990 Tim Skinner					
11	Tusk ❦	5b	86°			
	❶(5b.N.S.) 20.4.1991 Tim Skinner:					
12	Tusk Direct Start ❦	5c	88°			
	❶(5c.N.S.) 6.9.1996 Robin Mazinke					

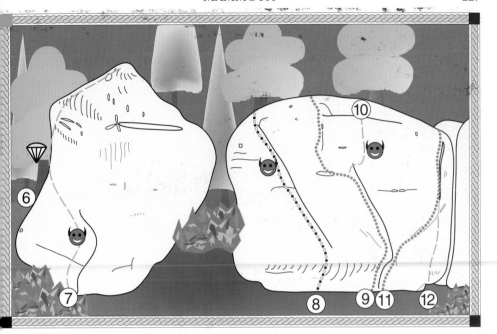

13   24
Innominate and Prowess area - Eridge

ERIDGE GREEN ROCKS - TOPO 2

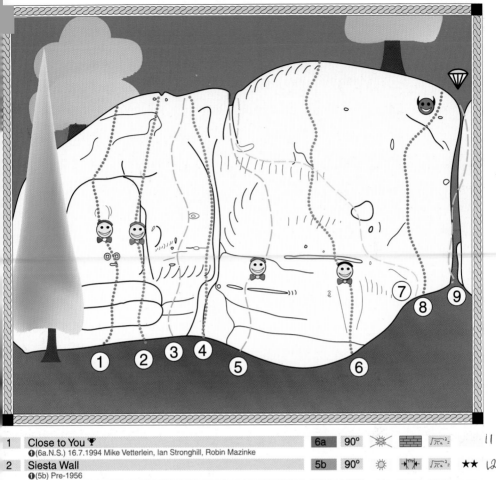

1	Close to You ⍦	6a	90°				11
	❶(6a.N.S.) 16.7.1994 Mike Vetterlein, Ian Stronghill, Robin Mazinke						
2	Siesta Wall	5b	90°				★★ 12
	❶(5b) Pre-1956						
3	Innominate Buttress ⍦	5c	90°				★
	❶(5c.N.S.) 2000						
4	Innominate Crack	5b	90°				★★★ 13
	❶(5a) Pre-1956						
5	Last of the Summer Wine	5c	86°				★ 14
	❶(5c.N.S.) 19.9.1993 Steve Durkin, R. Darnell: (5c) 19.9.1993 ⍦ R. Darnell						
6	Big Fat Tart	5b	80°				★★ 15
	❶(5c.N.S.) 31.5.1992 A.Hughes: (5c)5.1992 ⍦ Matt Smith						
7	Equilibrium Wall	5a	70°				★★ 16
	❶(5b) Pre-1956						
8	Hottie ⍦	6a	94°				★ 17
	❶(6a.N.S.) 1981-89						
9	Boulder Chimney	2b	90°				18
	❶(2b) Pre-1956						

16

Equilibrium Wall 5b, Virginet Bernier

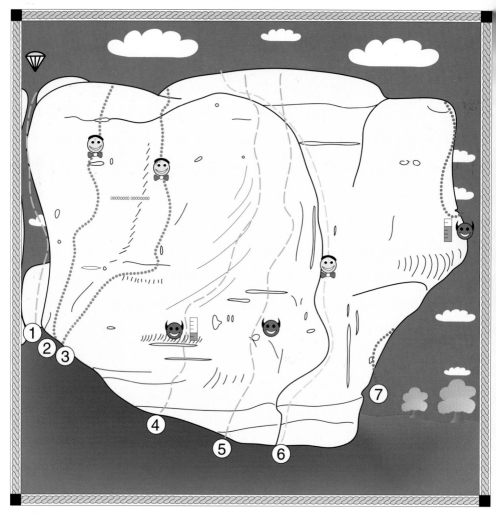

1	Boulder Chimney	2b	75°			
	❶(2b) Pre-1956					
2	Nuthin' Fancy	5b+	80°			★
	❶(5c) 5.9.1992 Tim Skinner					
3	Libra	5b+	88°			★★
	❶(5c) 1969-81					
4	Too Short	5c	87°			★★
	❶(5c.N.S.) 16.11.1991 Robin Mazinke: (5c) 5.1993 ☙ Matt Smith					
5	Trainer Drainer	5c	88°			★
	❶(5c.N.S.) 8.8.1990 Andy Hughes: (5c) 5.1993 ☙ Matt Smith					
6	Hanging Crack	5a	80°			★★★
	❶(5a) Pre-1956					
7	Prowess	6a+	98°			★★★
	❶(6b.N.S.) 10.7.1991 Mike Vetterlein: (6b) 15.6.1997 ☙ Robin Mazinke					

30
Parisian Affair 6a, Luc Percival

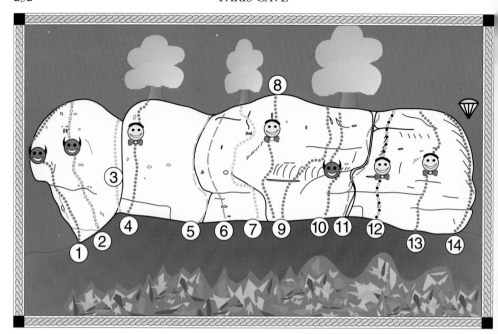

1	Prowess	6a+	97°				★★★
	❶(6a/b.N.S.) 10.7.1991 Mike Vetterlein: (6a+) 15.6.1997 ♥ Robin Mazinke						
2	Nonpareil ♥	6c+	99°				★★★
	❶(6c.N.S.) 11.6.1992 Paul Widdowson						
3	Flake Crack	3a	78°				★★
	❶(1b) Pre-1956						
4	Cracking Up	6a	77°				★
	❶(6a) 1989-92						
5	Bivouac Chimney	1b	67°				
	❶(1b) Pre-1956						
6	Geronimo	4b	82°				
	❶(4b) 1.6.1993 Robin Mazinke, Mike Vetterlein, Steve Durkin						
7	Truncate	3a	77°				★
	❶(3a) 1969-81 Tim Daniells						
8	Parisian Affair	6a	100°				★★
	❶(6a) 4.1984 Guy McLelland, Chris Arnold						
9	Too Short to Mention	6a	110°				★★
	❶(6a) 1981-89						
10	Even Shorter Mention	6a	120°				★★
	❶(6a) 4.1991 P. Stone, M. Smith						
11	6.00a.m. Route	4b	88°				★
	❶(4b) Pre-1956						
12	Condom Corner	6b	90°				★
	❶(5c) 4.1984 Guy McLelland, Chris Arnold						
13	Safe Sex ♥	6a	87°				★
	❶(6a.N.S.) 1.6.1993 Robin Mazinke						
14	Dr. Kemp's Cure ♥	6a	85°				★
	❶(6a.N.S.) 1.6.1993 Robin Mazinke, Mike Vetterlein						

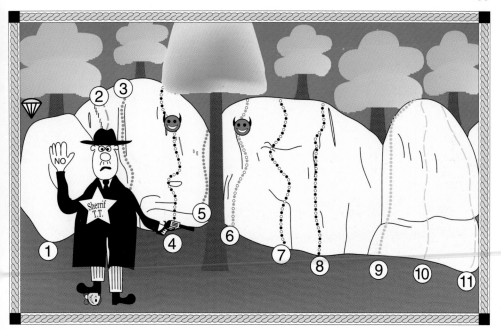

1	BoulderArête ❶(3a) Pre-1956	6a	75°				★	
2	Tree Climb ❶(4a) 1969-81	4c	76°					37
3	Thin Layback ❶(5b) 1969-81	5b	88°				★★	38
4	Scratch ❶(5c.N.L.) 1969-81: (5c) 1980 ♛ David Atchison-Jones	6b	88°				★★	39
5	Amnesian ❶(5b) 1969-81	5b	88°					40
6	Moments of Pleasure ❶(6c.N.S.) 1994 Luc Percival: (6c) 30.8.1995 ♛John Patterson	6c	98°				★★	41
7	Woodstock ♛ ❶(6a/b.N.S.) 8.1994 Ian Stronghill	6b	96°				★★★	42
8	Dutch Cap Arête ❶(6b.N.S.) 7.1990 P. Stone: (6b) 20.8.1995 ♛ John Patterson	6b	94°				★	43
9	Mosquito ❶(4c) 1969-81	4c	76°					44
10	Tiger Moth ❶(5a) 1969-81	5a	76°				★	45
11	Buzzard's Saw gets Christened ❶(5b.N.S.) 29.11.1992 Robin Mazinke: (5a) 29.4.1993 ♛ Tim Skinner	5a	76°					46

1	Mosquito	4c	76°				★
	❶(4c) 1969-81						
2	Tiger Moth	5a	76°				★★
	❶(5a) 1969-81						
3	Buzzard's Saw gets Christened	5a	76°				
	❶(5b.N.S.) 29.11.1992 Robin Mazinke: (5a) 29.4.1993 ❦ Tim Skinner						
4	Sadness is 35, and living at Home	5c	87°				★
	❶(5c.N.S.) 1992-5 Doug Reid: (5c) 17.8.1995 ❦ John Patterson						
5	Rota	4a	80°				★
	❶(4a) 1959-69						
6	Demon Wall	5c	88°				★★
	❶(5c) 1959-69						
7	Easy Life ❦	6b	99°				★★
	❶(6b.N.S.) 11.6.1992 Paul Widdowson						
8	Tallywhackle's Climb ❦	6a	94°				
	❶(5c.N.S.) 1981-9						
9	Descent Chimney	3b	90°				
	❶(3b) 1969-81						
10	Bulging Corner	5c	90°				★
	❶(5b) 1959-69						
11	Enigma	6b	95°				★★
	❶(6b.N.S.) 20.2.1990 Mike Vetterlein: (6b) 26.9.1994 ❦ John Patterson						
12	Long Man's Neighbour	4b	95°				
	❶(4a) Pre-1956						
13	Long Man's Slab	5b	95°				★★
	❶(5b) Pre-1956						
14	Scirocco ❦	6b	95°				★★★
	❶(6b.N.S.) 12.9.1991 M.Smith						

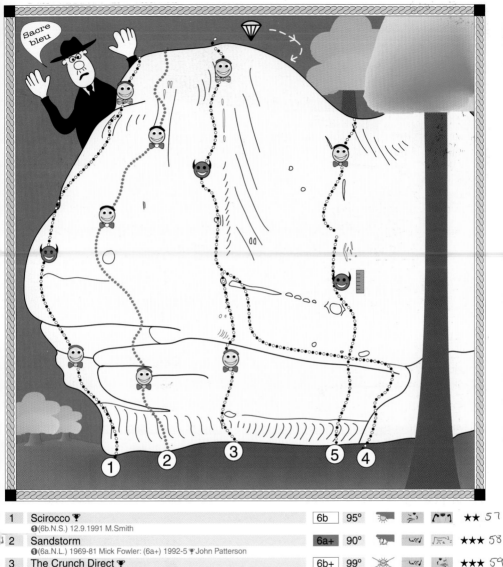

1	Scirocco	6b	95°	★★ 57
	❶(6b.N.S.) 12.9.1991 M.Smith			
2	Sandstorm	6a+	90°	★★★ 58
	❶(6a.N.L.) 1969-81 Mick Fowler: (6a+) 1992-5 John Patterson			
3	The Crunch Direct	6b+	99°	★★★ 59
	❶(6b.N.L.) 1982 Guy McLelland			
4	The Crunch	6b	95°	★★★
	❶(6b.N.L.) 1980-1 Mick Fowler			
5	More Cake For Me	6a+	97°	★★★ 60
	❶(6b.N.S.) 9.1989 Paul Hayes, Matt Saunders, Barry Knight			

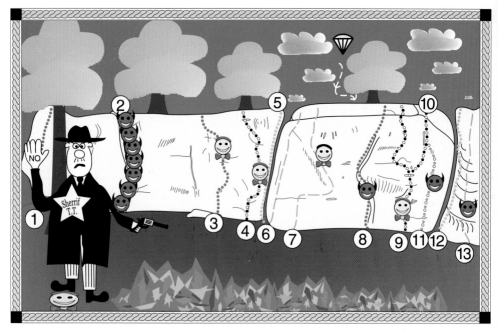

1	The Crunch Direct ⚑ ❶(6b.N.L.) 1982 Guy McLelland	6b+	99°					★★★
2	Amphitheatre Crack ❶(5b) Pre-1956	5b	87°					
3	Slug ❶(6a.N.L.) 1970-81 Mick Fowler: (6a) 1992-5 ⚑ John Patterson	6a	98°					★
4	Flail Trail ❶(6a.N.S.) 9.1990 Jasper Sharpe: (6b) 30.8.1995 ⚑John Patterson	6b	101°					★
5	Amphitheatre Chimney ❶(3a) Pre-1956	3a	88°					★★★
6	Branchdown ❶(5c.N.L.) 1969-81 Mick Fowler: (5c) 6.8.1996 ⚑ Tim Skinner	5c	88°					★★
7	Leech ❶(5c.N.L.) 1969-81 Mick Fowler: (5c) 5.9.1992 ⚑ Tim Skinner	5c	82°					★★
8	Forgotten Crack ❶(6a.N.L.) 1969-81 Martin Boysen: (6a) 1992-5 ⚑ Gary Wickham	6a+	110°					
9	Smile of the Beyond ❶(6a.N.L.) 30.9.1979 Mick Fowler: (6b) 1982⚑ David Atchison-Jones	6b	95°					★★★
10	Bernadette ❶(6b.N.S.) 17.3.1984 Barry Knight, Guy McLelland: (6b) 1982-7 ⚑Barry Knight	6b	95°					★★★
11	Caped Avenger ⚑ ❶(6c.N.S.) 9.1990 Jasper Sharpe	6c	95°					★★
12	Torpedo Route ❶(3b) Pre-1956	3b	85°					
13	Getafix ❶(5c.N.L.) 1969-81 Mick Fowler: (6a) 1981 ⚑David Atchison-Jones	5c+	125°					★

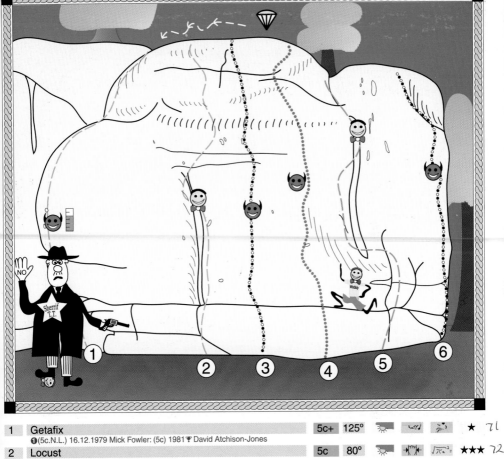

1	Getafix		5c+	125°				★	71
	❶(5c.N.L.) 16.12.1979 Mick Fowler: (5c) 1981 ♟ David Atchison-Jones								
2	Locust		5c	80°				★★★	72
	❶(5c) 1959-69								
3	Finance		5c	80°				★	73
	❶(5c.N.S.) 1981-89: (5c) 5.9.1992 ♟ Tim Skinner								
4	Higher Purchase ♟		6b	80°				★	74
	❶(6b.N.S.) 1981-89: (6b) 1993-6 ♟ Doug Reid								
5	Dusk Crack		4b	75°				★★	75
	❶(4b) Pre-1956								
6	Meaty Thighs ♟		6b	93°				★	76
	❶(6b.N.S.) 1.9.1992 Alan Grigg								

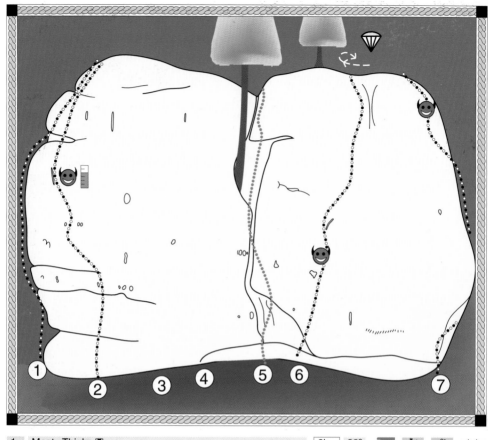

1	**Meaty Thighs** ♟	6b	92°				★★
	❶(6b.N.L.) 1.9.1992 Alan Grigg						
2	**The Beguiled**	6b	92°				★★★
	❶(6b.N.S.) 9.9.1994 Guy McLelland: (6b) 1992-5 ♟John Patterson						
3	**Project**	7*	93°				
	❶(7*) 2000*						
4	**Project**	7*	93°				
	❶(7*) 2000*						
5	**Hour Glass**	5b	88°				
	❶(5b) 1978 Mick Fowler						
6	**Snail Trail** ♟	6b	98°				★★★
	❶(6b.N.S.) 1981-9 Ed Stone						
7	**Zugzwang** ♟	6b	96°				★★★
	❶(6b.N.S.) 11.6.1992 Paul Widdowson						

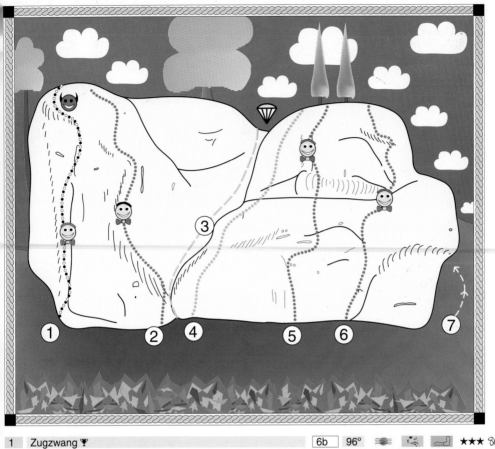

1	Zugzwang ♈		6b	96°				★★★ 80
	❶(6b.N.S.) 11.6.1992 Paul Widdowson							
2	Emerald ♈		6a	79°				★★ 81
	❶(6a.N.S.) 30.7.1990 Mike Vetterlein							
3	Easy Gully		1a	60°				
	❶(1a) Pre-1956							
4	Arête		4c	77°				
	❶(4c) Pre-1956							
5	Sandstone Hell ♈		6a	98°				★ 82
	❶(6a.N.S.) 30.7.1990 Mike Vetterlein							
6	Nonododododedendron ♈		6a	98°				★
	❶(6a.N.S.) 16.5.1998 Mike Eden, R. Mazinke							
7	5.11 Crack		6a	80°				★★ 83
	❶(6a.N.S.) 21.1.1990 Oliver Hill: (6a) ♈ Pre-2000							

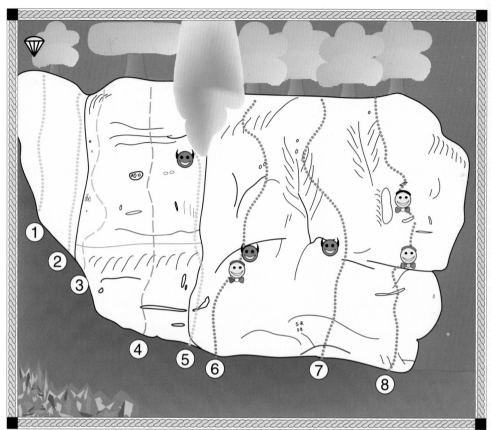

1	Greasy Slab	3b	65°			
	❶(3b) Pre-1956					
2	Embarkation Crack	3b	75°			
	❶(3b) Pre-1956					
3	Middleclass Ponce ❦	5c	88°			★★
	❶(5c.N.S.) 6.12.1992 Doug Reid, Robin Mazinke: (5c) 18.5.1997 ❦ Henry Widd					
4	Spot the Dog, and the Breath of Death	4b	78°			★★
	❶(4b) 6.12.1992 Doug Reid, Robin Mazinke					
5	Yew Crack	3b	88°			
	❶(3b) Pre-1956					
6	Tortoise on a Spin Out	6a	98°			★
	❶(6a) 3.1990 P. Stone: (6b) ?					
7	More Monkey than Funky	6a	92°			★
	❶(6a.N.S.) 28.1.1990 Oliver Hill: (6a) 29.4.1993 ❦ Tim Skinner					
8	Thrutch	5c+	94°			★★
	❶(5c) 1959-69					

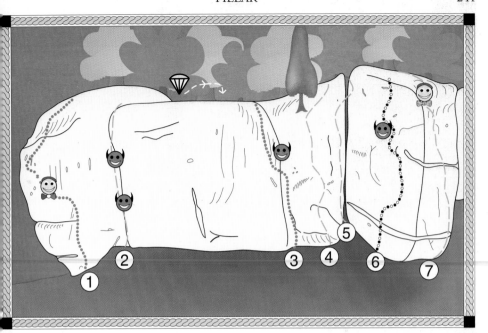

1	Earthrise	6a	88°				★★★ 92

1 Earthrise   6a   88°   ★★★ 92
❶(6a.N.S.) 23.7.1994: (6a) 5.1998 ♇ John Patterson

2 Empty Vee ♇   5c+   90°   93
❶(5c.N.S.) 27.1.1990 Mike Vetterlein

3 Triceratops ♇   6a   98°   ★ 94
❶(6a.N.S.) 1981-9

4 Impacted Stool   5c   87°   95
❶(5c.N.S.) 15.3.1992 Paul Widdowson, D.Reid, M.V: (5c) 6.1995♇ J.Patterson

5 Brian's Corner   5c   85°   ★★ 96
❶(5c.N.S.) 21.1.1990 Brian Kavanagh, M.V, O.Hill: (5c) 6.1995♇ J.Patterson

6 Kinetix ♇   6b   88°   ★★ 97
❶(6b.N.S.) 1981-9: (6b) 6.1998 ♇ John Patterson

7 The Pillar   5c   90°   ★★★ 98
❶(5c.N.L.) 1959-69: (5c) 11.9.1991♇ John Patterson

ERIDGE GREEN ROCKS - TOPO 16

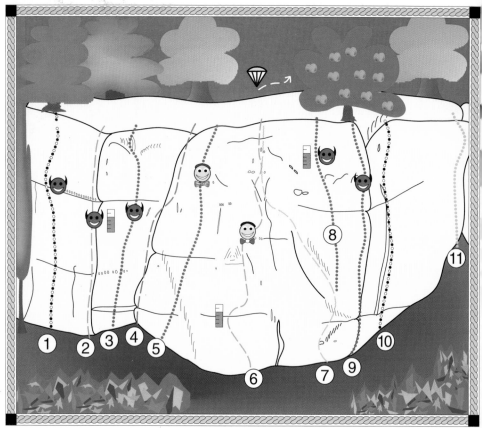

1	Waffer Thin		6b	90°				★
	❶(6b.N.S.) 1981-9: (6b) 11.9.1991 ♀ John Patterson							
2	Obelisk		5c+	90°				★★★
	❶(5c.N.L.) 9.6.1979 Mick Fowler,Mike Morrison: (5c) 11.9.1991 ♀ John Patterson							
3	Mein Herr ♀		6a	90°				
	❶(6a.N.S.) 1981-9							
4	Slanting Crack		4a	77°				
	❶(4a) Pre-1956							
5	Nigel Mantel ♀		6a	80°				★
	❶(6a.N.S.) 5.1990 Matt Smith, Ray Tipton							
6	Stirling Moss		5c	81°				★★
	❶(6a.N.S.) 1981-9: (5c+) 3.9.1991 ♀ John Patterson							
7	Scooped Slab		5a+	78°				★★★
	❶(5a) 1959-69							
8	Snap, Crackle, Pop,,,,, Splat!		6a	94°				★
	❶(6b.N.S.) 1981-9: (6a) 1981-9 ♀							
9	Afterburner		6a	95°				★★
	❶(6a) 4.1991 Matt Smith, P. Stone							
10	The Nail ♀		6b	95°				
	❶(6b.N.S.) 19.9.1992 Alan Grigg							
11	Black Crack		3b	70°				
	❶(3b) Pre-1956							

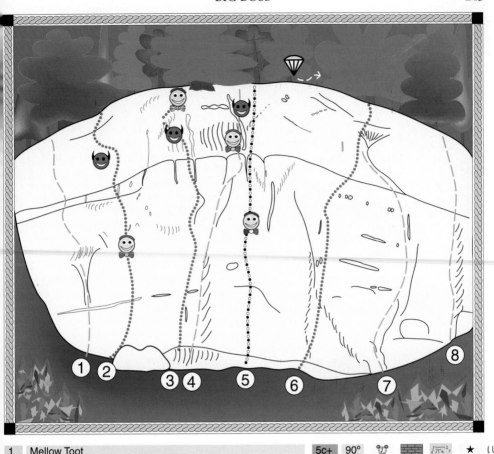

1	Mellow Toot		5c+	90°				★	110
	❶(6a.N.S.) 19.5.1991 A.Hughes: (5c+) 6.1998 ♈ John Patterson								
2	Big Boss ♈		6a+	99°				★★	
	❶(6a.N.S.) 5.1999 David Atchison-Jones								
3	Yellow Soot ♈		6a+	120°				★★	111
	❶(6a.N.S.) 9.9.1984 Guy McLelland								
4	Dilemma		5c+	105°				★★★	112
	❶(5c) 1959-69								
5	Ken Clean Air System ♈		6b	110°				★★	113
	❶(6b.N.S.) 21.1.1990 Mike Eden								
6	Iron Man Tyson		6a	98°				★	114
	❶(6a.N.S.) 1981-9: (6a) 5.1998 ♈ John Patterson								
7	Communist ♈		5c	88°				★	115
	❶(5c.N.S.) 14.1.1990 Oliver Hill								
8	Polly Ticks ♈		5c	94°					116
	❶(5c.N.S.) 1.1.1990 Oliver Hill								

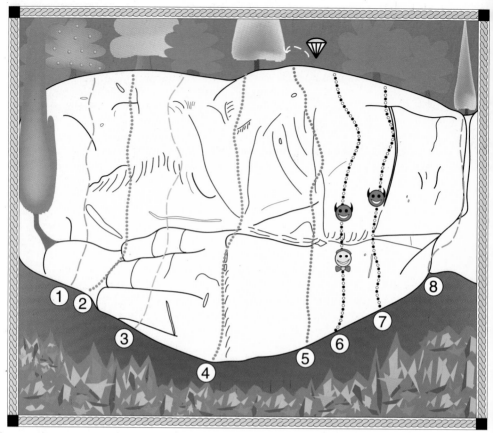

1	**Mamba's Come Home to Roost** ❶(4b) Pre-1956	4b	78°				
2	**The Pink Pengster** ⚑ ❶(5b.N.S.) 14.1994 Doug Reid	5b	79°				
3	**Tweedle Dee** ❶(5b.N.S.) 4.1.1990 Oliver Hill: (5b) 1990-2 ⚑	5b	79°				
4	**Tweedle Dum** ⚑ ❶(5c.N.S.) 4.1.1990 Oliver Hill	5c	83°				
5	**Stem Son** ❶(6a.N.S.) 4.1.1990 Oliver Hill: (6a) 5.1998 ⚑ John Patterson	6a	88°				★
6	**Evoloution** ⚑ ❶(6b.N.S.) Daimon Beail	6b	98°				★
7	**Lou** ❶(6b.N.S.) 31.5.1990 Paul Widdowson: (6b) 1992-5 ⚑ John Patterson	6b	96°				★★
8	**Toadstool Crack** ❶(4a) Pre-1956	4a	80°				

124

Genesis 5c, Virginet Bernier

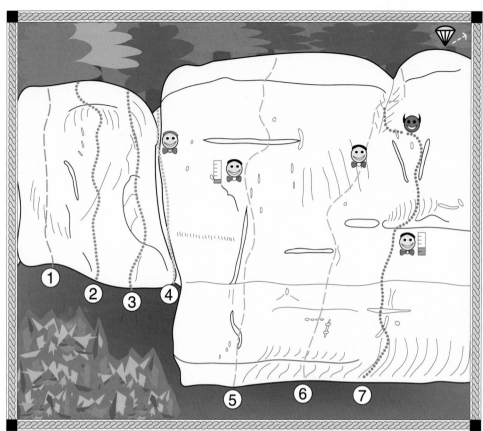

1	Just Cause ♥		4b	80°					
	❶(4b.N.S.) 14.1.1990 Oliver Hill								
2	Just CIA		5b	80°					
	❶(5b.N.S.) 14.1.1990 Oliver Hill: (5b) 12.1992 ♥Tim Skinner								
3	Just Ice		5b	80°					
	❶(5b.N.S.) 14.1.1990 Oliver Hill: (5b) 12.1992 ♥Tim Skinner								
4	Backyard		4c	80°					
	❶(4b.N.S.) 14.1.1990 Oliver Hill: (4c) 1992 ♥								
5	Genesis		5c+	90°				★★★	
	❶(6a.N.S.) 12.11.1989 G.Hill: (5c) 1992-5 ♥								
6	Steelmill		5c+	96°				★★★	
	❶(6a.N.L.) 10.6.1979 M.Fowler, A.Meyers, M.Morrison: (5c)1992-5 ♥J. Patterson								
7	Touchdown ♥		6a+	108°				★★★	
	❶(5c.N.S.) 1982 Mick Fowler								
8	Scorpion ♥		6a	110°				★★★	
	❶(6a.N.S.) 4.1.1990 G. Hill								
9	Lazy Chive ♥		6b	90°				★★★	
	❶(6b.N.S.) 31.5.1990 Paul Widdowson								
10	Revelations		6a	90°				★★★	
	❶(6a.N.S.) 17.11.1989 O. Hill: (6a) 21.9.1996 ♥Robin Mazinke								
11	Poofy Fingers Revenge ♥		6a	89°				★★	
	❶(6a.N.S.) 19.11.1989 G. Hill								
12	Green Bollard Chimney		2b	89°				★	
	❶(2b) Pre-1956								

134

Hadrian's Wall 5b, Phil Kelly

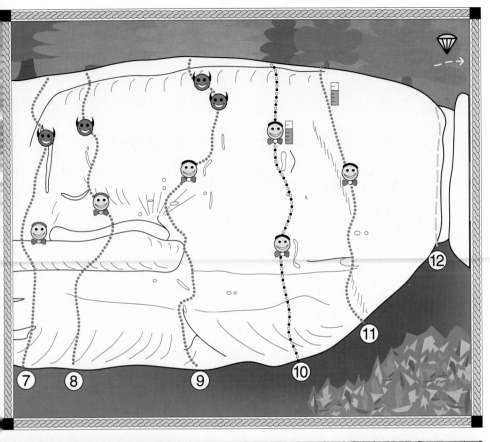

ERIDGE GREEN ROCKS - TOPO 21

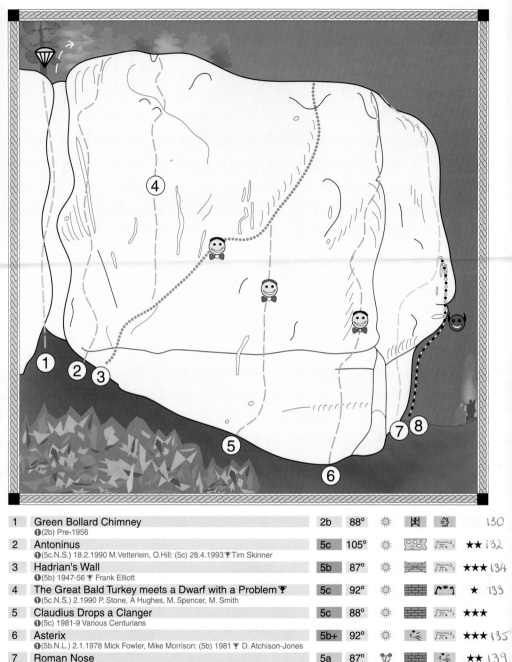

1	Green Bollard Chimney	2b	88°				130
	❶(2b) Pre-1956						
2	Antoninus	5c	105°			★★	132
	❶(5c.N.S.) 18.2.1990 M.Vetterlein, O.Hill: (5c) 28.4.1993 ♈Tim Skinner						
3	Hadrian's Wall	5b	87°			★★★	134
	❶(5b) 1947-56 ♈ Frank Elliott						
4	The Great Bald Turkey meets a Dwarf with a Problem ♈	5c	92°			★	133
	❶(5c.N.S.) 2.1990 P. Stone, A Hughes, M. Spencer, M. Smith						
5	Claudius Drops a Clanger	5c	88°			★★★	
	❶(5c) 1981-9 Various Centurians						
6	Asterix	5b+	92°			★★★	135
	❶(5b.N.L.) 2.1.1978 Mick Fowler, Mike Morrison: (5b) 1981 ♈ D. Atchison-Jones						
7	Roman Nose	5a	87°			★★	139
	❶(N.L.) Frank Elliott 1947-56: (5b) 1981 ♈David Atchison-Jones						
8	Roman Nose Direct	6b	140°			★	"
	❶(6b.N.S.) 1981-9: (6b) 4.5.1992 ♈ Tim Skinner						

126

Touchdown 6a, Luc Percival

SAVE £'s

With This Card

BREAKING-AWAY

10% OFF!

With This Card

DISCOUNT

YOUR FREE VALUE CARD

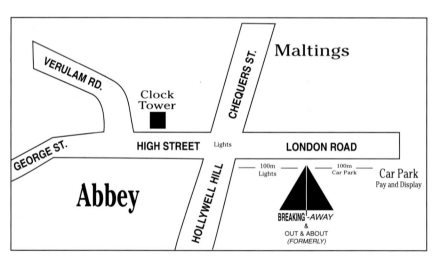

VERULAM RD.

GEORGE ST.

Clock Tower

HIGH STREET

CHEQUERS ST.

Maltings

Lights

LONDON ROAD

HOLLYWELL HILL

Abbey

100m
Lights

100m
Car Park

Car Park
Pay and Display

BREAKING-AWAY
&
OUT & ABOUT
(FORMERLY)

THE OUTDOOR SHOP.

When out and about
why not come and see us for all your
travel and outdoor requirements.
Pay us a visit at -

BREAKING-AWAY

DISCOVER THE ALTERNATIVE

All the top names in outdoor equipment
at unbeatable prices.
The Friendly, Outdoor Shop Alternative.
Quality Service, Expert Advice.

D.J.Izzard BA (prop.)
Open Six days a week
10.00 a.m. to 6.00 p.m.
9.30 a.m. to 5.30p.m.- Sat
Mail Order Available

**36 LONDON ROAD, ST. ALBANS, HERTS. AL1 1NG
PHONE 01727 833 586**

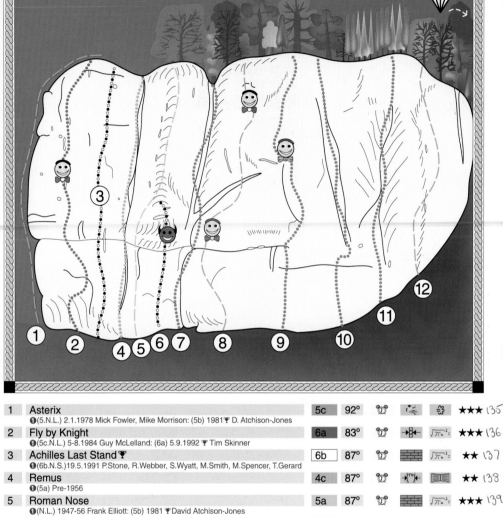

#	Name	Grade	Angle				Stars
1	**Asterix** ❶(5.N.L.) 2.1.1978 Mick Fowler, Mike Morrison: (5b) 1981♥ D. Atchison-Jones	5c	92°	👕	🏃	🔗	★★★ 135
2	**Fly by Knight** ❶(5c.N.L.) 5-8.1984 Guy McLelland: (6a) 5.9.1992 ♥ Tim Skinner	6a	83°	👕	↦◄	√π²	★★★ 136
3	**Achilles Last Stand** ♥ ❶(6b.N.S.)19.5.1991 P.Stone, R.Webber, S.Wyatt, M.Smith, M.Spencer, T.Gerard	6b	87°	👕	🧱	√π²	★★ 137
4	**Remus** ❶(5a) Pre-1956	4c	87°	👕	↦┃┤	▤	★★ 138
5	**Roman Nose** ❶(N.L.) 1947-56 Frank Elliott: (5b) 1981 ♥David Atchison-Jones	5a	87°	👕	🧱	√π²	★★★ 139
6	**Roman Nose Direct** ❶(6b.N.L.) 1981-9: (6b) 4.5.1992♥ Tim Skinner	6b	140°	👕	↩	🔗🔗	★
7	**Romulus** ❶(5b) Pre-1956	5b	86°	👕	🧱	↦☺◄	★ 140
8	**Good Route, Poor Line** ♥ ❶(5c.N.L.) 7-8.1984 Paul Hayes	5c+	86°	👕	🧱	√π²	★★ 141
9	**Good Route, Good Line** ❶(5b.N.L.) 7-8.1984 Tim Daniells: (5c) 13.5.1993 ♥ Chris Murray	5b+	86°	👕	🧱	√π²	★★ 142
10	**Layaway** ❶(5b) 1969-81	5b	86°	👕	🏃	〰	★ 143
11	**Hipposuction** ❶(5b.N.S.) 22.12.1991 Doug Reid and Crowds: (5b) 28.4.1993 ♥Tim Skinner	5b	86°	👕	▤	⤸	★ 144
12	**Appetite for Destruction** ♥ ❶(5c.N.S.) 25.5.1996 R. Mazinke, M. Vetterlein, Ian Butler	5c	86°	👕	⤳	🔗	

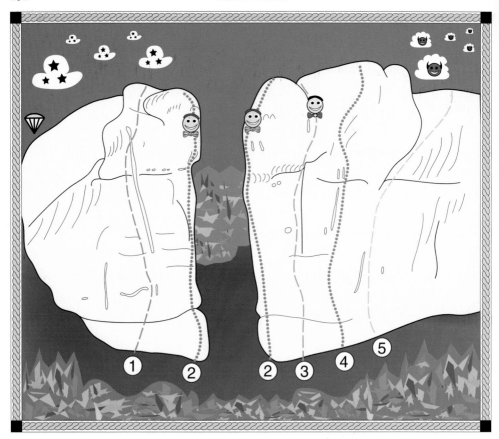

1	Capstan Wall	4a	82°	☀	🧱	⤚ᵐ⤙	★★
	❶(4b) Pre-1956						
2	Concorde	5b	88°	☀	⌇	⌇	★★★
	❶(5b) 1975 ♇ Mick Fowler, John Stevenson						
3	Viking Line	5c	88°	☀	⤚⊞⤙	▦	★★
	❶(5c.N.S.) 17.3.1996 R. Mazinke, M. Vetterlein: (5c) 8.1996 ♇ Tim Skinner						
4	Misty Wall ♇	5b	87°	☀	🧱	⤚ᵐ⤙	★
	❶(5b.N.S.) 17.3.1996 R. Mazinke, M. Vetterlein, S. Durkin						
5	Shanty Wall	5a	82°	🐫	🧱	▦	
	❶(5a) Pre-1956						

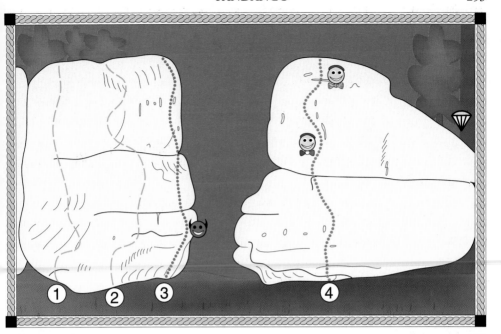

1	Fruits ♈		5c	70°				152
	❶(5c.N.S.) 11.7.1991 Robin Mazinke							
2	Eric		5b+	81°			★★	153
	❶(5b) 1947-56 Frank Elliott							
3	Life in the Old Dog Yet ♈		6a	114°			★★★	154
	❶(6a.N.S.) 17.8.1993 Chris Arnold							
4	Fandango		5b+	97°			★★★	155
	❶(6a.N.L.) 1959-69: (5c) 1981 ♈David Atchison-Jones							

146
Concorde 5b, David Atchison-Jones; photo, Angela White

154
Life in the Old Dog Yet 6a, Malcolm McPherson

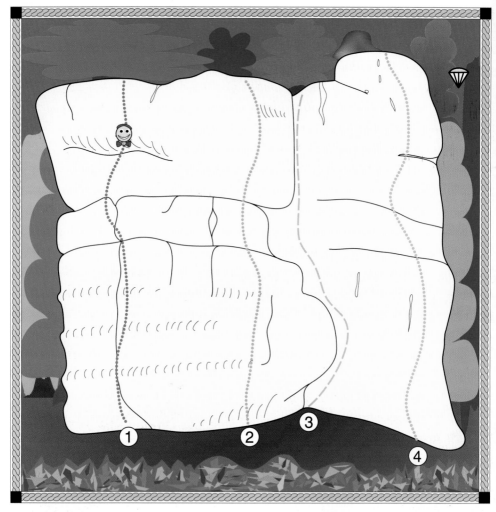

1	Keystone Cop		5b	82°			
	❶(5b.N.S.) 7.4.1996 Robin Mazinke						
2	Keystone Face		4c	82°			
	❶(4a) Pre-1956						
3	Keystone Crack		1b	65°			
	❶(1b) Pre-1956						
4	Keystone Wall		3b	75°			
	❶(3a) Pre-1956						
5	Paisley		5b	88°			★
	❶(5b) 13.5.1993 ⚥ Chris Murray						
6	Hartleys		4b	88°			★
	❶(4a) 1968-81						
7	Flutings		4b	88°			★★
	❶(4b) Pre-1956						
8	Fluted Fancy		4c	88°			★
	❶(4c) Pre-1956						

166
Short Work 5c, Luc Percival

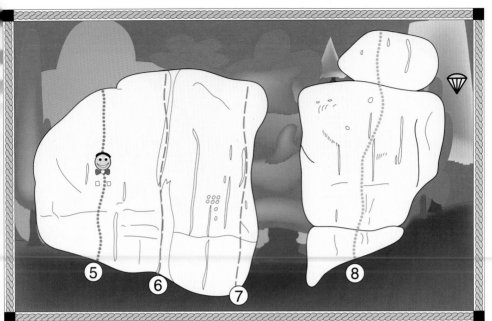

ERIDGE GREEN ROCKS - TOPO 27

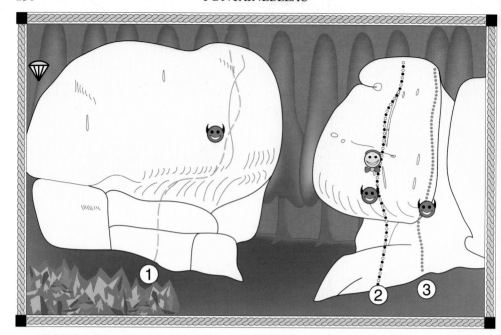

ERIDGE GREEN ROCKS - TOPO 28

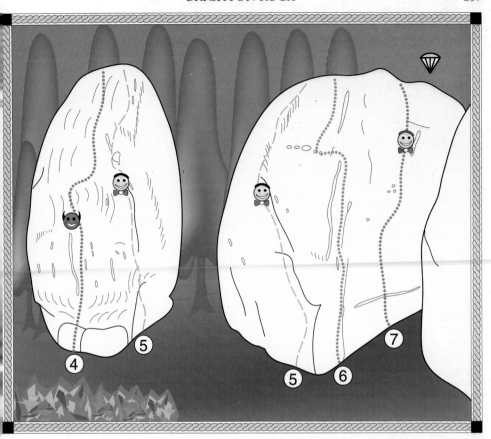

1	Fontainebleau		5c	135°				★	162
	❶(5b) Pre-1956 ♈								
2	Oliver and his Amazing Underpants		6b+	136°				★★	163
	❶(6b) 4.1991 Matt Smith ♈								
3	Fernkop Corner		5b	110°				★★	164 ?
	❶(4b) Pre-1956								
4	Hyphenated Jones ♈		6a	101°				★★	165
	❶(6a.N.S.) 23.7.1994 Mike Vetterlein								
5	Short Work		5c	112°				★★	166
	❶(5c) 13.5.1993 Tim Skinner ♈								
6	Sonny Dribble Chops		5b	88°				★★★	167
	❶(5b) 11.1989 Paul Stone, Michael Spencer ♈								
7	Brighton Rock		6a	85°				★	168
	❶(6a.N.S.) 11.1989 Paul Stone: (6a) 13.5.1993 ♈Chris Murray								

168
Brighton Rock 6a, Luc Percival

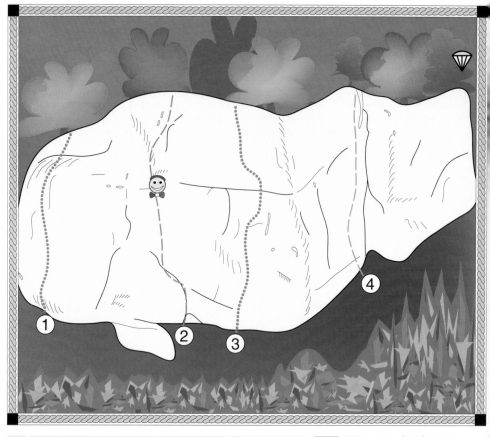

1	Wobble		5b	68°				★	
	❶(5b) 13.5.1993 ☫Tim Skinner								
2	Pedestal Wall		4b	81°				★	
	❶(4b) Pre-1956								
3	Elastic Headbands		5b	81°				★★	
	❶(5b) 2.1990 A. Hughes, M. Spencer								
4	Another Wet Bank Holiday		5c	89°					
	❶(5c.N.S.) 3.4.1994: (5c) 14.7.1994 ☫Mike Vetterlein								

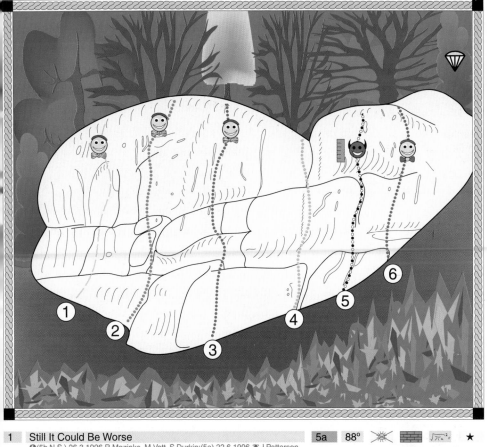

1	Still It Could Be Worse	5a	88°				★
	❶(5b.N.S.) 26.3.1996 R.Mazinke, M.Vett. S.Durkin:(5a) 22.6.1996 ♈ J.Patterson						
2	Ooh - Er Missus	5b	88°				★
	❶(5c.N.S.) 26.3.1996 R.Mazinke, M.Vetterlein: (5b) 22.6.1996 ♈ John Patterson						
3	Local Vigilantes ♈	6a	92°				★
	❶(6a.N.S.) 7.4.1996 Robin Mazinke						
4	Tree Root	4c	98°				★
	❶(4c) 26.3.1996 ♈ Robin Mazinke, M.Vetterlein, Steve Durkin						
5	Seize Cent Soixante Quatre ♈	6b	110°				★
	❶(6b.N.S.) 22.6.1996 John Patterson						
6	I'm Not Worried, I'm a Tractor	6a	110°				★
	❶(6a.N.S.) 26.3.1996 Robin Mazinke: (5c) 6.1996 ♈ Tim Skinner						

Portcullis 5c, Malcolm McPherson

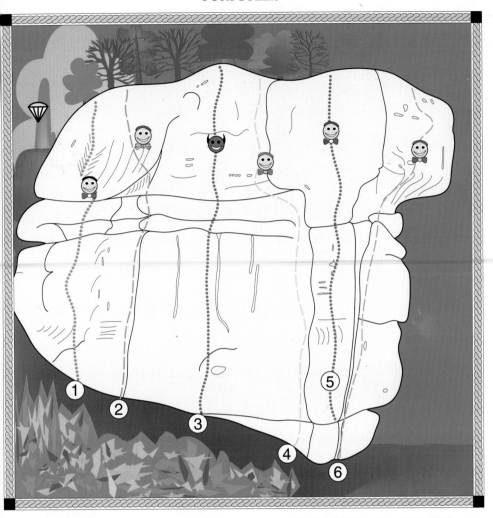

1	**Optical Racer** ❶(5b.N.S.) 11.1989 M. Smith, R. Tipton: (5b) 1989-94 ⚑	5b	90°				★ 174
2	**Barbican Buttress** ❶(5a) Pre-1956 ⚑	4b	90°				★★ 175
3	**Steamroller** ❶(5c.N.L.) 2.4.1978 M.Morrison, M. Fowler: (6a) 1992-5 ⚑ John Patterson	6a	90°				★★★ 176
4	**Battlements Crack** ❶(5b) Pre-1956⚑	5a	90°				★★★ 177
5	**Aero** ❶(6a.N.L.) 22.7.1979 Mick Fowler: (6a+) 6.1998 ⚑ John Patterson	6a+	90°				★★★
6	**Portcullis** ❶(N.L.) Frank Elliott 1947-56: (5c) 1981-9 ⚑	5c	120°				★★★ 178

Vetterlein continues 179 to 195

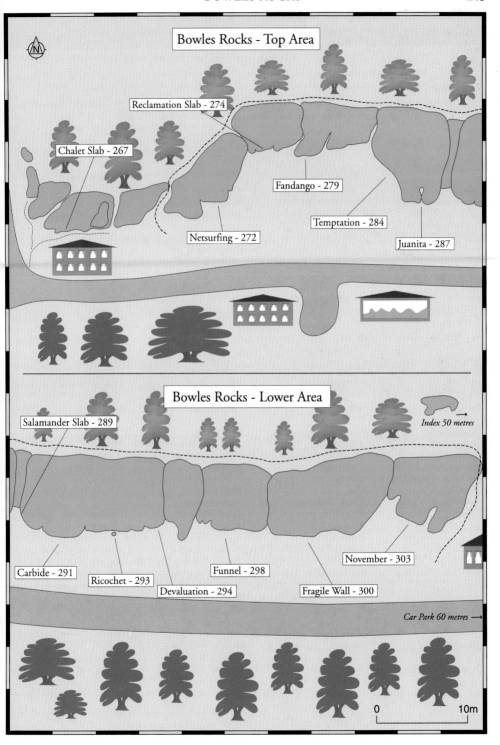

Bowles Rocks - Top Area

Reclamation Slab - 274

Chalet Slab - 267

Fandango - 279

Temptation - 284

Netsurfing - 272

Juanita - 287

Bowles Rocks - Lower Area

Salamander Slab - 289

Index 50 metres

November - 303

Carbide - 291

Ricochet - 293

Funnel - 298

Devaluation - 294

Fragile Wall - 300

Car Park 60 metres →

0   10m

A posh crag: With its own ski slope – all 100 yards of it; Swimming pool – well, an indoor brick edifice, bang in front of the crag! I ask you, should planners be shot? In any event, Bowles outdoor centre seems here to stay - and to be honest, it does run well, and offers a superb climbing facility. The rocks are managed by a trust, and can be quite busy at anytime with courses; even so, there are plenty of routes to go round. There is a higher density of quality climbs here, than anywhere else locally. The rock is dry and quite fingery on the less worn climbs. A true, all year round venue with bouldering, traversing, and fine long routes.

GRADED LIST

6c
Skallagrigg
Them Monkey Things
Pastry Chef
Carbide Finger
One Nighter
The Wrecker
Kinnard
Sabre Cut
Zoom
6b+
Recurring Nightmare
Nutella
The Thing
6b
Temptation
Tobacco Road
Poff Pastry
Upside Downies
Boiling Point
Knuclebones
White Verdict
Coast to Coast
Cardboard Box
Sandman Direct Finish
One-Buzzards is Missing
Zugabe
Geoff's Route
6a+
Love
Sandman
Patella
The Ly'in
Finale
Lady in Mink
Sugarplum
Target Direct
6a
Serenade Arête
Slyme Cryme
Urban Jock
Fandango Right Hand
Proboscis
Station to Station
Conjuror
Digitalis

Cutting Edge
Cheese Sandwich
Hate
Burlap
Nightmare
5c+
Banana
Juanita
Mick's Wall Direct
Blue Moon
Fandango
Aphrodite
Mental Balance
The Big Stretch
Perspiration
5c
Koffler
Salamander Slab
Pastry
Target
Nero
Mick's Wall Arête
Inspiration
Reclamation Slap
Mohrenkop
Oliver's Twist
5b+
Chalet Slab Direct
Rib
Manita
Coathanger
Umbilicus
Encore
Pigs Ear
August Variation
Chris
5b
U.N.
Swastika
Seltzer
Lee Enfield
Jackie
Chalet Slab Direct
Mick's Wall
Cenotaph Corner Two
Two Step

T.N.T.
Abracadabra
5a+
Burlap Arete
T.T.
Hennesey Heights
Drosophila
5a
Pull Through
Joripundia
Elevator
Fragile Arête
Pig's Nose
Larchant
Devaluation
Gully Wall
Helter Skelter
4c
Bull's Nose
Court's Climb
Six Foot
Escalator
October
Alka
Nealon's
E.S.Cadet Nose
High Traverse
Sloth (Sapper)
Four-by-Two
Cave Crack
Santa's Claws
Corner Layback
4b
Ricochet
Badger's Head
Roman Nose
Tory Variation
Kemp's Delight
Babylon
Dival's Diversion
Sylvie's Slab
Bovril
Index
Corbett Slab
Nelson's Column
Wally

Baby Boulder
4a
Barham Boulder
Rad's Cliff
Fragile Wall
Dubonnet
Kennard's Climb
Corbett Nose
YoYo
Scirocco Slab
3c
Dib
Funnel
Ballerina
Netwall
3b
Hibiscus
Chalet Slab Left
Reclamation Slab
3a
Well's Reach
Skiffle
Sing Sing
Claire
Pat's Progress
Free Willy
Charlie's Chimney
2b
Renison Gully
Running Jump
Rec- Slab Right
Grotto Chimney
2a
Red Peg
William's Layback
Birch Crack
Harden Gully
Chelsea Chimney
Grotty Groove
1
Reclamation Gully
Easy Gully
November

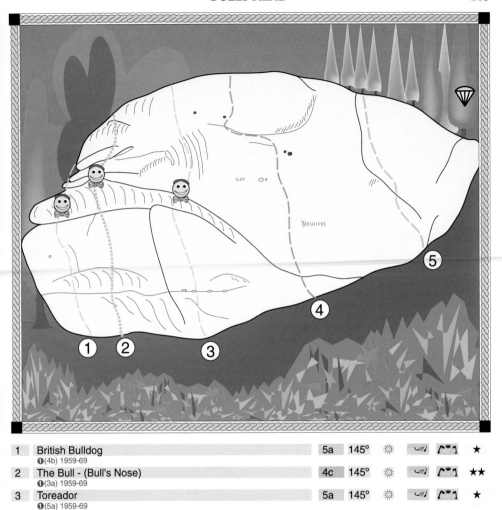

1	British Bulldog	5a	145°	☀			★
	❶(4b) 1959-69						
2	The Bull - (Bull's Nose)	4c	145°	☀			★★
	❶(3a) 1959-69						
3	Toreador	5a	145°	☀			★
	❶(5a) 1959-69						
4	Badger's Head	4a	87°	☀			★
	❶(3a) 1959-69						
5	Badgering the Badgers Badger	2a	77°	☀			
	❶(2a) 1959-69						

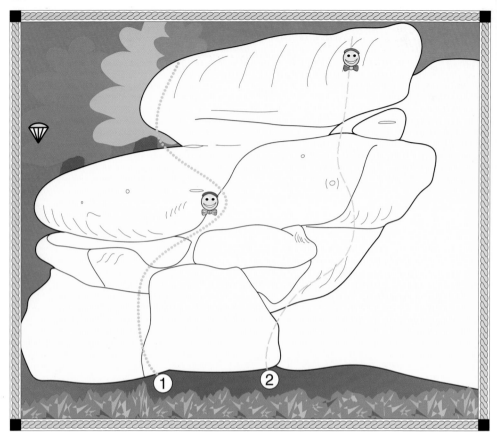

If you are on your way to the rocks, and you have forgotton your guide, then you are probably not reading this but remember you can buy this guide near the rocks at the following:-
Groombridge Village Shop
The Crown pub Groombridge, The Huntsman pub Eridge,
Country Trails shop in Tunbridge Wells.

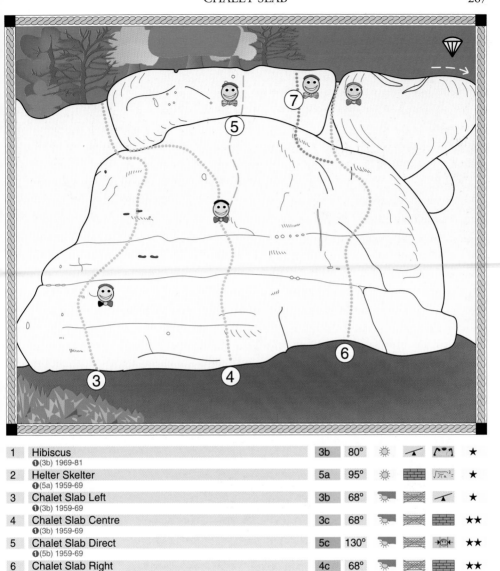

1	Hibiscus	3b	80°				★
	❶(3b) 1969-81						
2	Helter Skelter	5a	95°				★
	❶(5a) 1959-69						
3	Chalet Slab Left	3b	68°				★
	❶(3b) 1959-69						
4	Chalet Slab Centre	3c	68°				★★
	❶(3b) 1959-69						
5	Chalet Slab Direct	5c	130°				★★
	❶(5b) 1959-69						
6	Chalet Slab Right	4c	68°				★★
	❶(3b) 1959-69						
7	Chalet Slab Right Direct	5b	90°				★★
	❶(4a) 1959-69						

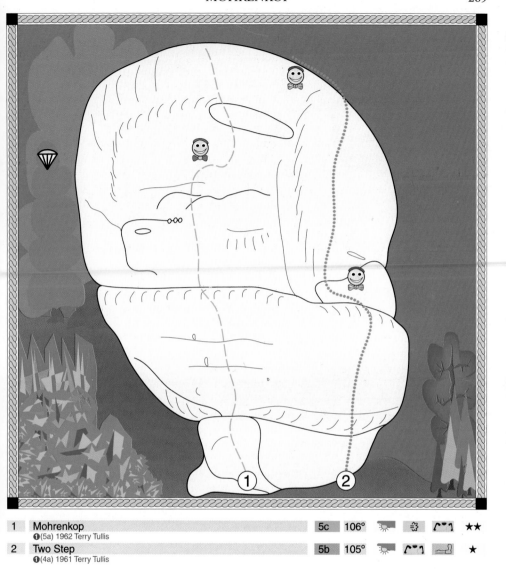

1	Mohrenkop		5c	106°				★★
	❶(5a) 1962 Terry Tullis							
2	Two Step		5b	105°				★
	❶(4a) 1961 Terry Tullis							

Chalet S;ab Left 3b, Jean Murray

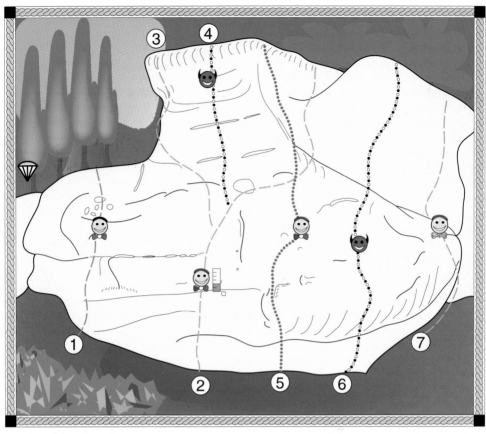

1	Roman Nose	4b	108°				★
	❶(4b) 1961 Terry Tullis						
2	Umbilicus	5c	108°				★★
	❶(5c) 1969-81 Gordon DeLacy, Tim Daniells						
3	Unrepentant	5c+	108°				★★
	❶(5c) 1969-81 Mick Fowler						
4	Unbeliveable ⚑	6b	127°				★★★
	❶(6a.N.L.) 1981 Guy McLelland, Barry Knight						
5	Froggatt Fudge	6a+	106°				★
	❶(6a) 1981 David Atchison-Jones						
6	Geoff's Route	6b	104°				★
	❶(6b.N.S.) 1981-9 Geoff Pearson: (6b) 1981-9 ⚑						
7	Blue Moon	5c+	120°				★★★
	❶(5b) 1969-81						

Umbilicus 5c, Ken Barber
Blue Moon 5c+, Ken Barber

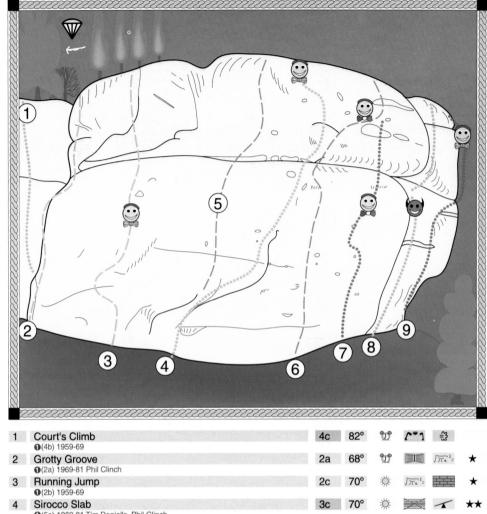

1	**Court's Climb**	4c	82°				
	➊(4b) 1959-69						
2	**Grotty Groove**	2a	68°				★
	➊(2a) 1969-81 Phil Clinch						
3	**Running Jump**	2c	70°				★
	➊(2b) 1959-69						
4	**Sirocco Slab**	3c	70°				★★
	➊(5a) 1969-81 Tim Daniells, Phil Clinch						
5	**Net Surfing**	4a	75°				★
	➊(3c) 1959-69						
6	**Netwall**	4b	79°				★★
	➊(2b) 1959-69						
7	**Knitwall**	6a	87°				★
	➊(6a) 1981 Guy McLelland						
8	**Corner Layback**	4c	112°				★★
	➊(4a) 1959-69						
9	**Aphrodite**	5c+	97°				★
	➊(6a.N.L.) 7.1982 David Atchison-Jones: (6a) 8.1982 ♟ David A-J						
10	**Zoom**	6c	120°				★
	➊(6c) 3.1982 David Atchison-Jones ♟						
11	**Santa's Claws**	4c	92°				★★
	➊(4a) 1969-81						
12	**Knucklebones**	6b+	92°				★
	➊(6b.N.S.) 11.1992 Chris Murray: (6b) 27.6.1995 ♟ Chris Murray						
13	**Coast to Coast** ♟	6b	100°				★
	➊(6b.N.S.) 1992-5 Chris Murray						

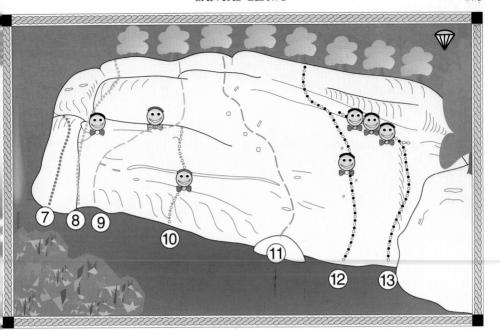

Knucklebones 6b, Barry Knight

BOWLES ROCKS - TOPO 7

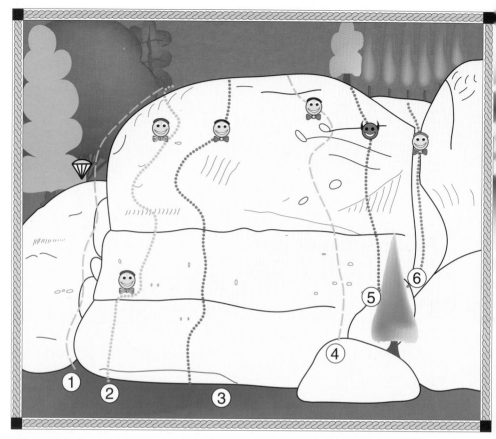

1	Reclamation Gully		1b	60°				
	❶(1b) 1959-69							
2	Reclamation Slab Left		3a	70°				★★
	❶(2a) 1959-69							
3	Reclamation Slap		6a	74°				★★
	❶(5c.N.L.) 15.7.1987 D. Turner, E.Stone, B.Pritchard: (5c)1.1994 ☗ Carl Martin							
4	Reclamation Slab		2b	70°				★
	❶(2a) 1959-69							
5	Mental Balance		6a	75°				★
	❶(5b.N.L.) 7-8.1984 Paul Hayes, Chris Arnold: (5b) 1984 ☗ Paul Hayes							
6	Cenotaph Corner 2		5b	87°				
	❶(5c.N.S.) 10.10.1992 B. Kavanagh,M-Vett,T-Skin: (5c) ☗10.10.1992 T. Skinner							

Banana 6a, Matt Martin

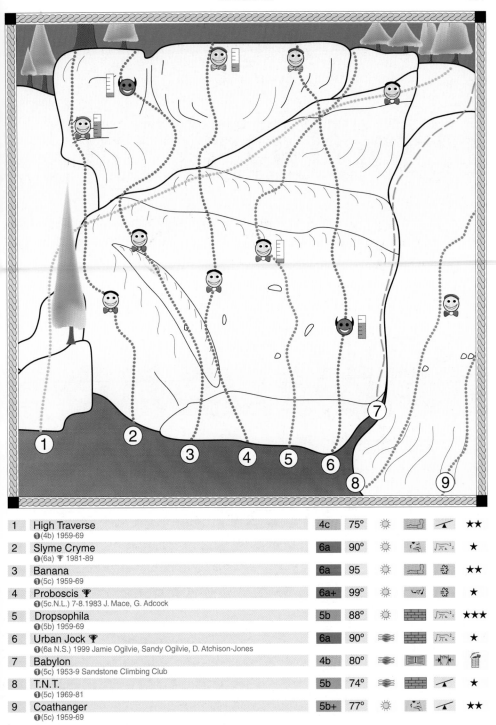

1	High Traverse ❶(4b) 1959-69	4c	75°	☀			★★
2	Slyme Cryme ❶(6a) ⚑ 1981-89	6a	90°	☀			★
3	Banana ❶(5c) 1959-69	6a	95	☀			★★
4	Proboscis ⚑ ❶(5c.N.L.) 7-8.1983 J. Mace, G. Adcock	6a+	99°	☀			★
5	Dropsophila ❶(5b) 1959-69	5b	88°	☀			★★★
6	Urban Jock ⚑ ❶(6a N.S.) 1999 Jamie Ogilvie, Sandy Ogilvie, D. Atchison-Jones	6a	90°	≈			★
7	Babylon ❶(5c) 1953-9 Sandstone Climbing Club	4b	80°	≈			
8	T.N.T. ❶(5c) 1969-81	5b	74°	≈			★
9	Coathanger ❶(5c) 1959-69	5b+	77°	☀			★★

Fandango bouldering Wall

You don't need much
for
BOULDERING

You do need the best.

Call

PEGLERS

of

ARUNDEL

01903 - 884684
www.peglers.co.uk

9am - 6pm 7 days per week

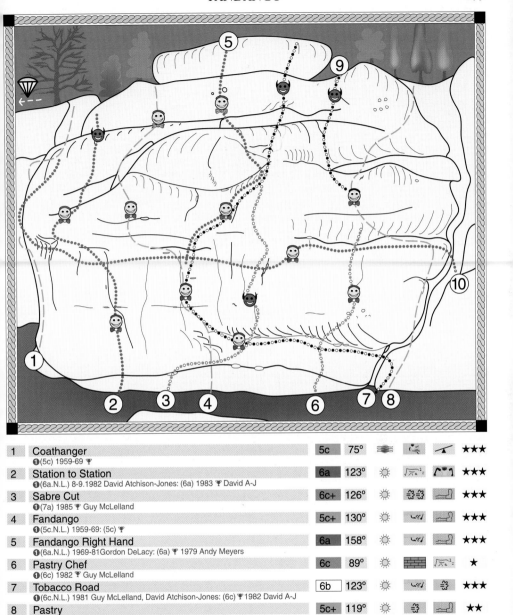

1	Coathanger	5c	75°				★★★
	❶(5c) 1959-69 ⚑						
2	Station to Station	6a	123°				★★★
	❶(6a.N.L.) 8-9.1982 David Atchison-Jones: (6a) 1983 ⚑ David A-J						
3	Sabre Cut	6c+	126°				★★★
	❶(7a) 1985 ⚑ Guy McLelland						
4	Fandango	5c+	130°				★★★
	❶(5c.N.L.) 1959-69: (5c) ⚑						
5	Fandango Right Hand	6a	158°				★★★
	❶(6a.N.L.) 1969-81Gordon DeLacy: (6a) ⚑ 1979 Andy Meyers						
6	Pastry Chef	6c	89°				★
	❶(6c) 1982 ⚑ Guy McLelland						
7	Tobacco Road	6b	123°				★★★
	❶(6c.N.L.) 1981 Guy McLelland, David Atchison-Jones: (6c) ⚑1982 David A-J						
8	Pastry	5c+	119°				★★
	❶(5c.N.L.) 1969-81: (5c) ⚑ 1982 David Atchison-Jones						
9	Poff Pastry ⚑	6b	147°				★★
	❶(6a/b.N.L.) 6.10.1983 Guy McLelland						
10	Sugarplum	6a+	106°				★★★
	❶(6b) 1978-80 Gordon DeLacy						

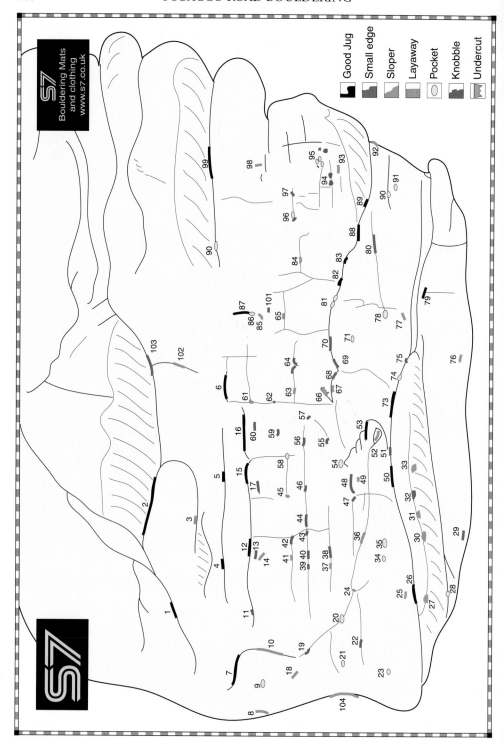

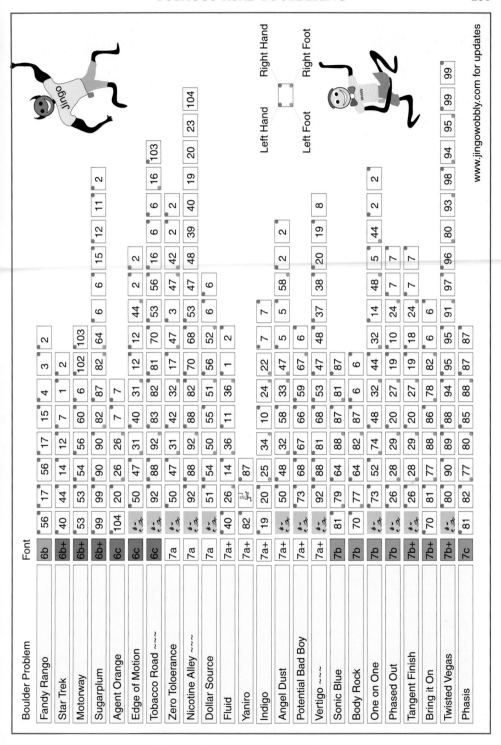

Legend: Left Hand · Right Hand · Left Foot · Right Foot

www.jingowobbly.com for updates

Boulder Problem	Font																		
Fandy Rango	6b	56	17	56	17	15	4	3	2										
Star Trek	6b+	40	44	14	12	7	1	2											
Motorway	6b+	53	53	54	56	60	6	102	103										
Sugarplum	6b+	99	99	90	90	82	87	82	64										
Agent Orange	6c	104	20	26	26	7	7												
Edge of Motion	6c	(feet)	50	47	31	40	31	12	44	2	6	2							
Tobacco Road ~~~	6c	(feet)	92	88	92	83	82	81	70	53	56	16	6	103					
Zero Toloerance	7a	50	47	31	42	32	17	47	3	47	2	2							
Nicotine Alley ~~~	7a	(feet)	92	88	92	88	82	70	68	53	47	48	39	40					
Dollar Source	7a	51	54	50	55	51	56	52	6	6	6								
Fluid	7a+	40	26	14	36	11	1	2											
Yaniro	7a+	82	(feet)	87															
Indigo	7a+	19	20	25	34	10	24	22	7	7									
Angel Dust	7a+	50	48	32	58	33	47	5	5	58	2								
Potential Bad Boy	7a+	73	68	67	66	59	67	6	6										
Vertigo ~~~	7a+	(feet)	92	88	81	68	53	47	48	37	38	20	19	8					
Sonic Blue	7b	81	79	64	88	81	87	87											
Body Rock	7b	70	77	64	82	87	6	6	6										
One on One	7b	73	52	74	48	32	44	32	14	48	5	44	2	2					
Phased Out	7b	26	28	29	20	27	19	10	24	7	7								
Tangent Finish	7b+	26	28	29	20	27	19	18	24	7	7								
Bring it On	7b+	70	81	77	88	86	78	82	6	6									
Twisted Vegas	7b+	(feet)	80	90	89	88	94	95	95	91	97	96	80	93	98	94	95	99	99
Phasis	7c	81	82	77	80	85	88	87	87										

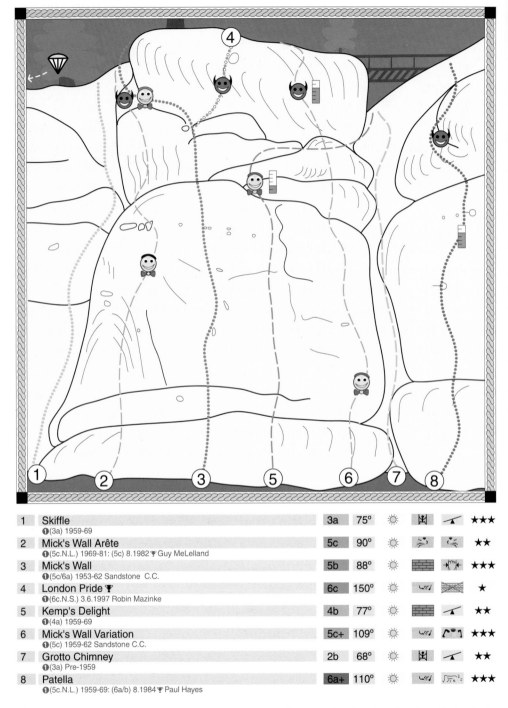

1	Skiffle		3a	75°	☀			★★★
	❶(3a) 1959-69							
2	Mick's Wall Arête		5c	90°	☀			★★
	❶(5c.N.L.) 1969-81: (5c) 8.1982 ♀ Guy MeLelland							
3	Mick's Wall		5b	88°	☀			★★★
	❶(5c/6a) 1953-62 Sandstone C.C.							
4	London Pride ♀		6c	150°	☀			★
	❶(6c.N.S.) 3.6.1997 Robin Mazinke							
5	Kemp's Delight		4b	77°	☀			★★
	❶(4a) 1959-69							
6	Mick's Wall Variation		5c+	109°	☀			★★★
	❶(5c) 1959-62 Sandstone C.C.							
7	Grotto Chimney		2b	68°	☀			★★
	❶(3a) Pre-1959							
8	Patella		6a+	110°	☀			★★★
	❶(5c.N.L.) 1959-69: (6a/b) 8.1984 ♀ Paul Hayes							

Patella 6a+, Mike Pollak - Struggling; Barry Knight - Crusing
Nutella 6b, Barry Knight - Puffing and nearly struggling

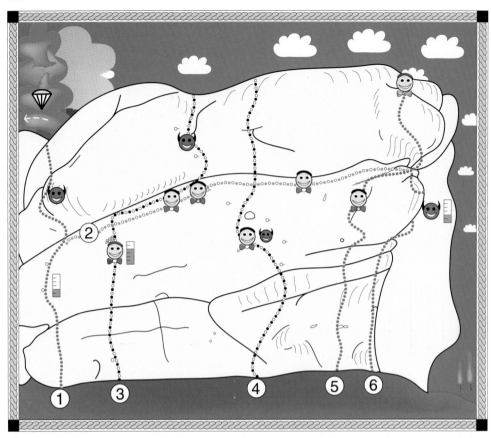

1	Patella	6a+	110°	☀	🌊	√×²̇	★★★

1 (5c.N.L.) 1959-69: (6a) 8.1984 ♈ Paul Hayes

2	Kinnard ♈	6c	105°	☀	🧫	⚡	★★★

1 (6a/b.N.L.) 8.1984 Paul Hayes

3	Nutella ♈	6b+	110°	☀	🧫	📖	★★★

1 (6c.N.L.) 15.7.1987 Dave Turner

4	Temptation	6b	100°	〰	🧫	〽	★★★

1 (6b.N.L.) 4-9.6.1983 Dave Turner: (6b) 7.1987 ♈ Matt Saunders

5	Digitalis	6a	115°	〰	🧱	🛋	★★★

1 (6a.N.L.) 1959-69: (6a) 1979-81 ♈ Ron Fawcett

6	Serenade Arête	6a	130°	☀	🌊	🧫	★★★

1 (6a.N.L.) 1969-81 John Durrant: (6a) 1981-2 ♈

Digitalis 6a, Emma Kelly

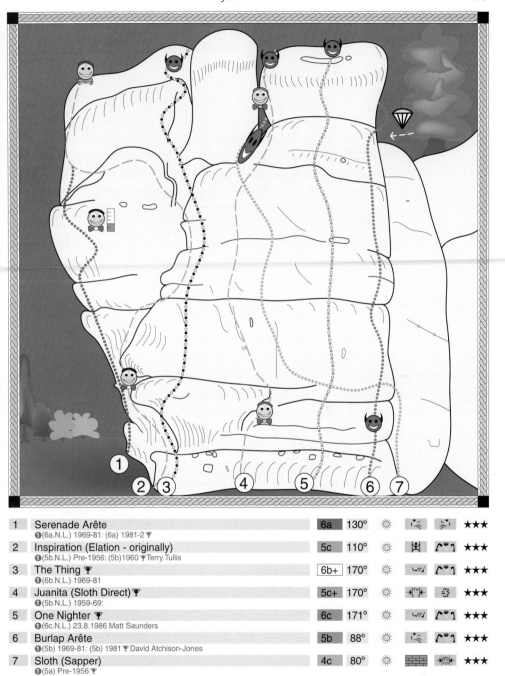

1	Serenade Arête	6a	130°	☀			★★★
	❶(6a.N.L.) 1969-81: (6a) 1981-2 ♈						
2	Inspiration (Elation - originally)	5c	110°	☀			★★★
	❶(5b.N.L.) Pre-1956: (5b)1960 ♈Terry Tullis						
3	The Thing ♈	6b+	170°	☀			★★★
	❶(6b.N.L.) 1969-81						
4	Juanita (Sloth Direct) ♈	5c+	170°	☀			★★★
	❶(5b.N.L.) 1959-69:						
5	One Nighter ♈	6c	171°	☀			★★★
	❶(6c.N.L.) 23.8.1986 Matt Saunders						
6	Burlap Arête	5b	88°	☀			★★★
	❶(5b) 1969-81: (5b) 1981 ♈ David Atchison-Jones						
7	Sloth (Sapper)	4c	80°	☀			★★★
	❶(5a) Pre-1956 ♈						

Sloth 4c, exit through the dreaded "Squeezeey hole"
Sloth 4c, Clive Knapp on lower wall

Yo Yo 4a, Kevin Murray

1	Burlap Arête		5b	88°				★★★
	❶(5b) 1969-81: (5b) 1981 ♇David Atchison-Jones							
2	Burlap		5c+	90°				★★
	❶(5c.N.L.) 1960 Terry Tullis: (5c) 1981 ♇David Atchison-Jones							
3	Yo Yo		4a	78°				★★★
	❶(3b) 1959-69 Sandstone C.C.							
4	White Verdict		6b+	80°				★★
	❶(6c.N.L.) 4.1983 David Atchison-Jones: (6b+) 23.6.1994 ♇John Patterson							
5	The Ly'in		6b	80°				★★
	❶(6b.N.L.) 1983-4 Chris Arnold: (6a+) 1998 ♇John Patterson							
6	Sing Sing		3a	68°				★★★
	❶(3a) 1959-69 Sandstone C.C.							
7	Manita		5c	85°				★★
	❶(5c) 1970-9 Gordon DeLacy							
8	Jackie		5b	84°				★★★
	❶(5b) 1969-81							
9	Joripurundia - Pete's Perseverence		5a	75°				★★★
	❶(5a) 1959-69 ♇John Smoker							
10	Nero		5c	105°				★★★
	❶(5c.N.L.) 1969-81: (5c) 8.1983 ♇Paul Stone							
11	Cheese Sandwich		6a	115°				★
	❶(6a.N.L.) 1981-9: (6a) 1992-5 ♇							
12	Salamander Slab		5c	115°				★★★
	❶(5c.N.L.) 1959-69: (5c) 1959-69 ♇							
13	Perspiration		5c	155°				★★★
	❶(5c.N.L.) 1959-62 John Smoker: (5c) 1959-69 ♇							

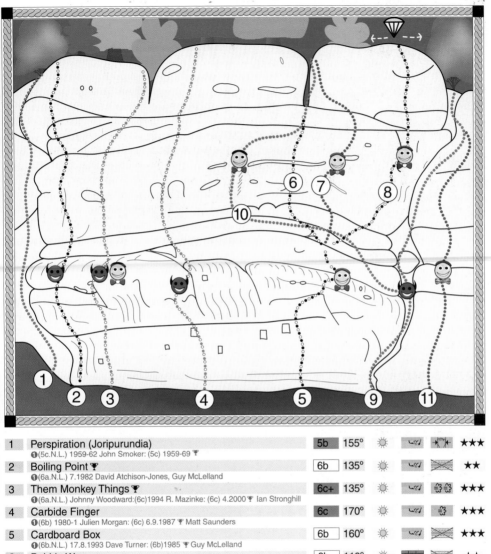

1	Perspiration (Joripurundia)	5b	155°	☀			★★★
	❶(5c.N.L.) 1959-62 John Smoker: (5c) 1959-69 ⚑						
2	Boiling Point ⚑	6b	135°	☀			★★
	❶(6a.N.L.) 7.1982 David Atchison-Jones, Guy McLelland						
3	Them Monkey Things ⚑	6c+	135°	☀			★★★
	❶(6a.N.L.) Johnny Woodward:(6c)1994 R. Mazinke: (6c) 4.2000 ⚑ Ian Stronghill						
4	Carbide Finger	6c	170°	☀			★★★
	❶(6b) 1980-1 Julien Morgan: (6c) 6.9.1987 ⚑ Matt Saunders						
5	Cardboard Box	6b	160°	☀			★★★
	❶(6b.N.L.) 17.8.1993 Dave Turner: (6b)1985 ⚑ Guy McLelland						
6	Bubble Wrap	6b	110°	☀			★★
	❶(6b.N.S.) 12.9.1996 Robin Mazinke						
7	Nightmare	6a	98°	☀			★★★
	❶(6a.N.L.) 1969-81Gordon DeLacy: (6b) 1992-5 ⚑John Patterson						
8	Recurring Nightmare ⚑	6c	105°	☀			★★★
	❶(6c.N.L.) 9.1986 Paul Hayes, Matt Saunders						
9	Abracadabra	5b+	84°	☀			★★
	❶(5c.N.L.) 1959-62 Sandstone C.C: (5b) 1959-69⚑						
10	Swastika	5b	84°	☀			★★★
	❶(5b.N.L.) 1959-62 Sandstone C.C: (5b) 1959-69 ⚑						
11	Conjourer	6a	95°	☀			★★
	❶(5c) 1969-81 Tim Daniells: (6a) 1969-81 ⚑ Gordon DeLacy						

Then Monkey Things 6c, Ian Stronghill

What to do when it's cold and wet?

1. Stay in bed.
2. Get fat on a greasy breakfast
3. Read your latest issue of On the Edge (again).
4. Visit High Sports and keep your mind, body and soul in shape.

High Sports Climbing Wall

Open Monday to Friday
12 noon until 10pm
Weekends
9.30am until 7.30pm

High Sports

Unit 6 Orchard Business Centre, Bonehurst Road
Salfords, Nr Redhill, Surrey RH1 5EL
Tel/Fax: 01293 822884   www.high-sports.co.uk

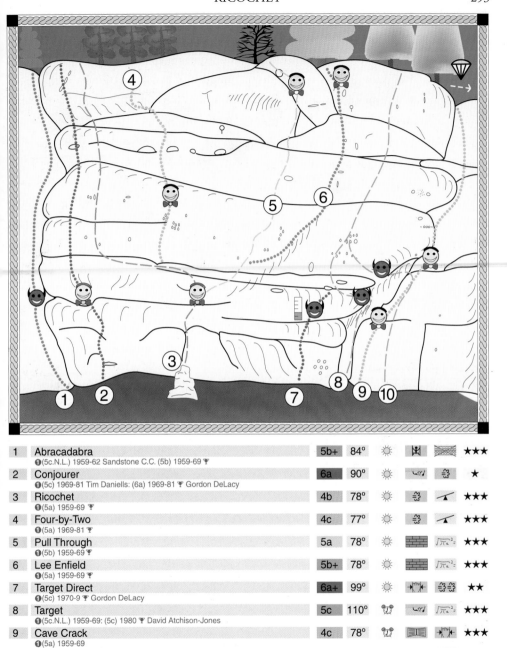

1	Abracadabra	5b+	84°	☀			★★★
	❶(5c.N.L.) 1959-62 Sandstone C.C. (5b) 1959-69 ☘						
2	Conjourer	6a	90°	☀			★
	❶(5c) 1969-81 Tim Daniells: (6a) 1969-81 ☘ Gordon DeLacy						
3	Ricochet	4b	78°	☀			★★★
	❶(5a) 1959-69 ☘						
4	Four-by-Two	4c	77°	☀			★★★
	❶(5a) 1969-81 ☘						
5	Pull Through	5a	78°	☀			★★★
	❶(5b) 1959-69 ☘						
6	Lee Enfield	5b+	78°	☀			★★★
	❶(5a) 1959-69 ☘						
7	Target Direct	6a+	99°	☀			★★
	❶(5c) 1970-9 ☘ Gordon DeLacy						
8	Target	5c	110°	🐭			★★★
	❶(5c.N.L.) 1959-69: (5c) 1980 ☘ David Atchison-Jones						
9	Cave Crack	4c	78°	🐭			★★★
	❶(5a) 1959-69						
10	The Big Stretch ☘	5c	145°	🐭			★★
	❶(5c.N.L.) 1983-5 David Atchison-Jones, Paul Hayes						

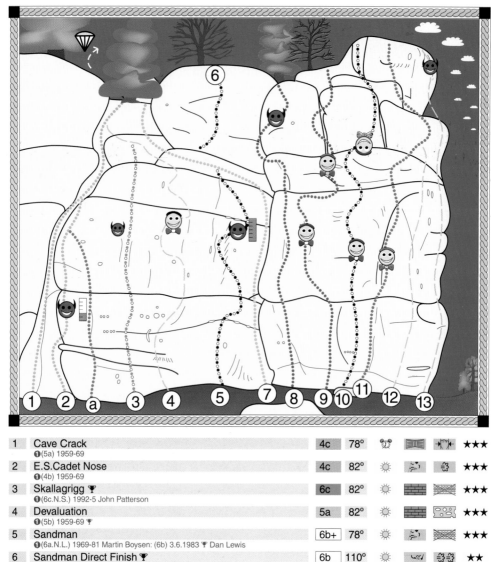

1	Cave Crack ❦ ❶(5a) 1959-69		4c	78°				★★★
2	E.S.Cadet Nose ❶(4b) 1959-69		4c	82°				★★★
3	Skallagrigg ❦ ❶(6c.N.S.) 1992-5 John Patterson		6c	82°				★★★
4	Devaluation ❶(5b) 1959-69 ❦		5a	82°				★★★
5	Sandman ❶(6a.N.L.) 1969-81 Martin Boysen: (6b) 3.6.1983 ❦ Dan Lewis		6b+	78°				★★★
6	Sandman Direct Finish ❦ ❶(6b.N.L.) 1.10.1986 Ed Stone		6b	110°				★★
7	Charlie's Chimney ❶(3a) Pre-1959		3a	80°				★★★
8	Love ❶(6a.N.L.) 1969-81 Blob Wyvill: (6a) 1982 ❦ David Atchison-Jones		6a+	151°				★★
9	Hate ❶(6a.N.L.) 1960 John Smoker: (6a) 13.7.1975 ❦ Mick Fowler		6a	132°				★★★
10	Upside Downies ❶(6b.N.L.) 6.1989 David Atchison-Jones		6b	82°				★★★
11	Pigs Ear ❶(5b.N.L.) 1959-69 Sandstone C.C. (5c) 1959-69 ❦		5b+	151°				★★★
12	T.T. ❶(5a) 1960 ❦ Terry Tullis		5a+	95°				★★
13	Pigs Nose ❦ ❶(5a) Pre-1959		5a	99°				★★★

Target 5c, Rya Tibawi

Devaluation 5a, Angela White

Pig's Nose 5a, Anna Gosden

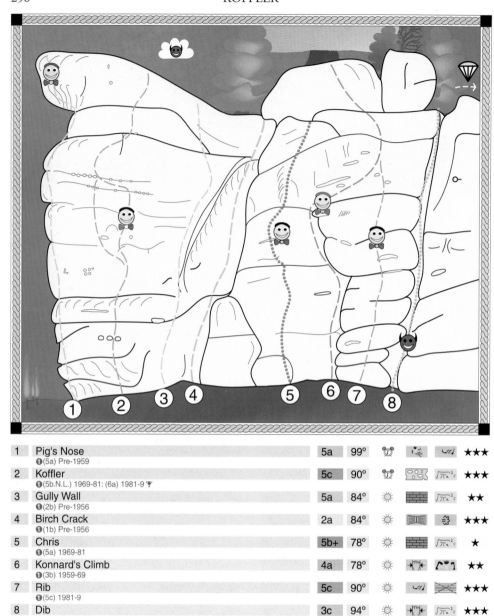

1	Pig's Nose		5a	99°				★★★
	❶(5a) Pre-1959							
2	Koffler		5c	90°				★★★
	❶(5b.N.L.) 1969-81: (6a) 1981-9 ♛							
3	Gully Wall		5a	84°				★★
	❶(2b) Pre-1956							
4	Birch Crack		2a	84°				★★★
	❶(1b) Pre-1956							
5	Chris		5b+	78°				★
	❶(5a) 1969-81							
6	Konnard's Climb		4a	78°				★★
	❶(3b) 1959-69							
7	Rib		5c	90°				★★★
	❶(5c) 1981-9							
8	Dib		3c	94°				★★★
	❶(4a) 1959-69							

Hate 6a, Carrie Atchison-Jones

1	Dib	3c	94°	☀	▸⫴⫸	√πₐ²=	★★★
	❶(4a) 1959-69						
2	Corbett's Nose	4a	112°	☀	⌣ᵂ	⧉	★★
	❶(4a) 1959-69						
3	Corbett's Slab	4b	83°	☀	▦	√πₐ²=	★★
	❶(4a) 1959-69						
4	Nelson's Column	4b	78°	☀	▦	√πₐ²=	★★★
	❶(4c) 1969-81						
5	Dival's Diversion	4b	83°	☀	▦	⟵	★★★
	❶(44) 1959-69						
6	Funnel	3b	75°	☀	▦	⟵	★★★
	❶(5a) 1959-69						
7	U.N.	5b	108°	☀	⧉	⌐•⌐	★★★
	❶(5a) 1959-69						
8	The Wrecker ♈	6c	160°	☀	⌣ᵂ	⧉⧉	🗑
	❶(6b.N.L.) 1959-69 John Smoker						
9	Well's Reach	3a	75°	☀	▤	√πₐ²=	★★
	❶(3a) 1959-69						
10	One of our Buzzards is Missing ♈	6b	153°	☀	⧉	⌐•⌐	★★
	❶(6b.N.S.) 20.3.1994 Robin Mazinke						
11	Harden Gully	2a	65°	☀	▤	√πₐ²=	★★
	❶(2a) 1959-69						

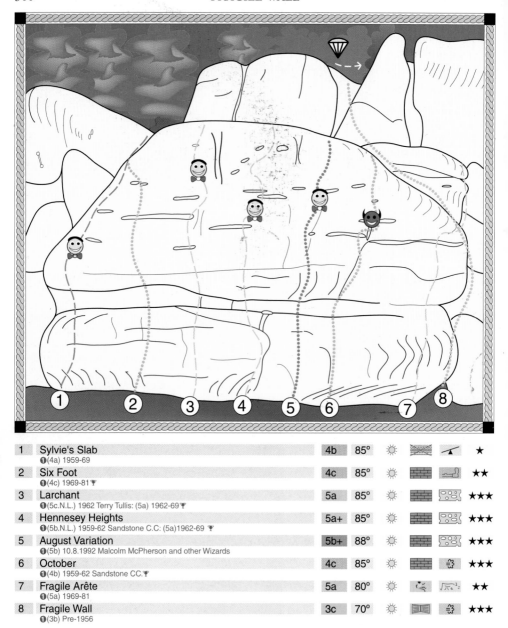

1	Sylvie's Slab ❶(4a) 1959-69	4b	85°	☀			★
2	Six Foot ❶(4c) 1969-81 ⚑	4c	85°	☀			★★
3	Larchant ❶(5c.N.L.) 1962 Terry Tullis: (5a) 1962-69 ⚑	5a	85°	☀			★★★
4	Hennesey Heights ❶(5b.N.L.) 1959-62 Sandstone C.C: (5a)1962-69 ⚑	5a+	85°	☀			★★★
5	August Variation ❶(5b) 10.8.1992 Malcolm McPherson and other Wizards	5b+	88°	☀			★★★
6	October ❶(4b) 1959-62 Sandstone CC.⚑	4c	85°	☀			★★★
7	Fragile Arête ❶(5a) 1969-81	5a	80°	☀			★★
8	Fragile Wall ❶(3b) Pre-1956	3c	70°	☀			★★★

Hennesey Heights 5a+, Jo Da Silva

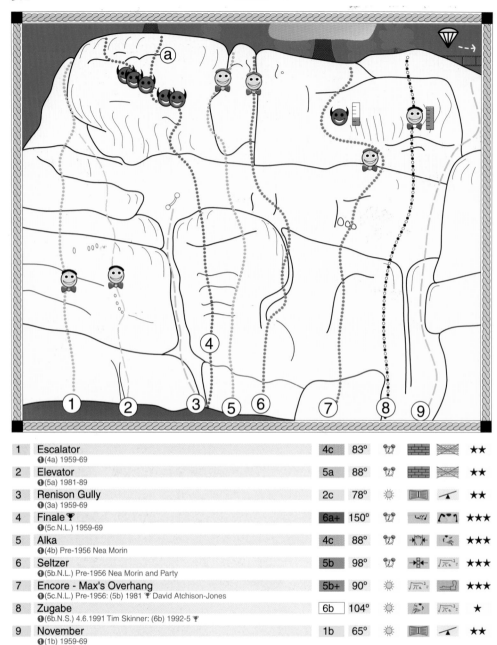

1	Escalator	4c	83°	★★
	❶(4a) 1959-69			
2	Elevator	5a	88°	★★
	❶(5a) 1981-89			
3	Renison Gully	2c	78°	★★
	❶(3a) 1959-69			
4	Finale ♈	6a+	150°	★★★
	❶(5c.N.L.) 1959-69			
5	Alka	4c	88°	★★★
	❶(4b) Pre-1956 Nea Morin			
6	Seltzer	5b	98°	★★★
	❶(5b.N.L.) Pre-1956 Nea Morin and Party			
7	Encore - Max's Overhang	5b+	90°	★★★
	❶(5c.N.L.) Pre-1956: (5b) 1981 ♈ David Atchison-Jones			
8	Zugabe	6b	104°	★
	❶(6b.N.S.) 4.6.1991 Tim Skinner: (6b) 1992-5 ♈			
9	November	1b	65°	★★
	❶(1b) 1959-69			

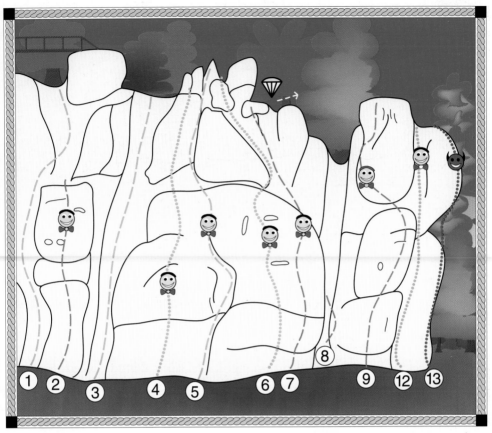

1	November	1b	65°				★★
	❶(1b) 1959-69						
2	Baby Boulder	4b	80°				★
	❶(3a) 1959-69						
3	Hot Cross Bun - Easy Gully	1a	68°				★
	❶(1a) 1959-69						
4	Ballerina	3c	70°				★★
	❶(4a) 1969-81						
5	Red Peg	2a	70°				★★
	❶(2b) 1959-69						
6	Claire	3a	73°				★
	❶(3a) 1959-69						
7	Barham Boulder	4a	80°				★★★
	❶(3b) 1959-69						
8	Rad's Cliff	4a	80°				★★
	❶(3a) 1969-81						
9	Bovril	4b	84°				★★
	❶(4a) 1959-69						
10	Wally	4b	90°				★★★
	❶(4b) 1959-69						
11	Oliver's Twist	5c	99°				★★★
	❶(5c.N.L.) 3.12.1989 M.Smith:(5c) 5.9.1983 ❣T.Skinner:						
12	Nealon's	4c	90°				★★★
	❶(4a) 1959-69						
13	A Lady in Mink	6a+	140°				★★★
	❶(6a.N.L.) 1975-81 Johnny Woodward: (6a+) 23.6.1994 ❣ John Patterson						

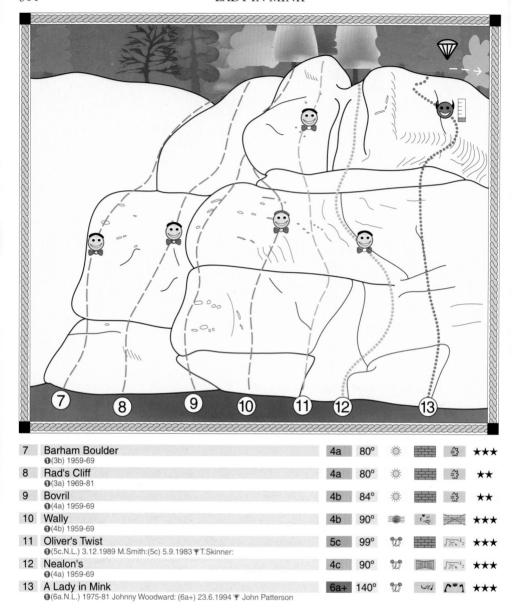

7	**Barham Boulder**	4a	80°				★★★
	❶(3b) 1959-69						
8	**Rad's Cliff**	4a	80°				★★
	❶(3a) 1969-81						
9	**Bovril**	4b	84°				★★
	❶(4a) 1959-69						
10	**Wally**	4b	90°				★★★
	❶(4b) 1959-69						
11	**Oliver's Twist**	5c	99°				★★★
	❶(5c.N.L.) 3.12.1989 M.Smith:(5c) 5.9.1983 ♈T.Skinner:						
12	**Nealon's**	4c	90°				★★★
	❶(4a) 1959-69						
13	**A Lady in Mink**	6a+	140°				★★★
	❶(6a.N.L.) 1975-81 Johnny Woodward: (6a+) 23.6.1994 ♈ John Patterson						

Fragile Wall, 4a, Mark Lythgoe

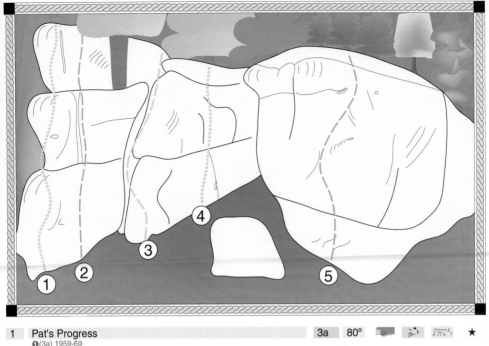

1	**Pat's Progress** ❶(3a) 1959-69	3a	80°				★
2	**Dubonnet** ❶(4a) 1959-69	4a	90°				★
3	**William's Layback** ❶(2a) 1959-69	2a	78°				★
4	**Free Willy** ❶(3a) 23.4.1995 ♀Robin Mazinke	3a	77°				★
5	**Index** ❶(4b) 1962 Terry Tullis	4b	98°				★

BOWLES ROCKS - TOPO 25

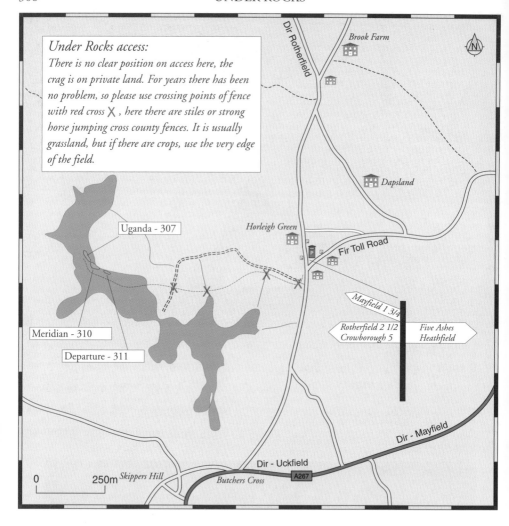

Under Rocks access:

There is no clear position on access here, the
crag is on private land. For years there has been
no problem, so please use crossing points of fence
with red cross X , here there are stiles or strong
horse jumping cross county fences. It is usually
grassland, but if there are crops, use the very edge
of the field.

Brook Farm

Dapsland

Uganda - 307

Horleigh Green

Fir Toll Road

Mayfield 1 3/4

Meridian - 310

Departure - 311

Rotherfield 2 1/2   Five Ashes
Crowborough 5   Heathfield

Dir Rotherfield

Dir - Mayfield

0   250m   *Skippers Hill*

Dir - Uckfield

Butchers Cross   A267

INTRODUCTION

Well away from the main outcrops is the quiet village of Mayfield, which reminds
us of what most of Sussex would have once been like. The countryside around is
still unspoilt and very much rolling grassland with occasional copses of deciduous trees. Under Rocks remains hidden, far into the heartland of this area, and
without concerted effort - will not be discovered. It has always been an ideal
spring venue with its southerly aspect, and a summer haven with the heavy shade
of the trees that enshroud it. It has a history of giving fine hallucinations to those
that visit it under the spell of the funkblasters and aliens.

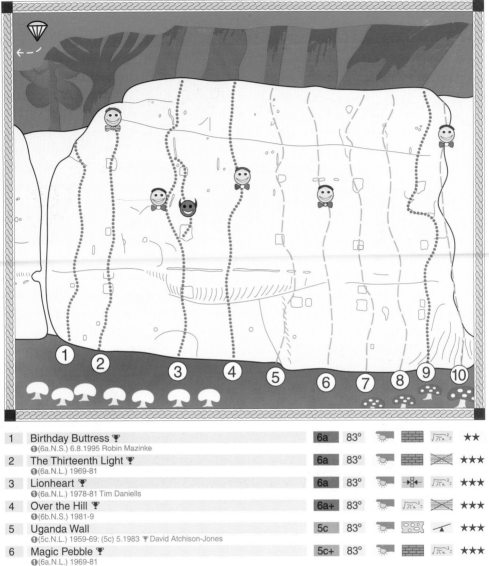

1	Birthday Buttress ♛	6a	83°	★★
	❶(6a.N.S.) 6.8.1995 Robin Mazinke			
2	The Thirteenth Light ♛	6a	83°	★★★
	❶(6a.N.L.) 1969-81			
3	Lionheart ♛	6a	83°	★★★
	❶(6a.N.L.) 1978-81 Tim Daniells			
4	Over the Hill ♛	6a+	83°	★★★
	❶(6b.N.S.) 1981-9			
5	Uganda Wall	5c	83°	★★★
	❶(5c.N.L.) 1959-69: (5c) 5.1983 ♛ David Atchison-Jones			
6	Magic Pebble ♛	5c+	83°	★★★
	❶(6a.N.L.) 1969-81			
7	Fireball	5c	83°	★★★
	❶(5c.N.L.) 1959-69 Tim Daniells: (5c) 1981 ♛ David Atchison-Jones			
8	Dogs of War -(Undercover) ♛	5c+	83°	★★★
	❶(6a.N.S.) 27.3.1993 Alan Grigg			
9	Pressure ♛	6a	83°	★★★
	❶(6a.N.L.) 7.1982 Guy McLelland, David Atchison-Jones			
10	Central Crack	5c	83°	★★★
	❶(5c.N.L.) 1959-69: (5c) 1981-9 ♛			

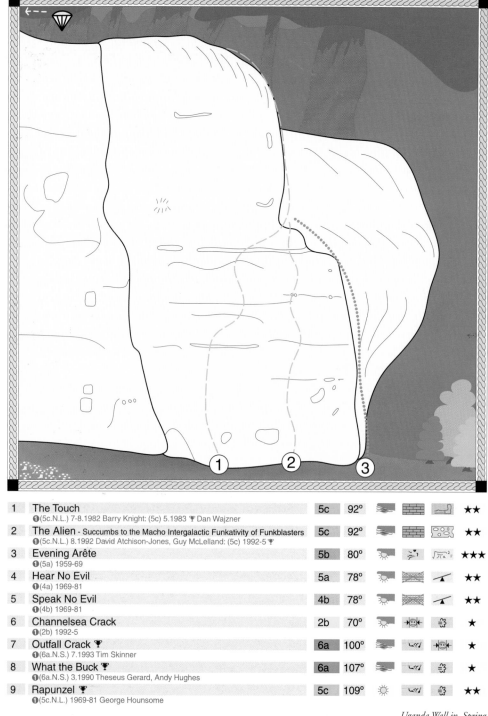

1	**The Touch**	5c	92°				★★
	❶(5c.N.L.) 7-8.1982 Barry Knight: (5c) 5.1983 ❦ Dan Wajzner						
2	**The Alien** - Succumbs to the Macho Intergalactic Funkativity of Funkblasters	5c	92°				★★
	❶(5c.N.L.) 8.1992 David Atchison-Jones, Guy McLelland: (5c) 1992-5 ❦						
3	**Evening Arête**	5b	80°				★★★
	❶(5a) 1959-69						
4	**Hear No Evil**	5a	78°				★★
	❶(4a) 1969-81						
5	**Speak No Evil**	4b	78°				★★
	❶(4b) 1969-81						
6	**Channelsea Crack**	2b	70°				★
	❶(2b) 1992-5						
7	**Outfall Crack** ❦	6a	100°				★
	❶(6a.N.S.) 7.1993 Tim Skinner						
8	**What the Buck** ❦	6a	107°				★
	❶(6a.N.S.) 3.1990 Theseus Gerard, Andy Hughes						
9	**Rapunzel** ❦	5c	109°				★★
	❶(5c.N.L.) 1969-81 George Hounsome						

Uganda Wall in Spring

UNDER ROCKS - TOPO 2

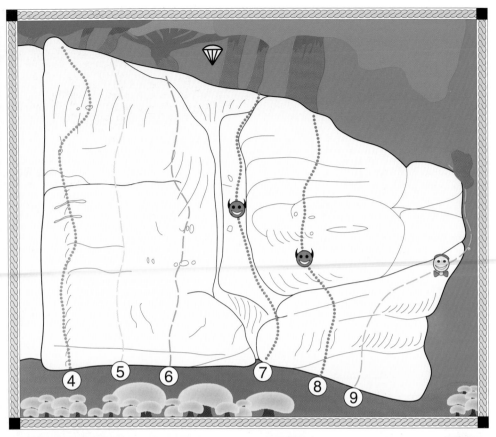

UNDER ROCKS - TOPO 3

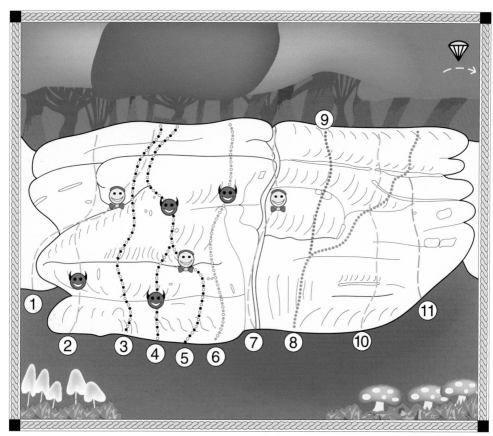

1	Rapunzel ♈		5c	109°				★★
	❶(5c.N.L.) 1969-81 George Hounsome							
2	Bow Locks ♈		5c	122°				★★★
	❶(5c.N.S.) 28.8.1994 Mike Vetterlein, J.Patterson, R. Mazinke							
3	Mastercard ♈		6b	126°				★★
	❶(6b.N.S.) 19.5.1990 Paul Widdowson							
4	Meridian Direct		6b	134°				★★★
	❶(6c) 12.1989 Paul Stone							
5	Meridian		6b	124°				★★★
	❶(6b.N.L.) 7.1982 David Atchison-Jones: (6b) 1995 ♈ Chris Murray							
6	Funnel Web ♈		6c	131°				★★★
	❶(6b.N.S.) 2.1990 Paul Stone							
7	Dark Crack ♈		5c	99°				🗑
	❶(5b.N.L.) 1969-81 Tim Daniells: (5c) 4.1983 ♈ David Atchison-Jones							
8	Peregrine		5b	90°				★★
	❶(5a) 1969-81							
9	One Up, All Up - Except Matt ♈		6a	100°				★★
	❶(6a.N.S.) Paul Stone, Andy Hughes, Mike Spencer							
10	Kestrel ♈		5c	90°				★
	❶(5c.N.S.) 28.8.1994 Mike Vetterlein, J.Patterson, R. Mazinke							
11	Merlin		4a	90°				
	❶(4a) 28.8.1994 Mike Vetterlein, J.Patterson, R. Mazinke							

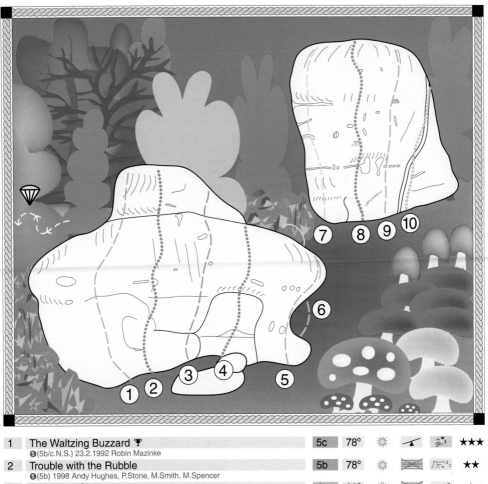

1	The Waltzing Buzzard 🏆	5c	78°	☀			★★★
	❶(5b/c.N.S.) 23.2.1992 Robin Mazinke						
2	Trouble with the Rubble	5b	78°	☀			★★
	❶(5b) 1998 Andy Hughes, P.Stone, M.Smith, M.Spencer						
3	Departure Slab	4a	82°	☀			★
	❶(1b) 1959-69						
4	Magic Mushroom	5b	120°	☀			★
	❶(5b) Delirious Climbers						
5	Manteloid	5c	146°	☀			★
	❶(5c.N.S.) 3.1990 Matt Smith: (5c) 5.1993 🏆 Matt Smith						
6	Thorny Crack	1b	80°	☀			
	❶(1b) 1992-5						
7	Lamplight	5a	86°	☀			★★★
	❶(5a) 1969-81						
8	No Ghosts	5b	86°	☀			★★
	❶(5b) 1969-81						
9	Wind and Wuthering	5c	86°	☀			★★
	❶(6a) 3.1990 M. Spencer						
10	Roger's Wall	3a	86°	☀			★
	❶(3a) 1969-81						

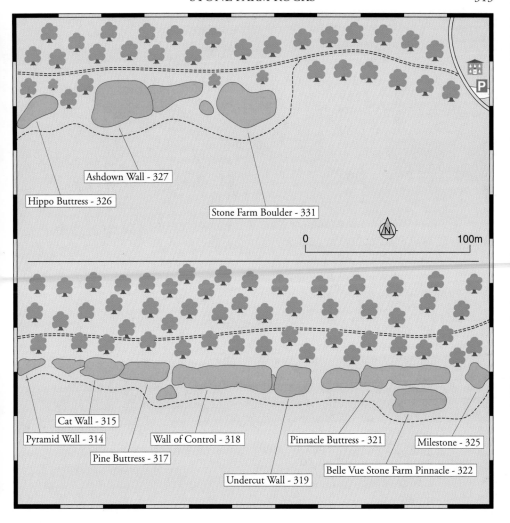

Ashdown Wall - 327

Hippo Buttress - 326

Stone Farm Boulder - 331

Cat Wall - 315

Pyramid Wall - 314

Pine Buttress - 317

Wall of Control - 318

Undercut Wall - 319

Pinnacle Buttress - 321

Belle Vue Stone Farm Pinnacle - 322

Milestone - 325

INTRODUCTION

Stone Farm Rocks are the lonely Western outpost of the East Sussex Sandstone outcrops. It consists of small 20 foot boulders, set into the top of a south-facing hill, overlooking the peaceful Weirwood reservoir. There is an excellent array of easy climbs for beginners, and some lovely bouldering in both the easy and hard grades. The crag is exposed to wind in most parts, which affords quick and easy drying. A lovely spot for a picnic, without having to arduously carry the picnic hamper and champagne, too!!! far from the car. The crag is now owned by the British Mountaineering Council (funny! No mountains here!), and that has allowed climbers, good assured access. The first large boulder encountered, from the stagger up, is the Isolated boulder: There is no easy way up or down this; so great caution should be exercised with summit conquest, and possible airborne head plants, on the way down.

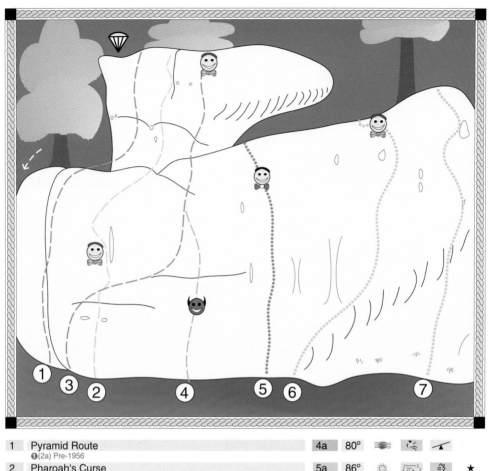

1	Pyramid Route ❶(2a) Pre-1956	4a	80°				
2	Pharoah's Curse ❶(5a) 2.3.2000 ⚑ Graham West	5a	86°				★
3	Kneeling Boulder ❶(4a) Pre-1956	4b	82°				★★
4	Gizeh Step up ❶(5c) 1980 ⚑ Guy Mclelland, Barry Knight	5c	85°				★
5	Keops Progress ❶(5b) Pre-1956	5b	80°				★
6	One Hold Route ❶(4b) Pre-1956	3b	76°				
7	Obscene Gesture ❶(3a) Pre-1956	3a	75°				

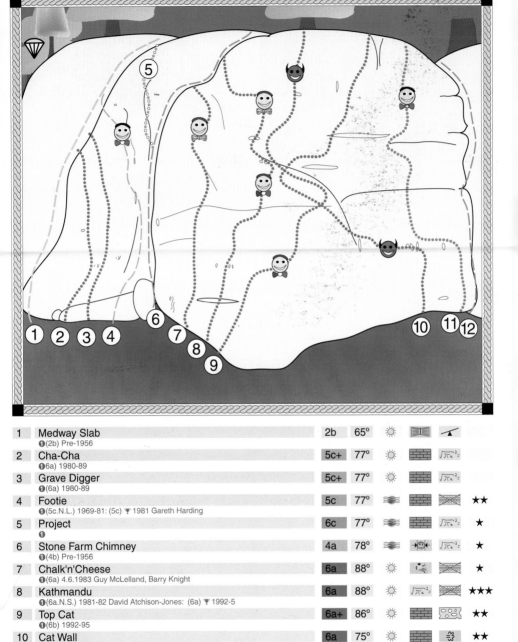

1	Medway Slab	2b	65°			
	①(2b) Pre-1956					
2	Cha-Cha	5c+	77°			
	①(6a) 1980-89					
3	Grave Digger	5c+	77°			
	①(6a) 1980-89					
4	Footie	5c	77°			★★
	①(5c.N.L.) 1969-81: (5c) ⚑ 1981 Gareth Harding					
5	Project	6c	77°			★
	①					
6	Stone Farm Chimney	4a	78°			★
	①(4b) Pre-1956					
7	Chalk'n'Cheese	6a	88°			★
	①(6a) 4.6.1983 Guy McLelland, Barry Knight					
8	Kathmandu	6a	88°			★★★
	①(6a.N.S.) 1981-82 David Atchison-Jones: (6a) ⚑ 1992-5					
9	Top Cat	6a+	86°			★★
	①(6b) 1992-95					
10	Cat Wall	6a	75°			★★
	①(5b) Pre-1956					
11	Sweet Carol	5b	75°			★
	①(5b) 1981 ⚑ David Atchison-Jones					
12	Stone Farm Crack	4b	75°			★★
	①(5a) Pre-1956					

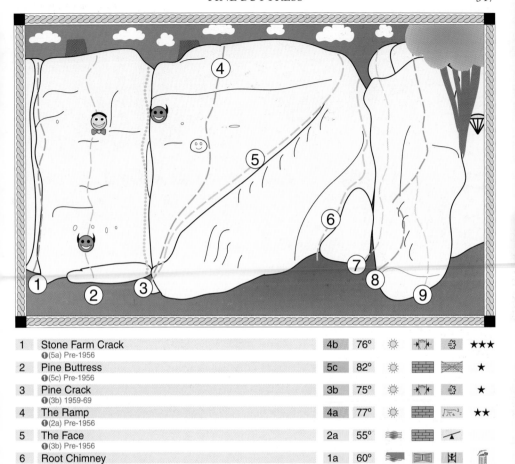

1	Stone Farm Crack	4b	76°	☀	→ᴵᵐᴵ←	≋	★★★
	❶(5a) Pre-1956						
2	Pine Buttress	5c	82°	☀	▦	≋≋	★
	❶(5c) Pre-1956						
3	Pine Crack	3b	75°	☀	→ᴵᵐᴵ←	≋	★
	❶(3b) 1959-69						
4	The Ramp	4a	77°	☀	▦	√π̄ₑ²	★★
	❶(2a) Pre-1956						
5	The Face	2a	55°	≋	▦	⚖	
	❶(3b) Pre-1956						
6	Root Chimney	1a	60°	≋	▤	⚒	🗑
	❶(2a) Pre-1956						
7	Slab Buttress Left	5a	80°	≋	▦	√π̄ₑ²	
	❶(5a) Pre-1956						
8	Slab Buttress	4b	77°	≋	⌇	√π̄ₑ²	★
	❶(5a) Pre-1956						
9	Slab Buttress Direct	5a	82°	≋	⌇	√π̄ₑ²	★
	❶(5a) Pre-1956						

BOREAL

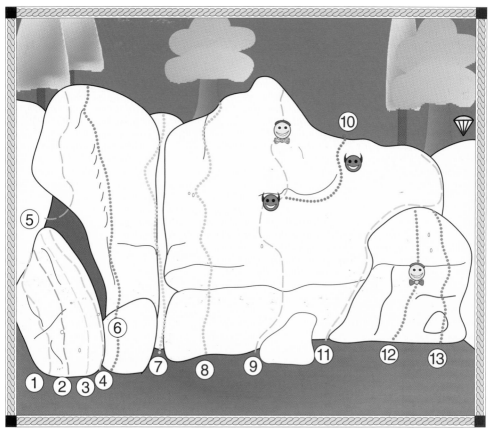

1	**Slab Left Hand** ❶(3a) Pre-1956	2b	65°				
2	**Slab Direct** ❶(4a) Pre-1956	4a	65°				★
3	**Slab Eliminate** ❶(5a) Pre-1956	5a	65°				
4	**Slab Arête** ❶(2a) Pre-1956	2a	60°				
5	**Yew Just Crimp** ❶(5c/6a) 14.3.1999 A. Rowland ♈	5c+	88°				★
6	**Yew Arête** ❶(4a) Pre-1956	5b	80°				
7	**Garden Wall Crack** ❶(5b) Pre-1956	3a	77°				★
8	**Remote** ❶(4b) 1959-69	4c	82°				★★
9	**Control** ❶(5c) 1981-9	5c	93°				★★
10	**Control Freak** ♈ ❶(6a.N.S.) 5.1993 Matt Smith	6a	95°				★★
11	**Holly Leaf Crack** ❶(3a) Pre-1956	1b	45°				
12	**Problem Boulder** ❶(3a) Pre-1956	5b	95°				
13	**Problem Boulder** ❶(3a) Pre-1956	5b	95°				

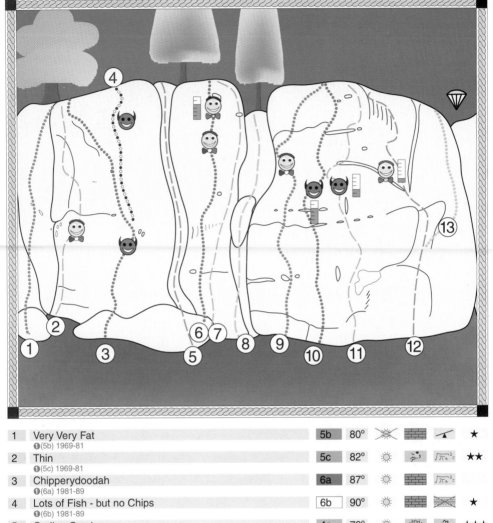

1	Very Very Fat	5b	80°				★
	●(5b) 1969-81						
2	Thin	5c	82°				★★
	●(5c) 1969-81						
3	Chipperydoodah	6a	87°				
	●(6a) 1981-89						
4	Lots of Fish - but no Chips	6b	90°				★
	●(6b) 1981-89						
5	Curling Crack	4a	78°				★★★
	●(3a) Pre-1956						
6	Illusion	6a+	88°				★★
	●(6b.N.S.) 1981-9 Barry Franklin: ♈						
7	Disillusion ♈	5c	92°				★
	●(5c.N.S.) 29.9.1985 Barry Franklin						
8	Inside or Out?	2b	67°				
	●(1b) 1959-69						
9	Front Face	5b	73°				★
	●(5a) 1959-69						
10	Excalibur	6a+	95°				★★
	●(5b) 7.1981 ♈ David Atchison-Jones						
11	Roller Bong - (Mania)	5c+	95°				★★
	●(5c) 7-8.1984 Paul Hayes						
12	Undercut Wall	4b	77°				★★
	●(2b) Pre-1956						
13	Arête of the Universe	3c	77°				
	●(2b) Pre-1956						

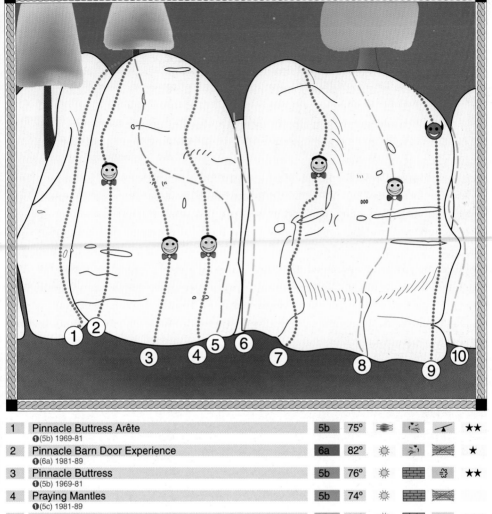

1	**Pinnacle Buttress Arête** ❶(5b) 1969-81	5b	75°				★★
2	**Pinnacle Barn Door Experience** ❶(6a) 1981-89	6a	82°				★
3	**Pinnacle Buttress** ❶(5b) 1969-81	5b	76°				★★
4	**Praying Mantles** ❶(5c) 1981-89	5b	74°				
5	**Pinnacle Buttress Original Route** ❶(4a) Pre-1956	4a	66°				★★★
6	**Easy Crack** ❶(1b) 1959-69	2a	60°				
7	**Bare Necessities** ❶(6a) 6.8.1984 Paul Hayes, Gareth Harding	6a	93°				★
8	**Bare Essentials** ❶(5c.N.L.) 1969-81: (5c) 1981 ♛ Gareth Harding	5c	94°				★★
9	**Belly Up ♛** ❶(6a.N.S.) 11.1995 Tim Skinner	6a	95°				★
10	**Pinnacle Chimney** ❶(1b) 1959-69	2a	75°				

Undercut Wall 4a, John Smyth

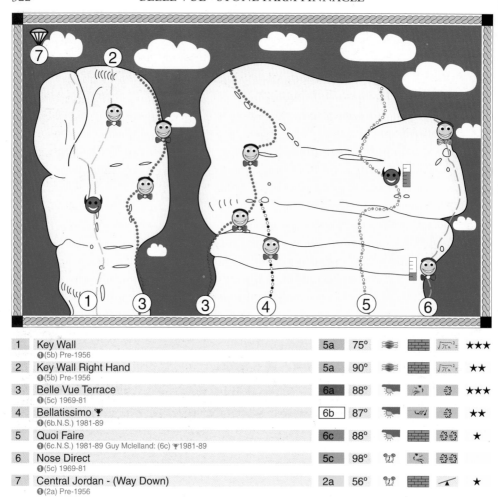

1	**Key Wall** ❶(5b) Pre-1956	5a	75°				★★★
2	**Key Wall Right Hand** ❶(5b) Pre-1956	5a	90°				★★
3	**Belle Vue Terrace** ❶(5c) 1969-81	6a	88°				★★★
4	**Bellatissimo** ♈ ❶(6b.N.S.) 1981-89	6b	87°				★★
5	**Quoi Faire** ❶(6c.N.S.) 1981-89 Guy Mclelland: (6c) ♈1981-89	6c	88°				★
6	**Nose Direct** ❶(5c) 1969-81	5c	98°				
7	**Central Jordan - (Way Down)** ❶(2a) Pre-1956	2a	56°				★

Belle Vue Terrace 6a, David Atchison-Jones

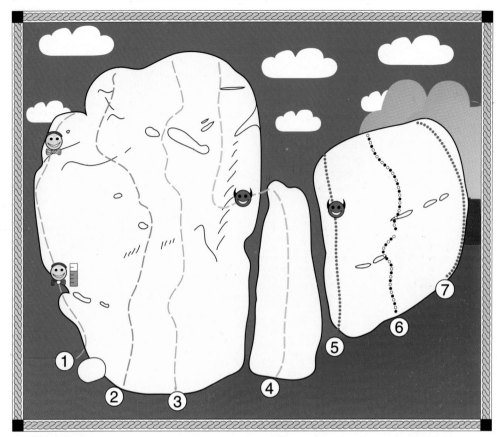

1	**Nose Direct** ❶(5c) 1969-81	5c	95°				★★
2	**East Jordan Route** ❶(4a) Pre-1956	4a	87°				★
3	**Leisure Line** ❶(5c) 1981-89	5c	88°				★
4	**Central Jordan - (Way Down)** ❶(2a) Pre-1956	2a	56°				★
5	**Absent Friends** ❶(6a) 15.9.1990 M. Spencer	6a	80°				
6	**Arthur's Little Problem** ❶(6b) 5.7.1987 John Sharratt or Paul Hayes	6b	81°				
7	**Arthur's Cruise** ❶(6a) 1981-89	6a	80°				

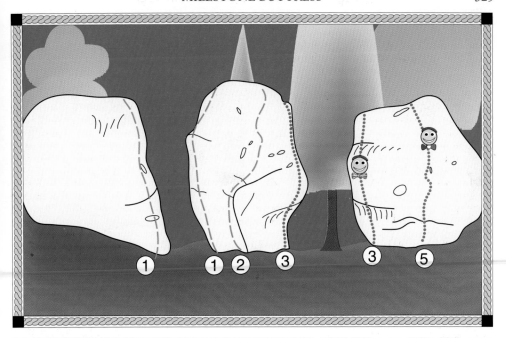

1	Milestone Arête	4a	75°			
	❶(3a) 1959-69					
2	Milestone Stride	4b	76°			
	❶(3a) Pre-1956					
3	Milestone Mantelshelf	6a+	90°			
	❶(6a) 1981-89					
4	Strider	5b				
	❶(5b) 1980-1 Martin Crocker					
5	Concentration Cut	6a	90°			
	❶(5c) 1981-89					

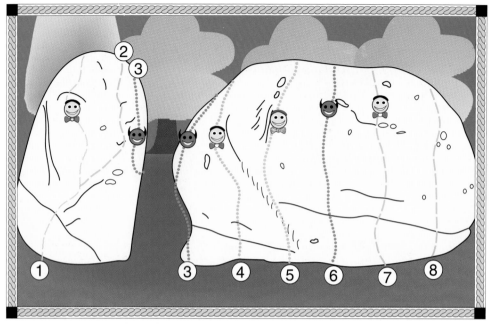

1	Jump Start	5a	80°	★
	①(5a) Pre-1956			
2	Pleasure Dome	1a	70°	
	①(1a) Pre-1956			
3	Backhander	5b	70°	★★
	①(5b) Pre-1956			
4	Hairy Scary	4c	77°	★★
	①(4c) Pre-1956			
5	Grooving Away	3a	77°	★
	①(3a) Pre-1956			
6	Font Blue	5b	76°	★★
	①(5b) Pre-1956			
7	Step Up	1c	74°	★
	①(1c) Pre-1956			
8	Bin the Trainers	2a	68°	★
	①(2a) Pre-1956			

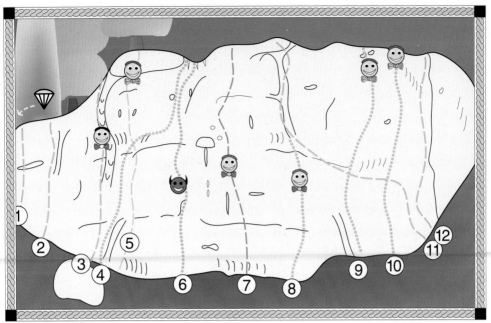

1	Tiny Wall	2b	74°				
	❶(2b) Pre-1956						
2	Thomas the Tank	2a	76°				
	❶(2a) Pre-1956						
3	Open Chimney	2c	68°				
	❶(3b) Pre-1956						
4	Bulging Corner	3a	90°				★★
	❶(3b) Pre-1956						
5	Transparent Accelerating Bannana	5a	97°				★
	❶(5b) 8.1982 David Atchison-Jones						
6	Bulging Wall	4c	99°				★★
	❶(5c) 1981-89						
7	Ashdown Wall	4b	111°				★★
	❶(4b) Pre-1956						
8	Prelude	2c	86°				★
	❶(3a) Pre-1956						
9	Epitaph	3a	79°				★
	❶(3a) Pre-1956						
10	Choo Choo Mama	3b	65°				★
	❶(3a) Pre-1956						
11	Introductory Climb	2a	75°				★
	❶(1b) Pre-1956						
12	Dinosaurs Don't Dyno	1a	75°				
	❶(1a) 1981-89						

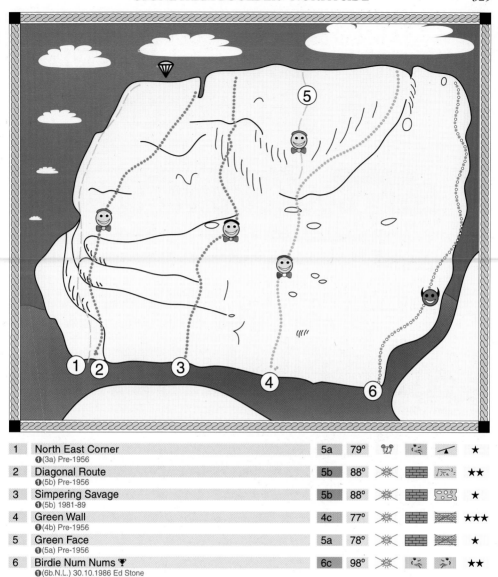

1	**North East Corner**	5a	79°				★
	❶(3a) Pre-1956						
2	**Diagonal Route**	5b	88°				★★
	❶(5b) Pre-1956						
3	**Simpering Savage**	5b	88°				★
	❶(5b) 1981-89						
4	**Green Wall**	4c	77°				★★★
	❶(4b) Pre-1956						
5	**Green Face**	5a	78°				★
	❶(5a) Pre-1956						
6	**Birdie Num Nums** 🏆	6c	98°				★★
	❶(6b.N.L.) 30.10.1986 Ed Stone						

Epitaph 3a, Carrie Atchison-Jones

GROUP use is HARD
on your KIT

for EQUIPMENT that
can TAKE IT

Call **PEGLERS**

of **ARUNDEL**

01903 - 884684
www.peglers.co.uk

9am - 6pm 7 days per week

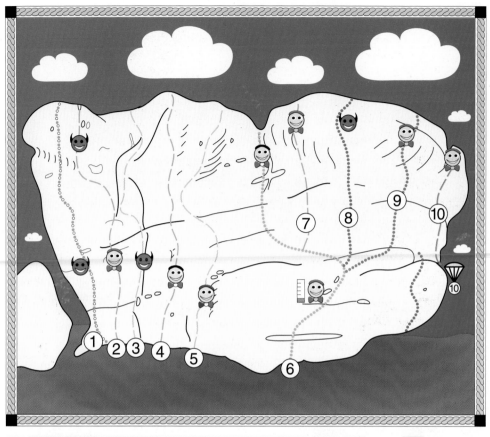

1	Guy's Route ♀	6c	100°				★
	➊(6b.N.L.) 1981-89 Guy Mclelland						
2	Hungry Heart ♀	5c	90°				★★
	➊(6a.N.L.) 1980 David Atchison-Jones, Jon Kenton						
3	Leaning Crack	5a	80°				★★★
	➊(4b) Pre-1956						
4	Ducking Fesperate	5c	80°				★
	➊(6a) 1981-89: ♀						
5	South West Corner Scoop	5a	83°				★★★
	➊(4b) Pre-1956						
6	Primitive Groove	4c	85°				★★★
	➊(4b) Pre-1956						
7	Mad as a Hatter	5c	130°				★
	➊(6a) 1981-89						
8	Boulder Wall	6a	135°				★
	➊(6a) 1969-81						
9	Time Warp	5b	120°				★
	➊(5b) 8.1992 ♀David Atchison-Jones						
10	South East Corner Crack - (Easy way Down)	4b	95°				★★
	➊(3b) Pre-1956						

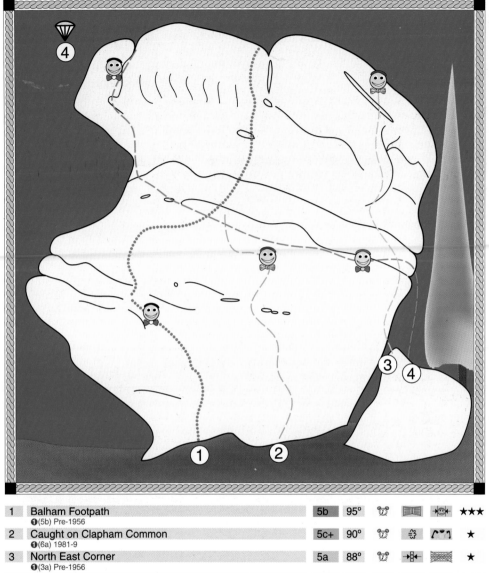

1	Balham Footpath	5b	95°				★★★
	❶(5b) Pre-1956						
2	Caught on Clapham Common	5c+	90°				★
	❶(6a) 1981-9						
3	North East Corner	5a	88°				★
	❶(3a) Pre-1956						
4	South East Corner Crack - (Easy way down)	4a	120°				★★★
	❶(3b) Pre-1956						

Stone Farm Boulder, West Side
Balhan Footpath 5b, David Atchison-Jones

砂岩

イギリスには、とても気持ちのいい緑の木々と田園があります。それは雨がよく降るという事を意味しますが、ロンドン南東部はその点たいへん優位で、カラッとしていて疑いなくイギリスの中で最もお天気の良い場所です。4月から10月までの気候はクライミングをするのには申し分なく、ハリソンズ・ロックスではたまの日曜日に限って沢山の人で混むことはありますが、むしろ実際のクライマーよりピクニック用バスケットの上をヒョイヒョイと歩くことになるでしょう。クライミングは砂岩の小さな露岩にあり、幾つかの孤立したピナクルを持ち、長いエッジの形態をとっています。それはだいたい7～10メートルぐらいの高さで緩やかに起伏していて、樹木の茂った低地の丘に位置しています。岩はもともと柔らかく、激しい雨の降った後は特に脆くなります。その砂岩は、フォンテンブローのダム・ジョアンネやエレファントに見かけは似ていますが、それほど肌理も細かくなく、かたいクォーツのスイ積物ではありません。それはドイツ南西部にあるプファルツ地域の一部、特にバードルフによく似ています。柔らかい為にいつもの決まった場所は、ひどく擦り切れ、とても丸くなったホールドを提供することとなり、それは初心者クライマーを非常に疲れさせます。難しい登り場所では、小さいホールドは概ねなくなり、結果としてオーバーハングの性質上の理由から、これらのルートはサービスととてもパワフルなオラウータンのような熟達した腕前が必要です。地元のクライマー達はこの地域を単に「岩」と呼んでいて、ほとんどの露岩はファーストネームだけで呼ばれています。

露岩

ハリソンズ・ロックスは、普通のクライマーにとってとても重要なクライミングエリアで、そこには350以上の登攀場所があります。大部分は西に面していて、心地の良い午後の日光を沢山受けています。登攀は8メートルの高さで色々違ったタイプのクライミングができます。それはメーンの駐車場から歩いて15分の、森のはずれの美しい環境の中にあります。他の主要な露岩のボウルズ・ロックスは、普通のクライマーにとっては申し分なく、またアウトドアセンターとしても利用できます。そこでのクライミングは素晴らしいのですが、ハリソンズの'自然のままの'感触は欠けています。ハイロックスで--疑問の余地なく--トップレベルのクライマーは最高の登攀ができます。そのルートは主に10メートルの高さで110度のアングルの為とても長い道のりのように見えます。残念ながら'ハイ'は沢山の日陰かあり、かなりの湿気がこもっていますが、それでもクライミングの邪魔になるという訳ではないのですが、ただそのせいで6bの登攀場所となってしまい、全部がとても難しくなっています。他のより小さな露岩は、大部分が静かで神聖です。つまりそれは最高品質のクライミングと、平和と平穏の中で楽しめる登攀場所の素晴らしい機会を提供するということです。

テクニック

フォンテンブローを初めて訪れた時のように、ただ地元のクライマーがどんなに優れているか驚かれることでしょう。そしてそれはだいたい単なるローカル・テクニックなのです。もちろん険しい登攀場所は違いますが、大部分のクライマーにとって筋骨たくましいことや、それどころかスタミナさえも必要ないのです。岩は砂質で摩擦を得るのは難しく、登攀前の靴底の手入れは絶対必要なことで、岩に触る前にまず足拭き用の小さな絨毯布を持っている地元の人たちを見かけることができます。砂ははげ落ちやすいので岩だなの登攀には、小さなタオルはホールドを拭ったり摩擦を確実にするのに便利です。岩が滑りやすい時は、タオルをフットホールドに置けば、靴はきれいなままで必要不可欠な摩擦も得られます。フットホールドは傾斜していることが多いので、足首は岩に靴底全体を接触させるゆとりを取れる

くらいにとてもリラックスしなければいけません。大部分のやさしい登攀場所は完全なバランスでできますし、ヒールフックの標準的使用はとても価値があります。登攀場所の多くは頂上が難問で、すばらしいマンテリング（プールから出る時のように、体を引き上げる動作）のテクニックが必要とされます。このフィニッシュが難しいので、単独でここをやれるクライマーはほんの少ししかいません。このガイドブックには沢山のボルダリングのセクションがありますが、その中のやさしい区域を訪れる事が、ここでのクライミングのタイプのとてもよい手引きになります。

用具

標準的な軽いロックシューズがここでは申し分なく、ボルダリングマットはいつも便利です。クライミングは危険な活動ですし、クライマーには各自の安全に責任があります。そこにはボルトアンカーも崖の頂上には木もありますが、安全を請け合うことはできません！万一失敗する場合も考えてひとつではなく、いつも幾つかのアンカーを選びましょう。重要なのは--ランニング（ロッキング・ゲート）カラビナを、崖のちょうど頂上のへりを越えた向こう側へ組み立てて、伸びないクライミングテープを使うことです。つまり、岩をこすって摩擦を起こさないということです。（ハリソンズやボウルズには 5 メートルのテープ、他の戻り道沿いに木がある露岩には 15 メートルのテープ）クライミングがトップロープでなされるなら、比較的短い優秀な良品の 30 メートルの長さが必要でしょう。それぞれのクライマー用に丈夫なハーネスとセルフロッキングのビレイの装置が、さらに望ましいです。

このガイドブックの使い方

このガイドブックには至る所に、フロントカバーのジャケットの内側にお見せしたシンボルがデザインされています。それぞれの崖は芸術的にスケッチされ、それに--フォンテンブローと全く同じグレードで、ルートに特別な色で示しています。ハッピー・フェイスはハードムーブを示しています。レッド・デビルは本当に危険なムーブ示し、背の低いクライマーには特別に難しかったり不可能な登攀場所を図解するために、ときどきリーチルーラー（背の低い人には難しい登攀場所）と合わせて示してあります。地形図の下のルートの索引で、登攀場所の名前・グレード・初登攀の記録と日付・初の単独登攀の記録を示しています。登攀場所の最新の総体的なグレードは、登攀場所でも最も難しい部分の角度の隣に見ることができます。南に面している幾つかの登攀場所が、木々の鬱蒼とした陰になっているところもあり、日光のカテゴリー実際に陽があたる岩に対して用いました。クライミングに適切なように、登攀場所の種類を示した 2 つのシンボルがあります。アレート（狭くギザギザした尾根）は側面が登攀場所になるという意味で示され、オーバーハングはもし既に登攀場所の角度が図解されているようなら示されていない、等です。星印は--地元のエリアを考慮に入れての--品質を知らせるものです。カバーの内側に入っている地図は露岩への道しるべです。それぞれの露岩においては、それぞれの特有の分野を見付ける別個のプランがあります。

制限

岩が柔かいため侵食が主要な問題になっています。どのクライマーもその問題をよく知っていて、侵食を広がらせないよう、また侵食の速度を早めるような可能性のあることは何もしないように努めなければなりません。できれば、どうか管理されたマナーを守ってください。つまりホールドをはぎ取らないでください。そして頂上ではロープをはずし、歩いて下まで降りてください。ロープを使って降りたりアプザイメン（懸垂下降）やルートに細工することは、岩を非常に急速に破壊することになるのは明白ですし、もちろん不必要なことです。

もしあなたがピナクルや下山の難しいボルダーに登攀するのを試みるなら、まず登る前に補助手段なしでの下山ができるのか確認してください。下降方向を図解するパラシュートにナンバーがふってあれば、この登攀場所では下山に使ってください。どうぞ2ページにわたる写真を検討してください。それはこのエリアにおいて、的を得た実際的な良いアイデアと悪いアイデアのほとんどを図解しています。鳥はこの砂岩の上にはたいてい巣をかけないので、季節の鳥のための制限を受けないことは私たちにとって好都合です。エリッジ・グリーンでは珍しい植物やヌルヌルした緑の苔や地衣類がありますから、クライマー達はこの特別区域を説明するガイドをつくり、このエリアでの自発的な登攀禁止計画を見事に成功させてきています。大体の制限区域はしばしば変更され、通常はナショナル・クライミング・オーガニゼーションの案内標識が、それぞれの露岩の入り口に掲示するでしょうし、それは信頼できる掲示板としても役に立つでしょう。

グレード

イギリスのグレードはしばしば個々のハードムーブに使われます。この砂岩エリア内では、グレードは登攀場所の全般の難しさをクラックス（難点）ムーブの図解をスマイルとデビルで表すことにしました。それぞれの露岩は、難易度順の登攀場所のリストを持ち、それぞれのエリアからのグレードは、このガイドブックの始めから終わりまで大体において同じようにしました。ルートの幾つかは‘削除’と‘確かなホールドを使ったクライミングのみ’の使用を要求することによってグレードを修正します。（シンボルがこれをより正確にしています）ボルダリング向けにフォンテンブロー・グレードを使いましたが、それにより少し難しめになり、中・上級グレードに余計に機会を与える傾向になりました。

宿泊施設とトラベル

ハリソンズ・ロックスにはジュリー・タリス・メモリアル・キャンプサイトがあります。それは小さくて気持ちの良い敷地で、小さいキャンピング・テント用の場所もあり、ただ新しい薄い木材に囲まれています。安い宿泊費で、トイレやお湯も出る基本的な洗う場所もあります。ハリソンズ・ロックスの駐車場と共に施設は、理解ある人々が訪れるたびに残していった寄付によって供給されています。利用する時は是非ご協力ください。何年にもわたっての高い水準の管理がどんなに貴重な事かを証明しています。その成果として、岩や大体のエリアは素晴らしく衛生的にクリーンで、他のポピュラーなクライミング開催指定地のようではなく、十分に経営され全ての人に真価を認められています。ベッドと朝食を提供してくれる地元の好意的なパブや農園もあります。車は露岩に行くには便利ですが、ロンドンからタンブリッジ・ウエルズ行きの幹線列車があります。そこからいつもタクシーがハリソンズまでの6マイル（約9.7キロ）の小旅行のためにお客さんを待っています。そのかわりバスは絶えずルートを、断続的にこっちからあっちへと往復の変更をして走っています！

ウォールアンドエッジ	アレート-左登攀	ハードムーブ
マントリング	あれーと-右登攀	危険なムーブ
バランス	コーナー	午前中の日光
ノーグリップ	ヒールフック	終日の日光
テクニカル	パワー	午後の日光
フィンガーポケット	ロングリーチ	日陰